Shawn M. Lehman

Introduction to Evolutionary Anthropology

Second Custom Edition

Taken from:
Introduction to Evolutionary Anthropology
by Shawn M. Lehman

Pearson Learning Solutions, 330 Hudson Street, New York, New York 10013
A Pearson Education Company
www.pearsoned.com

Printed in Canada

1 2 3 4 5 6 7 8 9 10 XXXX 18 17 16 15

000200010271953051

NB/AP

ISBN 10: 1-323-23890-5
ISBN 13: 978-1-323-23890-5

For Christine, Joshua, and Maxim, always and forever.

—S.M.L.

Shawn M. Lehman is an associate professor in the Department of Anthropology at the University of Toronto. Among his field experiences are expeditions to jungles in Venezuela, Guyana, Suriname, and Madagascar. He earned his Ph.D. in anthropology at Washington University in St. Louis. His doctoral research focused on the biogeography of nine primate species in Guyana, South America. Following his doctoral work, he undertook research on the conservation biogeography of lemurs in Madagascar. Dr. Lehman and his students are currently exploring innovative approaches to determine how landscape changes in forest composition influence lemur ecology in Madagascar. He is also a dedicated and enthusiastic lecturer, having been nominated three times for TVO's Best Lecturer Competition.

BRIEF CONTENTS

CONTENTS

Biological evolution is integral to research in fields ranging from anthropology to zoology, making it one of the most fascinating subjects in science. Biological evolution is topical, biological evolution is engrossing, and biological evolution holds the answers to some of the world's most fascinating anthropological questions. For example, paleoanthropologists seek answers to the intriguing questions of who we are and where we came from. Anthropologists studying primates work to determine what role these fascinating creatures play in tropical ecosystems, and they help us understand the human condition. Medical anthropologists delve into the evolutionary essence of why, after 100 000 years or so of natural selection, humans still suffer from myriad health issues. Forensic anthropologists represent an applied field more popular now than ever before, due in part to associated television shows and bestselling books. Despite the fact that just about everyone has an inherent interest in biological evolution, there exists a rather perplexing issue: introductory textbooks in biological anthropology often come across as, in the words of many of my students, dull and boring. *Introduction to Evolutionary Anthropology* represents a new, exciting perspective on the field of evolutionary anthropology for first-year students at universities and colleges.

Distinctive Aspects of *Introduction to Evolutionary Anthropology*

Focus on Biological Evolution

This book focuses on biological evolution with an anthropological perspective. Each chapter deals exclusively with evolutionary concepts, particularly those that are rarely mentioned in other introductory textbooks. For example, *Introduction to Evolutionary Anthropology* consistently employs phylogenetics and cladistic trees as tools for understanding patterns and processes in human evolution. Readers are given the tools to interpret phylogenetic trees rather than the overly complex methods for constructing them.

Originality, Personality, and Energy

I provide unique examples of evolutionary research and my own personal experiences to make seemingly complex evolutionary concepts accessible to students. Each chapter commences with a first-person narrative in which I highlight a personal experience with the topic that follows. Some examples and stories are humorous, others are adventurous, and a few are serious. These stories connect students to the pervasive influence of biological evolution in their world, putting a personal touch on what can be a very impersonal process in large, introductory classes. The energetic writing style and topical examples are designed to engage students, without sacrificing the quality of the science.

Chapter Brevity

Chapters are concise, enabling students to work quickly through their assigned readings. Students are then ready to assimilate lesson plans during lectures or podcasts. Consequently, this book is designed to fit within a single-semester course.

Unique Application of Illustrations, Cartoons, and Humour

In addition to many original line drawings and colour photographs, *Introduction to Evolutionary Anthropology* uses a novel series of editorial cartoons to help students see the humorous side of common misconceptions about evolutionary anthropology. I see humour as a powerful pedagogical tool, when applied appropriately. Consequently, the book contains, here and there, humorous reflections and anecdotes to help students learn about the field that fascinates us as professional anthropologists. Some URLs in the end-of-chapter Internet Resources provide amusing videos of ideas and concepts within the associated chapter.

Highlights of the Chapters

Chapter 1: Introduction to Evolutionary Anthropology

This chapter introduces students to the modern, holistic application of anthropological theory in the following five disciplines: sociocultural, linguistics and semiotics, archaeology, medical, and biological anthropology. With this background, the biological subfield of evolutionary anthropology is introduced, as is the scientific method. I then provide a short review of the historical development of evolutionary concepts, including an appraisal of Charles Darwin's life and of how he came to formulate his theory of natural selection. The chapter concludes with a short review of Gregor Mendel's work on trait inheritance and a discussion of why creationism and "intelligent design" are scientifically bankrupt.

Chapter 2: Microevolution and Evolutionary Anthropology

In this chapter, I introduce the main processes and patterns in modern evolutionary theory as they pertain to microevolution. What's microevolution? Put simply, it refers to small changes in evolution, such as a change in a population's gene pool over a succession of generations. I begin the review by looking at the genetic basis of inheritance. My use of simplified examples of transcription and translation enables students to better understand what exactly was going on at the genetic level in Mendel's experiments. From there, I delve into genetic changes at the population level. Finally, I review the four mechanisms of biological evolution: mutation, genetic drift, gene flow, and natural selection. I conclude the chapter by clearing up common misconceptions regarding natural selection and mutation.

Chapter 3: Macroevolution and Evolutionary Anthropology

This chapter covers macroevolution, which encompasses large-scale changes at or above the species level extending over geologic eras and resulting in the formation of new taxonomic groups. I explore fundamental issues of species concepts and how species evolve. I then expand the review of modern evolutionary theory from the species level to that of a community of different species in space and time. Finally, I describe the modern synthesis, which establishes the primacy of biological evolution for understanding the history of life on our planet.

Chapter 4: Living Primates

The purpose of this chapter is to introduce students to the exciting science of primate studies in evolutionary anthropology. Students use an up-to-date taxonomy for primates to provide order for a general review of living primates. I then provide specifics on how to differentiate the various taxonomic groups within the Order. There is an extensive and lively discussion of fundamental aspects of the evolutionary anthropology of primates, including body size, ecology and behaviour, and conservation.

Chapter 5: Primate Origins

This chapter offers a review of the evolutionary anthropology of non-human primates in the fossil record. The major goal of the chapter is to give students an understanding of how and why primates evolved from the time of the dinosaurs up until the emergence of the first hominins. Each section starts with a review of the major global patterns of geography and climate. This information is needed to understand how environmental factors influenced primate macroevolution. I undertake a brief review of the major morphological characteristics and ecological interpretations of the primates associated with that epoch. Finally, I piece together the phylogenetic relationships of early primates.

Chapter 6: The First Hominins

In this chapter, students meet species that may be our earliest common ancestors with living apes. Specifically, students learn about major trends in the evolutionary anthropology of human origins during the Pliocene and Pleistocene epochs. Major fossil species receive a brief review of their morphological characteristics and ecology. This chapter sets the stage for understanding the broad evolutionary patterns that resulted in human origins.

Chapter 7: Human Origins: Rise of the Genus *Homo*

This chapter introduces students to paleoanthropology as an exciting and rewarding academic pursuit. I discuss the evolutionary anthropology of human origins starting with the emergence of the first species in our genus (*Homo*). Students also learn about the origins of and changes in tool use over the course of millions of years. Finally, I piece together the phylogenetic relationships of hominins.

Chapter 8: Human Variation

In this chapter, students learn that evolutionary anthropologists are at the forefront of science in documenting phenotypic and genetic diversity of modern humans. This research seeks to provide us with an improved understanding of where we came from and why we look the way we do. Thus, the purpose of this chapter is to discuss the evolutionary anthropology of human variation. I start with looking at the main hypotheses on human origins, followed by a review of human adaptations, ranging from body size to disease. Finally, I provide a detailed, evolutionary perspective on the fallacies of human race concepts and so-called racial abilities.

Chapter 9: Applied Anthropology

The book concludes with a discussion of the application of anthropological knowledge to solve practical problems. In the course of conducting their research, many evolutionary anthropologists have an opportunity to assist in resolving environmental issues with their study animals, or social and health problems with local human populations. I also discuss specifics of the practical application of anthropological knowledge in primatology, medical anthropology, and forensic anthropology. I conclude the chapter with a review of forensic anthropology—the application of skeletal biology to issues within a legal setting.

Supplements

The following instructor supplements are available for downloading from a password-protected section of Pearson Education Canada's online catalogue (www.pearsoned.ca/highered). Navigate to your book's catalogue page to view a list of those supplements that are available. See your local sales representative for details and access.

Instructor's Resource Manual: This manual includes additional resources and exercises that can be assigned to students to further their study and interest in anthropology.

PowerPoint Presentation Slides: The PowerPoint Presentation Slides offer key concepts and key figures from the text and can be used during lecture to highlight key points in the text.

Test Item File: This test bank created in Microsoft Word format includes a variety of questions, such as multiple choice, true/false, short answer, and essay-type questions that can be used for testing students on their understanding of core concepts discussed in the text. This test bank is also available in MyTest format (see below).

MyTest: MyTest is a powerful assessment generation program that helps instructors easily create and print quizzes, tests, exams, as well as homework or practice handouts. Questions and tests can all be authored online, allowing instructors ultimate flexibility and the ability to efficiently manage assessments at any time, from anywhere.

CourseSmart eTextbook

CourseSmart is a new way for instructors and students to access textbooks online anytime from anywhere. With thousands of titles across hundreds of courses, Course-Smart helps instructors choose the best textbook for their class and give their students a new option for buying the assigned textbook as a lower cost eTextbook. For more information, visit www.coursesmart.com.

This book represents a personal journey of sorts, ranging from my days as a young student-athlete at the University of Calgary to my current role as mentor to a new generation of anthropologists at the University of Toronto. Like all journeys, there are important people to acknowledge along the way. My patient undergraduate advisors, James Patterson and Linda Taylor, taught me that biological evolution is an integral part of the anthropological perspective. Because of their support and guidance, I was fortunate to attend graduate school at Washington University in St. Louis. During this time, I was privileged to learn from some of the top minds in evolutionary anthropology, particularly my Ph.D. advisor, Robert W. Sussman as well as Jim Cheverud, Glenn Conroy, Jane Phillips-Conroy, and Richard Smith. I am indebted to Robert Sussman and Linda Taylor for hammering, quite literally, my nascent skills in scientific and grant writing into something resembling that of a professional academic. I also thank my fellow graduate students at WashU, including Pamela Ashmore, Thad Bartlett, David Bergeson, Shimelis Beyene-Gebru, Ian Colquhoun, Ben Freed, Lisa Gould, Donna Hart, Kevin Kykendall, Laura Marsh, and Myron Shekelle.

Following graduate school, my understanding of evolutionary anthropology was greatly enhanced by faculty and students at SUNY-Stony Brook, including Summer Arrigo-Nelson, Diane Doran, Fred Grine, William Jungers, Curtis Marean, Jonah Ratsimbazafy, Karen Samonds, John Shea, and Chia Tan. I am particularly grateful to John Fleagle and Patricia Wright at SUNY-Stony Brook, whose collegiality and support continue to sustain my intellectual and career development.

I would like to thank a number of my colleagues and students in the Department of Anthropology at the University of Toronto who have been instrumental in my never-ending quest to learn and teach about our fascinating biological world, including Katherine Bannar-Martin, David Begun, Ryan Burke, Andrea Falkner, Tracy Kivell, Keren Klass, Keriann McGoogan, Mariam Nargolwalla, Esteban Parra, Susan Pfeiffer, Malcolm Ramsay, Larry Sawchuk, Michael Schillaci, Dan Sellen, Courtney Sendall, Mary Silcox, Travis Steffens, Kim Valenta, Angel Vats, and Katy Wilson. I acknowledge the incomparable administrative and business staff in the department office: Josie Alaimo, Kristy Bard, Annette Chan, Sophia Cottrell, Natalia Krencil, and Diane Yeager.

I would like to thank the acquisitions and development people at Pearson Education Canada, particularly Laura Forbes and Sally Aspinall, who took somewhat of a risk in letting me put my rather unique ideas into a textbook. From our first meeting, they embraced my desire to produce a textbook similar to my teaching pedagogy, resulting in a text different from any currently available to teachers and students. I greatly appreciate the editorial work done by Lisa Berland, Lila Campbell, Rema Celio, Charlotte Morrison-Reed, and Colleen Ste. Marie. They are a wonderful team to work with. For the new edition, I thank the many acquisitions editors, sales people, and managing editors who were supportive of this revised edition, particularly Michele Cronin and Elaine Logashov (who happened to use the first edition when she took my class!). I am indebted to colleagues, current and former students, and photographers who provided images and data for use in the text. A very special thanks goes to Angus Bungay for using his creativity, enthusiasm, and artistic talents to give such vibrant life to Cucu, Bento, and Geo; long may they live! I thank the anonymous reviewers whose suggested changes greatly improved drafts of the book during production and as part of the revision process. I am particularly grateful to colleagues who reviewed some of the chapters, including David Begun, Mariam Nargolwalla,

Joyce Parga, James Rising, Michael Schillaci, Mary Silcox, David Strait, and Patricia Wright. Any remaining errors or omissions are mine, and mine alone.

Finally, I thank my little family for their love and support, including the gentle presence of Persia, our old cat who was always close by when I wrote the first edition. My deepest love and respect go to my beautiful wife, Christine, and my exuberant sons, Joshua and Maxim; they are my world. Their support sustained me during the long months when completing this book and its revisions seemed almost impossible. I also thank Christine, Joshua, and Maxim for their patience and understanding in accepting that my research often takes me away physically, but never emotionally, from their loving presence.

CHAPTER 1

Introduction to Evolutionary Anthropology

GOALS

By the end of this chapter you should understand:

1. Research topics explored by evolutionary anthropologists.
2. Basics of the scientific method.
3. Historical development of evolutionary concepts.
4. Charles Darwin and the theory of natural selection.
5. Gregor Mendel's studies of trait inheritance.

CHAPTER OUTLINE

What Do Evolutionary Anthropologists Study?

How Do Evolutionary Anthropologists Conduct Their Research?

Development of Evolutionary Concepts

Introduction

I remember my first course in anthropology. Because my initial request for a course on biological evolution was denied due to enrolment limits, a friend suggested I take a popular course focusing on what he called "monkey stuff." Sounded interesting, I thought, so I enrolled in Introduction to Biological Anthropology. Being a newcomer to campus, I got lost and was late for the first class. As I hurried toward the classroom, I heard strange animal-like noises echoing off the lockers in the hallway. The noises got louder as I approached my designated room. I stepped into the classroom to discover the professor hooting like a wild monkey! As I negotiated through the seats already occupied by my fellow students, the professor told us about the course. In the weeks ahead, we would learn about the mechanisms of biological evolution, the ecology and behaviour of our closest biological relatives, and the anatomical trends in our biological evolution. In our studies, we sought to answer the question, what is it to be human? I knew by the end of the course that I wanted to be an anthropologist!

What's the first thing that comes to your mind when you hear the word *anthropology*? Perhaps you picture researchers studying primitive human cultures deep in the jungle, archaeologists struggling to locate treasures in the ruins of ancient cities, or scientists digging for fossils under the blazing sun in Africa. Certainly, some aspects of all these activities relate to **anthropology**. Anthropology is a **holistic** science comprising the following five disciplines: socio-cultural anthropology, linguistic and semiotic anthropology, archaeology, medical anthropology, and biological anthropology. Socio-cultural anthropology is the comparative study of human cultures and societies. Linguistic and semiotic anthropology focuses on how language and other systems of human communication contribute to the reproduction, transmission, and transformation of culture. Archaeology is the scientific study of the material evidence of human activities in the past. Medical anthropology focuses on human health and its relationship with culture, behaviour, and biology. Biological anthropology is the study of human and **non-human primates** in their biological and demographic dimensions. Evolutionary anthropology, a specialized subdiscipline within biological anthropology, is the application of modern evolutionary theory to studies of the **morphology**, **ecology**, and behaviour of human and non-human primates. This book employs an evolutionary perspective on humans and non-human primates. Why? Because as a famous evolutionary biologist stated, "Nothing in biology makes sense except in the light of evolution" (Dobzhansky, 1973).

Biological evolution and other associated processes influence every aspect of our lives (Groen et al., 1990). Do you like good food and drink? Our ability to taste, smell, and in some cases detoxify food results from evolutionary processes. Do you like looking at artwork or participating in sports? Our ability to see in colour and judge distance is the result of millions of years of natural selection. Do you like scary movies? If so, then perhaps you have noticed that watching a scary movie often makes the hairs stand up on your arms and the back of your neck. This uncontrolled response is similar to what happens to frightened cats: they fluff up. A tiny muscle, the arrector pilorum, can raise each hair on the human body. The body's response to being scared is to revert to an ancient mammalian trick of looking bigger and more imposing to some perceived external threat! As you will learn in the upcoming chapters, biological evolution has influenced and continues to influence humans, as it has all other life forms on Earth.

Evolutionary concepts are hidden in some of the most popular movies, television shows, and advertisements. For example, the computer-animated movie *Finding Nemo* is the story of a clownfish (*Amphiprion ocellaris*), named Marlin, who loses his wife and all but one of their offspring to a predator. The remainder of the movie describes Marlin's heroic efforts to find and save his son Nemo from captivity. However, clownfish biology is different from that portrayed in the movie: The death of the resident breeding female, such as Nemo's mom, results in one of the local males, like Marlin, changing sex to become the new breeding female. Yes, you read that correctly: Marlin should have become Marlina!

Anthropology ■ The global and holistic study of human culture and biology.

Holistic ■ Considering all aspects of the research subject.

Non-human primate ■ Any primate that is not a human.

Morphology ■ The study of the form and structure of organisms.

Ecology ■ The study of interrelationships of organisms and their environment.

Speaking of cartoons, you will see a number of editorial cartoons used in this text to help you understand the humorous side of common misconceptions about biological evolution (starting with Figure 1.1). This chapter will introduce you to the exciting science of evolutionary anthropology.

Figure 1.1

Introducing three characters—Cucu, Bento, and Geo—who at various points in the book provide a comical view of common misconceptions people have about evolutionary concepts.

What Do Evolutionary Anthropologists Study?

Evolutionary anthropologists and biologists seek answers to intriguing questions of where we come from, who we are, and why we are here (Futuyma, 1998). Evolutionary anthropologists specialize in primatology, paleoanthropology, human variation, medical anthropology, and forensic anthropology. Below is a brief introduction to these five research disciplines.

Primatology

Primatology is the scientific study of our closest **extant** biological relatives: non-human primate species. For now, we can define *species* as a single, distinct class of living creature with features that distinguish it from other living creatures. You can find a more detailed explanation of species concepts in Chapter 3. Primatologists conduct their research on a variety of **primate** species and research topics, ranging from descriptions of primate anatomy through field studies of wild animals to investigations of primate psychology. Primatologists are at the forefront of research efforts to conserve primates in vanishing tropical ecosystems. For example, Dr. Colin Chapman and his research team at McGill University have spent decades studying how primates respond to deforestation in Africa (Chapman et al., 2000, 2005). Their groundbreaking work indicates that even 15 to 25 years after logging, the abundance of some primate species have still not returned to levels recorded before logging occurred. They have linked this slow recovery to a fascinating pattern of temporal and spatial variations in parasites and the quality and abundance of food resources.

Extant ■ Living representatives of a species exist.

Primate ■ Any extant or extinct member of the order of mammals that includes lemurs, tarsiers, monkeys, apes, and humans.

Paleoanthropology

Paleoanthropology is the multidisciplinary study of the biological evolution of humans and non-human primates. Although paleoanthropologists are perhaps best known for excavating **fossils**, many researchers also investigate the advent of and changes in human cultural activities, including tool use, subsistence patterns, and disease. We know that the primate fossil record stretches back as far as 50 to 60 millions years (Fleagle, 1999). Ancient primates evolved and went **extinct** in response to a variety of geological and biological processes. Paleoanthropologists also investigate the evolutionary history of behaviour in human and non-human primates. For example, Dr. Mark Collard of Simon Fraser University combines biological evolution and archaeology to understand patterns of primate and human evolution (Collard and Wood, 2000; Lycett et al., 2007). Dr. Collard has suggested that the behavioural patterns of some primates result from social learning, and that these creatures share with humans the unique distinction of having culture.

Fossils ■ Organic remains that have been transformed by geological processes into a mineralized form.

Extinct ■ No living representative of a species exists.

Human Variation

Anthropologists study human variation to determine spatial and temporal variations in human features (Jobling et al., 2004). Observe your fellow humans the next time you are on campus or at another major urban centre, such as an international airport. You're likely to see that we come in an impressive array of sizes, shapes, and colours. We also have considerable skeletal and dental variations, which are, of course, much harder to see. Despite this variation, all humans are members of one species, which evolutionary anthropologists refer to as *Homo sapiens*. For example, Dr. Esteban Parra at the University of Toronto-Mississauga uses genetic markers to answer questions related to the biological evolution of skin pigmentation in human populations (Parra et al., 2001; Shriver et al., 2003). This research indicates that human skin pigmentation has been subject to strong selection pressures due to environmental factors rather than population history.

Medical Anthropology 医学人类学

Medical anthropology, the study of how social, environmental, and biological factors influence health and illness of individuals at the community, regional, national, and global levels, is a recent addition to evolutionary anthropology. Many medical anthropologists investigate spatial and temporal variations in human survival, disease, and health disparity. Dr. Robert Hoppa, of the University of Manitoba, investigates the interactions between environment, health, and behaviour in ancient human populations (Green et al., 2003; Hoppa, 2000). Dr. Hoppa and his research team are conducting groundbreaking studies of the skeletons of the indigenous peoples of Canada to reconstruct their cultural history at both the individual and population levels.

Forensic Anthropology 法医医人类学

Forensic stuff fascinates many people! If you watch television, then you are likely aware of popular programs, like *Bones* and the *CSI* series, that deal with forensic scientists and their work on homicide investigations. There are equally popular books dealing with forensic science, such as Patricia Cornwell's series on the fictional character Dr. Kay Scarpetta. While forensic science encompasses a variety of biological fields of research, such as genetics and toxicology, forensic anthropology focuses only on the skeletal remains of humans. By analyzing these remains, forensic anthropologists seek to determine the age, sex, stature, ancestry, and any trauma or disease of the deceased. For example, Dr. Mark F. Skinner from Simon Fraser University has consulted on hundreds of forensic cases in Canada (Bell et al., 1996; Skinner, 1987). Dr. Skinner has also investigated allegations of mass graves in Afghanistan, Bosnia, Serbia, and East Timor.

How Do Evolutionary Anthropologists Conduct Their Research?

Evolutionary anthropologists conduct three types of research: descriptive, causal, and applied (Bryman, 2001). Descriptive research involves collecting data about the study subjects or objects. If, for example, I were to walk through a forest recently damaged by logging and notice that some primate species were missing, I would be conducting descriptive research. However, although my observations are of conservation interest, they do not provide a means to determine what caused the primates to disappear. They could be gone because of hunting pressures, loss of critical food resources, sensitivity to habitat disturbance, or any number of other factors. Therefore, you can see that descriptive research does not demonstrate causal relationships. Causal research involves looking for one thing that causes another thing to happen or change. Returning to my previous example, I could look for a cause-and-effect relationship between ecological factors, such as the distribution and density of critical food resources and the loss of primate species in the logged forest.

Medical and forensic anthropologists tend to focus on applied research. In applied research, a scientist determines the means by which a specific, recognized need can be met (Miller and Salkind, 2002). Applied research can also be used in the previous example of deforestation effects on local primates. If one of my variables, such as the distribution of food resources, was a strong predictor of primate diversity, then applied research could involve planting various primate food trees in the remaining forest. In this way, I could determine whether the addition of specific food trees increased primate diversity. These research paradigms are directly relevant to formulating and testing scientific theory.

What's a Theory?

A scientific theory is a well-substantiated explanation of some aspect of the natural world that incorporates facts, laws, predictions, and tested hypotheses. A scientific theory is very different from a **common theory**. For example, I have a common theory that I always pick the slowest lineup to pay for items at a grocery store. Presumably, I have sufficient data to support my theory because I have been to grocery stores hundreds of times. Is my common theory supported by enough data to form a scientific theory? No! I need to set up a series of experiments to test the hypothesis that I consistently have longer wait times than other patrons in grocery stores. In this experiment, I would need to control for interpersonal differences in grocery quantities, unloading times from carts, cashier speed, payment methods, and so on. As you can see, things get rather detailed when someone conducts hypothesis testing in science. Therefore, unlike a common theory, a scientific theory is a widely accepted set of ideas that produce hypotheses that can be tested and refined by the scientific community.

Common theory ■ An idea based only on conjecture or personal opinion.

What's a Hypothesis?

A hypothesis is a testable statement about the natural world that a researcher uses to build **inferences** and explanations. Before conducting an experiment, a scientist evaluates and defines specific aspects of each hypothesis. From there, a scientist ensures that each hypothesis is **falsifiable**. Wait a second! You may be thinking that scientists are supposed to prove, not disprove, their hypotheses. This is not the case. A simple example can illustrate the critical importance of falsifiable hypotheses. Hypothetically, someone could suggest that giant, sentient cucumbers from an alternate universe brought the first life forms to Earth and other planets in our galaxy. The research should not proceed because, in part, the hypothesis is not falsifiable—there is no way to test whether this is or is not the case. Specifically, you cannot falsify the existence of an alternative universe in evolutionary anthropology, and there are no existing data to support the existence of giant, sentient cucumbers capable of interstellar travel. Thus, a hypothesis is not an "educated guess." A scientist uses observations from previous research to formulate and then test a hypothesis. For example, each year I teach a large course on introduction to anthropology. I also advise students on their study habits. Based on my observations, I could hypothesize as follows: If student grades in class are related to studying time, then people who study for longer time periods will have a higher final grade. An alternative hypothesis could be this: If student grades in class are related to studying quality, then people who have better study periods will have a higher final grade. Each hypothesis is falsifiable because I can collect data on the study habits of the students and their final grades. I could also set up some experiments to test my hypotheses using the scientific method.

Inference ■ A process of reasoning in which a conclusion is derived from one or more facts.

Falsifiable ■ A study design that enables the researcher to make observations that disprove a hypothesis.

The Scientific Method

Evolutionary anthropologists employ the scientific method as often as possible in their research. The scientific method involves investigating phenomena, acquiring new knowledge, or correcting and integrating previous knowledge (Cohen and Nagel, 1934). The scientific method generally involves five sequential processes: (1) observation of the phenomena, (2) formulation of a hypothesis concerning the phenomena, (3) development of methods to test the validity of the hypothesis, (4) experimentation, and (5) a conclusion that supports or modifies the hypothesis. Data collected by a scientist must be repeatable, observable, empirical, and measurable. The scientific method involves collecting **quantitative data**, which is information sometimes referred to as "hard" or numerical in nature, and **qualitative data**, which is information on just about anything that is non-numerical in nature. For example, a medical anthropologist can interview study subjects suffering from various parasitic illnesses. Because there is no direct, empirical means of measuring discomfort, the researcher may collect qualitative data on pain levels (by asking people to evaluate it as low, moderate, or extreme). Conversely, the researcher could collect quantitative data on the number and kinds of parasites found in the blood and fecal samples of the local people.

Development of Evolutionary Concepts

Before we get into modern evolutionary theory, it's important to have a short, historical review of the people that influenced the development of evolutionary concepts. Historians trace ideas on biological evolution back as far as 2600 years ago in ancient Greece and Asia, to the works of Aristotle and Zhuangzi. For example, Aristotle's observations of the anatomy of various aquatic mammals and fish were thousands of years ahead of their time. Almost 2400 years ago, Zhuangzi suggested that living things have the power to transform themselves to adapt to their surroundings. In 18th-century Europe, a series of monumental changes occurred in scientific explorations and discoveries related to biological evolution.

Historical Contributors

Carl Linnaeus (1707–1778) was a Swedish physician and **botanist**, with a strong interest in **classifying** plants and animals (Figure 1.2). Often referred to as "the father of modern **taxonomy**," Linnaeus began his work with forays into local gardens, expanded into remote areas of Sweden, and also received collections of animals from distant lands, including primates from equatorial regions of the world. Two of Linnaeus's most important contributions to modern science are his taxonomic system and the **binomial nomenclature**, which is a method scientists use to name plants and animals in descriptive Latin terms. Linnaean taxonomy classifies all living things in a ranked hierarchy, from the highest and most generalized category (a domain) down to the species level. Despite recent revisions to Linnaeus's classification levels, the basics of his system are still in use today. In the binomial nomenclature system, **genus** and species are written only in Latin. Scientists use Latin because it is no longer spoken, except by scholars, and therefore will not change over time. In addition, the typeset for the font should be offset (*italics* or underlined) from the main text because the writer is using a different language. In evolutionary anthropology and biology, the first letter of the genus is capitalized while the first letter of all other words is in lower-case letters. For example, the binomial nomenclature for humans is *Homo sapiens*. Thus, we are in the genus *Homo* (human) and our species designation is *sapiens* (wise). Linnaeus believed that he was simply organizing God's creations because at that time, there was no treatise on biological evolution.

Georges-Louis Leclerc (1707–1788) was a French aristocrat, mathematician, and naturalist. Although Leclerc contributed to various scientific fields, one of his most notable contributions to evolutionary concepts was his monumental 36-volume *Histoire Naturelle* (1749–1788). This remarkable series of books described everything known about **natural history** at that time. For example, some of his ideas formed core concepts in what would eventually become the modern science of **biogeography** (Brown and Gibson, 1998), which is the study of where organisms live, at what abundance and why they're there or not there. Leclerc's other primary contribution to the development of evolutionary concepts was the idea that species changed and evolved after they moved

Quantitative data ■ Information measurable or quantifiable on a numeric scale, such as body mass or the number of primate species in a protected area.

Qualitative data ■ Information based on observations that cannot be reduced to numerical expression.

Botanist ■ A scientist who studies plants.

Classify ■ The scientific method of placing an organism in a system based on order by classes or categories.

Taxonomy ■ The theory and practice of describing, naming, and classifying extant and extinct organisms.

Binomial nomenclature ■ The scientific method for assigning names to species and genera.

Genus (pl. *genera*) ■ A taxonomic group of species exhibiting similar characteristics.

Natural history ■ The study of animals, plants, and minerals.

Biogeography ■ The scientific study of the geographic distribution of organisms.

Figure 1.2

Nineteenth-century painting of Carl Linnaeus, dressed in the traditional Lapp costume of Scandinavia. He is holding one of his favourite plants (*Linnaea boreali*), which was named in his honour.

away from the place where they were created. This idea is broadly similar to Charles Darwin's Theory of Natural Selection.

Jean-Baptiste Lamarck (1744–1829) was also French, a decorated soldier, and, later, an academic. Like Linnaeus, Lamarck was fascinated by the taxonomic classification of plants and animals. His major contribution to evolutionary concepts was a reformulation and specification of a very old idea on how organisms change. Lamarck suggested that individuals lose those characteristics they do not use and develop useful characteristics, and that individuals can pass on these characteristics (or lack thereof) to their offspring. He believed that these changes were the result of an unknown nervous fluid. Moreover, Lamarck theorized that environmental changes could alter behaviour and biological organs. For example, application of Lamarck's ideas would mean that the excessively large muscles (the acquired character) developed by a professional athlete, such as the wrestler Hulk Hogan, must pass on to his offspring (inheritance of the acquired character). Clearly, Hulk Hogan's increased musculature is an acquired trait and not a heritable trait. Modern biologists have labelled these ideas by a variety of terms, including Lamarckism, the theory of "inheritance of acquired characters," and "soft inheritance." Although Lamarckism is no longer accepted by modern biologists, they agree that his published works were integral to the development of evolutionary concepts.

Georges Cuvier (1769–1832) was another aristocratic French naturalist. Cuvier's studies and publications on structural similarities and differences between organisms helped establish the scientific disciplines of **comparative anatomy** and **palaeontology**. These fields

Comparative anatomy ■ The study of anatomical features of animals of different species.

Paleontology ■ The study of fossilized life forms.

compare and contrast tissues of living and extinct organisms. He contributed to the development of evolutionary concepts through his work on the comparative anatomy of extant and extinct mammals. Although modern science accepts extinction as integral to evolutionary processes, in Cuvier's time his idea that extinction has occurred in some animals was in direct opposition to the widely accepted religious concept of **fixity of species**, which is a purely religious idea that a Supreme Being created all living things and that no changes have occurred since the moment of creation. Ideas about the fixity of species assert, quite incorrectly, that organisms do not change (evolve) or go extinct. Cuvier championed a controversial idea known as **catastrophism**, which, among many other things, states that the surface of our planet originated suddenly in the past by geological processes very different from those currently occurring. A key biological element of catastrophism is that it allows for changes in organisms but does not refute Biblical interpretations of the Earth's age. The prevailing view of contemporary European theologians and religious authorities was that the planet was only 5700 years old. Because the Catholic Church in 18th-century Europe wielded enormous political power, going against any of its major teachings was a perilous undertaking. However, Cuvier carefully avoided invoking a Biblical flood as the source of catastrophism, suggesting instead that there were multiple catastrophic events. In fact, he was strongly critical of contemporary evolutionary concepts, such as those proposed by Lamarck. Therefore, Cuvier's major contribution to evolutionary concepts was his assertion that species go extinct.

James Hutton (1726–1797) was a Scottish naturalist and geologist. He made many contributions to the founding of **geology** as a science. Hutton proposed that successive upheaval and erosion of sedimentary rock had been occurring for millions of years and would continue to occur forever. Hutton's ideas would eventually form important components of a **school of thought** known as **uniformitarianism,** which is a geological principle that holds that the Earth was formed and has evolved through the same natural geological processes operating today. Unfortunately, Hutton's complex writing style prevented his published work from receiving the public attention and acclaim he richly deserved.

Charles Lyell (1797–1875), another Scottish geologist, made numerous important contributions to geology, particularly in the fields of **stratigraphy** (the scientific study of how rock layers form) and **glaciology** (the study of how glaciers form). He was an enthusiastic field geologist, making many trips throughout Europe and even to North America. Lyell's three-volume *Principles of Geology* (1830–1833) greatly improved access to and support for uniformitarianism. Before publishing his own thoughts on biological evolution, one of Lyell's greatest, albeit indirect, contributions to the development of evolutionary concepts was his influence on young natural historians in Europe, such as Charles Darwin.

Charles Darwin and the Theory of Natural Selection

Charles Darwin (1809–1882) was an English geologist and naturalist (Figure 1.3). The son and grandson of wealthy country doctors, Darwin entered medical school in hopes of continuing the family medical tradition. Though uninterested in medical studies, he was fascinated by stories about the tropical forest told to him by John Edmonstone, a freed slave from Guyana in South America. Darwin also spoke regularly with local authorities on **zoology**, taxonomy, and basic concepts in biological evolution. He spent considerable time in the countryside collecting insects, a craze among British naturalists of the period. Not surprisingly, Darwin failed to progress beyond his second year of medical school. He then enrolled in theology at Cambridge University. He spent most of his free time with friends, collecting insects, learning natural history from local authorities, and reading natural history books. Despite these extracurricular activities, Darwin managed to complete his degree. Rather than immediately taking his holy vows, Darwin joined an expedition to survey geological formations in Wales. While

Fixity of species ■ A theory that derives from Biblical creation, in which each living thing has always existed and will always exist by God's acts of creation.

Catastrophism ■ The idea that catastrophic events altered geological features and caused the extinction of plants and animals.

Geology ■ The scientific study of the Earth, what it is made of, and how it changes over time.

School of thought ■ A group of people united in their shared belief in some ideas or concepts.

Uniformitarianism ■ A theory that natural processes, such as erosion, operating in the past are the same as those that operate in the present.

Stratigraphy ■ The study of rock layers (strata) and the relationships among them.

Glaciology ■ The study of glaciers and other natural phenomena involving ice.

Zoology ■ The scientific study of animals.

Figure 1.3

A photograph of Charles Darwin in his later years (c. 1869).

Darwin was in Wales, two of his Cambridge professors, John Henslow and George Peacock, recommended him for the unpaid position of naturalist aboard the HMS *Beagle*. The *Beagle* was to set sail for a two-year survey of South America. Darwin was eventually awarded the position after cajoling his father for support and following interviews with the ship's captain. You can imagine his excitement to finally fulfill his dreams of exploration and discovery!

The two-year trip extended to almost five years, as the HMS *Beagle* and her crew visited the eastern and western coasts of South America, the Galapagos Islands, Australia, various islands in the Indian Ocean, and South Africa. While at sea, Darwin read whatever natural history and geology books he could acquire, including Lyell's *Principles of Geology*. Darwin spent much of his time on land, exploring geological formations and collecting thousands of plant and animal specimens. You should note that at this time there were no antibiotics, water filters, or even mosquito repellents. Darwin spent months in environments that challenge even the best-prepared modern explorers and scientists. He made detailed notes on everything he saw and collected. Whenever possible, Darwin sent his collections and notes back to John Henslow at Cambridge University, who made these materials available to a select group of scientists. Consequently, Darwin was a respected naturalist on his return to England in 1836. In 1839, he married one of his cousins, Emma Wedgwood, and settled into the life of a gentleman researcher.

Darwin applied himself to determining how species evolved. His research was not composed solely of analyzing dead animals and fossils. Darwin also spoke with anyone knowledgeable about natural history, from dog and pigeon breeders to luminaries in the fields of geology and zoology (e.g., Charles Lyell). He also collaborated with expert naturalists in examining his specimens and categorizing them into distinct species. A bird expert studying Darwin's bird collection from the Galapagos Islands revealed that the birds represented 12 closely related species. Darwin theorized that one bird species must have arrived on the Galapagos from the mainland, and had then been altered in some way to eventually become different species. Darwin also read books on economics, such as Malthus's *An Essay on the Principle of Population*. Malthus proposed that human populations could potentially grow at geometric rates whereas food supplies can only increase at an arithmetic rate; he concluded that death, disease, and natural restraint limit human population growth. In other words, many more individuals are born than can possibly survive. Darwin applied certain aspects of Malthus's ideas about competition and checks to human population growth to animals in nature. Combining Malthus's theories with observations he made about the ability of animal breeders to use selective breeding to alter the physical form and behaviour of animals, Darwin formulated ideas about how nature selects for traits in animals. He reasoned that nature selects for or against individuals in the natural world—favourable variants or traits of *individuals* of a species should enable some to better compete in nature. By *selection* Darwin meant that the environment chooses certain physical aspects of an organism, so that some individuals are more likely to survive than others. Thus, if these favourable variants are passed on to offspring, then successive changes over an immensely long time will result in the formation of new species. Less favourable variants and species will disappear. Darwin had formulated the basics of the theory of natural selection!

Years passed between Darwin's first notions on natural selection and the publication of his complete theory. He initially shared only limited aspects of his ideas in letters to select researchers, such as Joseph Dalton Hooker, a famous English explorer with an interest in **botany**. Darwin's reticence stemmed predominantly from concerns about rejection of his ideas by other scientists, such as Charles Lyell. Lyell was, at that time, strongly opposed to evolutionary ideas similar to those Darwin was working on. In fact, some of the most powerful and influential naturalists were adamantly opposed to alternatives to Lamarckism. To avoid conflict, Darwin published books about his trip aboard the HMS *Beagle* and about the zoology of barnacles. He conducted his experiments, engaged in friendly debates with his colleagues about biological evolution, and only secretly worked on a paper describing his theory on natural selection. However, as publication of his theory approached, Darwin's quiet life as a naturalist and country squire was about to change dramatically.

In the summer of 1858, Darwin was shocked by the contents of an unpublished essay by Alfred Russel Wallace. Wallace (1823–1913) was a British naturalist and explorer who earned his living collecting and then selling organisms from the tropical forests of South America and Southeast Asia. In his essay, Wallace described ideas very similar to those in Darwin's theory of natural selection! Darwin finally felt obliged to present his ideas on biological evolution and natural selection to the scientific community. In 1858, papers by Darwin and Wallace were read at a special meeting of the Linnean Society in London, which created considerable excitement among the attendees. On November 22, 1859, 1250 copies of Darwin's *On the Origin of Species by Means of Natural Selection, or the Preservation of Favoured Races in the Struggle for Life* went on sale in London. Most copies of the book sold on the first day. Today, many scientists consider *On the Origin of Species* to be one of the greatest works of science ever published. Darwin spent the remainder of his professional life revising *On the Origin of Species* and publishing books on various scientific topics.

What did Darwin say in *On the Origin of Species*? Darwin synthesized his field experiences, discussions with animal breeders, experiments, and the work of others into two broad ideas on how species evolve. First, Darwin theorized that all extant and extinct species share a common ancestry, which he eventually called The Tree of Life (Figure 1.4). Closely related species have a more recent common ancestor, while

Botany ■ The scientific study of plants.

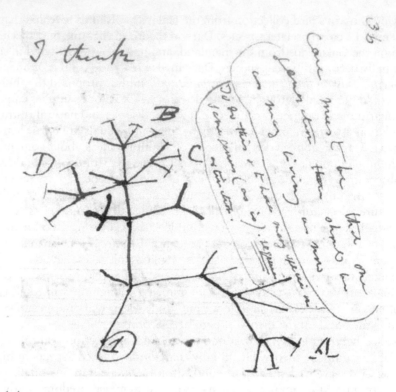

Figure 1.4

A page from Darwin's notebooks, showing his first attempts to illustrate an evolutionary tree, which he termed The Tree of Life.

more distantly related species have an older common ancestor. Thus, the supernatural creation of life and the spontaneous creation of species by Lamarckian mechanisms are unnecessary. Darwin saw the process of species formation as a slow, gradual accumulation of slight variations in traits of individuals. Second, Darwin laid out his compelling argument for the power and scope of natural selection. He described his observations on how humans create new variants of dogs though selective breeding, and extended this human selection for domesticates to how nature selects for certain characteristics of individuals, which then compete amongst each other for access to food and mates. Darwin elegantly wrote,

> Owing to this struggle for life, any variation, however slight and from whatever cause proceeding, if it be in any degree profitable to an individual of any species, in its infinitely complex relations to other organic beings and to external nature, will tend to the preservation of that individual, and will generally be inherited by its offspring. The offspring, also, will thus have a better chance of surviving, for, of the many individuals of any species which are periodically born, but a small number can survive. I have called this principle, by which each slight variation, if useful, is preserved, by the term of Natural Selection, in order to mark its relation to man's power of selection. (1859, p. 61)

It is impossible in one paragraph to summarize *On the Origin of Species*. Furthermore, it is beyond the scope of this book to review the considerable differences between how Darwin and Wallace saw natural selection operating. Darwin's knowledge and descriptions of biological diversity were remarkable, even by modern standards. Despite the limitations of 19th-century science, Darwin made accurate predictions about many biological facts that we now know only because of decades of research. *On the Origin of Species* is a remarkably detailed but easily read piece of science, and well worth the time to read and enjoy.

Misconceptions about Darwin's Ideas

There are some common misconceptions about Darwin's published works. Darwin did not originate the phrase, "survival of the fittest." This phrase was the creation of Herbert Spencer, a social philosopher and contemporary of Darwin. Spencer introduced the phrase in *Principles of Biology* (1864) after reading Darwin's *On the Origin of Species*. While Darwin did use it as a synonym for natural selection in the final editions of his book, modern biologists do not use "survival of the fittest" because it was originally intended to apply to human societies and because Spencer favoured Lamarckian concepts over natural selection. It is imperative that you understand that *societies change; they do not experience biological evolution*. Misguided attempts to apply Darwin's theory on natural selection to human societies have resulted in **Social Darwinism** and the atrocities of the Holocaust and Rwandan genocide. Proponents of Social Darwinism hold that the strongest or fittest individuals should survive and flourish in society, whereas weak and unfit individuals should be allowed to die. Moreover, "survival of the fittest" implies that organisms gain evolutionary success only by being competitive and aggressive (Figure 1.5), contradicting Darwin's notion that morality has a role to play in human evolution, and that cooperation and other positive social behaviours can also result in evolutionary success (Chapman and Sussman, 2004). Evolutionary anthropologists also criticize colloquial use of this phrase, which incorrectly emphasizes the physical attributes of an organism (e.g., body size, ferocity, and armament). In evolutionary anthropology and biology, **fitness** is a very different thing (Futuyma, 1998).

Darwin's ideas on natural selection and biological evolution resulted in considerable controversy among religious conservatives. These issues tend to revolve around the origins of life, the supposed impacts of Darwin's ideas on religious doctrine, and Darwin's personal views on religion. Some people conflate Darwin's views on the origins of life with the origins of the universe. Darwin's works refer to the evolution of biological systems, not to stellar and galactic phenomena. Second, some religious groups hold misconceptions about how Darwin's ideas on natural selection and biological evolution relate to their faith. **Creationism** became particularly prevalent in secular settings immediately after the publication of *On the Origin of Species*. Most creationists apply a literal interpretation of the Bible to the origins of life, particularly the parts dealing with God's creation of the universe. For example, Young Earth Creationists hold that the earth is only 10 000 years old, rather than the geological estimate of 4.5 billion years. Consequently, creationists see Darwin's work as an attack on fundamental aspects of their belief systems, requiring them to oppose his ideas. The weight of decades of scientific evidence supporting biological evolution led many people to abandon creationist ideas, and to understand that creation themes of the Bible represent symbolic rather than literal truths (Futuyma, 1982).

Some fundamentalist Christians refused to accept that Darwin's ideas have nothing to do with their personal faith. Consequently, these diehard believers morphed creationism into something called **intelligent design**. Intelligent design or "scientific creationism" represents an attempt to discredit the work of Darwin and other evolutionary anthropologists. This belief system lacks scientific support for an intelligent creator or design; adherents simply seek to discredit Darwin's ideas. For example, despite lacking any data to support the existence of "scientific creationism," some people advocate teaching this purely religious idea as an alternative to evolution in biology classes in publicly funded school systems. These misguided attempts have failed to gain

Social Darwinism The misguided application of the concepts of natural selection and biological evolution to the historical development of human societies, placing special emphasis on the idea of "survival of the fittest."

Fitness The average contribution of an allele or genotype to succeeding generations.

Creationism The largely Christian belief that all life was created by a supernatural deity (typically God), the existence of which is presupposed.

Intelligent design The largely Christian belief that living things occur because of intelligent cause, not as a result of undirected processes, such as evolution and natural selection.

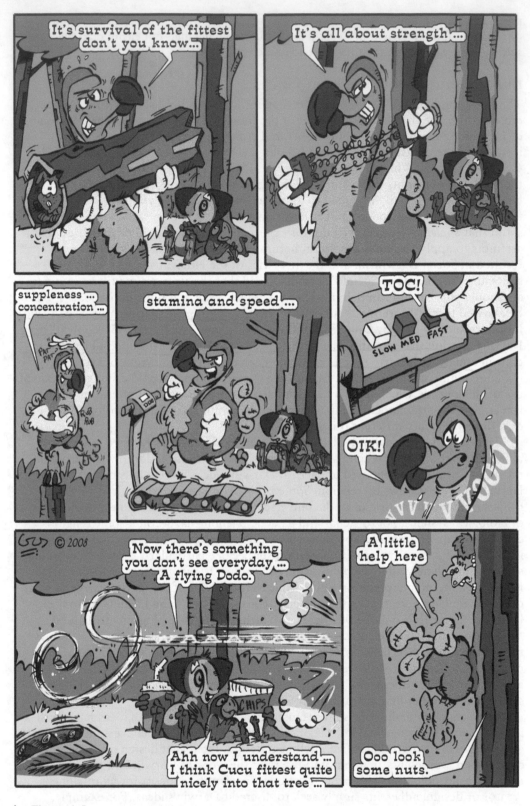

Figure 1.5
Satirical representation of misconceptions regarding the concept of "survival of the fittest."

traction in most school boards, and they have been consistently dismissed by the courts as a duplicitous means of promoting conservative religious opinions. The fact is that Darwin's ideas on biological evolution do not conflict with religion. Why? Because biological evolution deals with biology whereas religion relates to **theology**. In other words, religion has no role to play in biological evolution, or vice versa. Thus, when contacted by a young student about the seeming conflict between natural selection and faith, Darwin wrote, "Science has nothing to do with Christ, except insofar as the habit of scientific research makes a man cautious in admitting evidence" (darwin-online.org.uk).

Theology ■ The study of religion from a religious perspective.

Contrary to what can be found on creationist websites, Darwin was not an atheist; he was an avowed **agnostic**. Darwin's personal religious beliefs were complex and changed throughout his life. Although circumstance and Darwin's faith led him to try to join the Anglican clergy, his scientific discoveries and the early death of one of his beloved children resulted in his rejecting Christian beliefs. Finally, he did not undertake a deathbed conversion to Christianity.

Agnostic ■ A person holding the belief that God is unknown and unknowable.

You may be surprised to learn that Darwin did not use the term *biological evolution* at all in *On the Origin of Species*. The closest he came to doing so was in the last sentence of the book:

> There is grandeur in this view of life, with its several powers, having been originally breathed into a few forms or into one; and that, whilst this planet has gone cycling on according to the fixed law of gravity, from so simple a beginning endless forms most beautiful and most wonderful have been, and are being, evolved. (p. 490)

Darwin did support some aspects of Lamarckism. In fact, he followed Alfred Wallace's suggestion to use Lamarck's explanation of how traits could move from one generation to the next. In later publications, Darwin hypothesized that gemmules passed on traits from one generation to the next. He suggested that gemmules are particles of inheritance produced by organs and carried in the blood. However, experiments by contemporary researchers, including one of Darwin's half-cousins, failed to prove the existence of gemmules. Neither Darwin nor any contemporary scientist knew the biological mechanisms for hereditary variations (i.e., genetics). In other words, no one at that time knew how traits were passed from one generation to the next. A monk in Eastern Europe provided the answer to this vital piece of the evolutionary puzzle.

Introduction to Mendelian Genetics

Gregor Mendel (1822–1884) was a monk in what is the present-day Czech Republic. Mendel was fascinated by physical variations in plants. In his monastery, Mendel experimented with seven physical characteristics of the common pea plant (*Pisum sativum*). For example, his plants produced either yellow or green pods but not yellowish-green pods, purple flowers or white flowers, round seeds or wrinkled seeds, and so on (Figure 1.6). Pea plants are ideal study subjects for inheritance research because a researcher can manipulate their reproduction and maintain large numbers of plants in a small area. Pea plants have both male and female reproductive organs, so each plant can either self-pollinate or cross-pollinate with another plant. Mendel's methods were simple but illuminating. First, he used selective breeding on pea plants so that they always produced only one variant of each trait (e.g., either yellow or green pods). Next, he cross-pollinated the pure plant strains and observed the physical traits of the offspring. Thus, Mendel allowed the pure-breeding plants to pollinate each other, such that the yellow pod plants bred with the green pod plants. The first generation of plants grown from this cross-breeding exhibited only one of the two physical characteristics. In our example, the first offspring always produced yellow pods. Finally, he allowed these offspring to self-pollinate, which produced a second generation of plants. In this second generation of

Figure 1.6
White flower on a common pea plant.
Courtesy of Vladyslav Siaber/fotolia

plants, Mendel observed that the physical characteristics were consistently expressed by a ratio of approximately three to one (3:1). So, three out of every four offspring exhibited yellow pods whereas only one of the four had green pods.

Mendel concluded three things about physical variation and heredity. First, an organism's physical traits pass from one generation to the next by "units" or "factors." Second, each individual inherits one "factor" from each parent. Third, a trait may not show up in an individual, although the trait can still be passed from one generation to the next. Mendel reasoned that one "factor" must "mask" another. With considerable pride and excitement, he published results of his experiments in a scientific journal. Unfortunately, naturalists either derided or ignored his conclusions. Mendel's work was largely forgotten until European botanists rediscovered it in the early 20th century.

Mendel is now referred to as the "father of genetics" because he discovered the mechanisms of inheritance and because his work led directly to studies that established that biological evolution is the result of genetic variations. In the following section, we explore what really happened in Mendel's experiments.

What Actually Happened in Mendel's Experiments?

In time, modern scientists determined what exactly was happening in Mendel's pea plants. The varieties of Mendel's pea plants that are physically distinguishable are now called **phenotypes,** the observable traits of an organism (Figure 1.7). For example, the pod colour phenotypes were yellow and green. We also know that what he called "factors" are actually **genes.** The **genotype** represents the specific genes in an individual or population, whether or not they are expressed physically. In Mendel's experiment, each of the phenotypes was based on a specific genetic code, such as a gene that produces pod coloration. The question arises here as to how some physical features (phenotypes) could seem to skip a generation. You may be familiar with this pattern in that many people describe certain familial characteristics observable in parents passing through offspring to show up again in their grandchildren. In fact, Mendel struggled with how to explain this "skipping of generation" phenomenon in his pea plants. In the end, Mendel concluded that there must be two **alleles** (different forms of the same gene) for each physical characteristic: for example, one allele for yellow pods and one allele for green pods. We can represent the allele for yellow pods with an upper-case Y and the allele for green pods with a lower-case y. You will see in just a moment that there is a purpose in using upper and lower case.

In Mendel's model, each plant inherits one allele for each characteristic from each parent plant. Modern scientists have devised terms for describing these different alleles and how they relate to each other and the physical expression of traits. A **homozygous** condition occurs when an individual organism has two of the same allele at a gene (e.g., YY or yy for colour in the pea plants). Mendel's pure-breeding parent plants were homozygous for each physical trait. Put differently, each parent plant has the genes to produce either green pods or yellow pods. Because each parent plant had two copies of only one type of allele, and those types were different in each of the parent plants, the first generation of plants could only inherit different alleles, resulting in a **heterozygous** condition (e.g., Yy or yY). Only one of these alleles, the dominant one (yellow pod), can be seen in the plant. In other words, when Mendel cross-pollinated green pod plants with yellow pod plants, he got only plants that exhibited yellow pods. Although each of these plants carried the gene for green pods, this genetic material was not

Phenotype ■ Observable traits or characteristics of an organism.

Genes ■ Basic, functional units of heredity.

Genotype ■ Genetic makeup of an organism.

Allele ■ One of several forms of the same gene.

Homozygous ■ Identical rather than different alleles in the corresponding loci of a pair of chromosomes.

Heterozygous ■ Different rather than identical alleles in the corresponding loci of a pair of chromosomes.

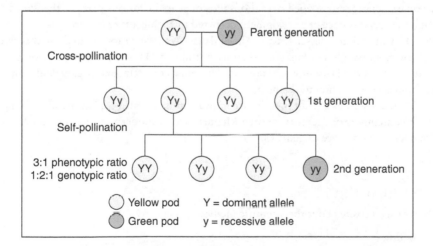

Figure 1.7

Graphical representation of Mendel's experiments with pea pods, focusing on one phenotypic trait (pod colour) and its associated alleles (yellow and green).

expressed by the plants. Thus, modern geneticists define a **dominant** allele, such as yellow pods, as a variant of a gene that prevents another from being expressed phenotypically. A **recessive** allele, such as green pods, is a gene that is expressed phenotypically only when it is in the homozygous condition. Based on these modern definitions, the allele for a yellow seed pod (Y) is always dominant to the allele for a green seed pod (y). Thus, any plant containing the Y (yellow pod) allele will always produce a yellow pod (i.e., YY, Yy, or yY). A plant will produce a green pod only if it inherits the recessive allele from each parent plant (i.e., yy). The gene ratio of Mendel's second generation of pea plants was 1:2:1, which is one homozygous dominant (YY) to two heterozygous dominant (Yy) to one homozygous recessive (yy).

By luck, Mendel selected pea plants as his test subjects. He was lucky because many, but not all, of the traits exhibited by the pea plants sort into dominant and recessive alleles on one gene. In modern humans, a few sets of physical traits result only from dominant or recessive alleles. For example, cheek dimples are a dominant trait in humans. However, other traits in pea plants and animals do not sort out into purely dominant or recessive alleles. In fact, most traits in humans do not result from alleles of only one gene. Eye colour, for example, is the result of a complex interaction of multiple alleles on multiple genes. These complex patterns are best left to more advanced studies. In the next chapter, we focus our attention on where genes are, what they are composed of, and how genetic information is transmitted within and between populations.

Summary

1. Evolutionary anthropology is the application of modern evolutionary theory to studies of the morphology, ecology, and behaviour of human and non-human primates. Evolutionary anthropologists study living non-human primates (primatology), extinct human and non-human primates (paleoanthropology), human diversity and variation, and the various evolutionary factors that influence human health (medical anthropology).

2. Research in evolutionary anthropology is grounded in evolutionary theory. Evolutionary anthropologists employ, whenever possible, the scientific method. In this method, researchers conduct descriptive, applied, or causal research to test hypotheses derived from evolutionary theory. This research produces quantitative and/or descriptive data.

3. Evolutionary concepts developed over thousands of years in various parts of the world, although the greatest pace of development occurred in 19th-century Europe.

4. Charles Darwin and, to a lesser extent, Alfred Russel Wallace co-formulated the theory of natural selection, which they based on their own studies and those conducted by other researchers. However, Darwin was unable to determine correctly how organismal traits passed from one generation to the next.

5. Gregor Mendel's studies of trait inheritance in pea plants revealed the mechanisms of heredity. Although contemporary scientists ignored Mendel's work, modern scientists credit Mendel as a founder of the science of genetics.

INTERNET RESOURCES

1. Check out this website about the scientific method:

   Science Buddies
   www.sciencebuddies.org/mentoring/project_scientific_method.shtml
   Further information on the scientific method can be found at this Science Buddies website.

2. Learn about some of the authorities on biological evolution:

Researcher Profile: Dr. Craig C. Mello
www.hhmi.org/research/investigators/mello_bio.html
Here you will find information about Dr. Craig C. Mello, who won the Nobel prize for his work on RNA.

Wikipedia: Nicholaas Tinbergen
http://en.wikipedia.org/wiki/Niko_Tinbergen
This site gives information about Niko Tinbergen, Noble prize winner for his work on animal behaviour.

Personal website for Dr. Patricia C. Wright
http://mysbfiles.stonybrook.edu/~pwright/
Learn about Dr. Patricia C. Wright, a John D. and Catherine T. MacArthur Foundation Fellow for her work in primate conservation.

Personal website for Dr. Linda Fedigan
www.ucalgary.ca/~fedigan/fedigan.htm
This website profiles Dr. Linda M. Fedigan, Royal Society of Canada Fellow for her work in primate behaviour.

Personal website of Dr. Richard Dawkins
http://richarddawkins.net/
This is the website of renowned author, Dr. Richard Dawkins.

New Scientist
www.newscientist.com
Catch up on the latest developments in science and technology.

Improbable Research
http://improbable.com/ig
Some of the hilarious yet real research conducted by scientists can be found at this website.

3. Find out more about Charles Darwin:

About Darwin
www.aboutdarwin.com
Here is everything you ever wanted to know about the life of Charles Darwin.

An Online Library of Literature
www.literature.org/authors/darwin-charles/the-origin-of-species
Read the original text of Darwin's On the Origin of Species.

The Alfred Russell Wallace Page
www.wku.edu/~smithch/index1.htm
Everything you ever wanted to know about Alfred Russell Wallace.

4. Find out more about Gregor Mendel:

Gregor Mendel Museum
http://www.mendelmuseum.muni.cz/en/
See pictures of Mendor's abbey and gardens, and learn more about his work.

Brother Gregory Investigates
www.brooklyn.cuny.edu/bc/ahp/MGInv/MGI.Intro.html
Try out some of Mendel's experiments at this story-based Brother Gregory Investigates website.

LITERATURE CITED

Bell, L., Skinner, M., and Jones, S. (1996). The speed of post mortem change to the human skeleton and its taphonomic significance. *Forensic Science International, 82,* 129–140.

Brown, J., and Gibson, A. (1998). *Biogeography.* Sunderland, MA: Sinauer Associates.

Bryman, A. (2001). *Social Research Methods.* Oxford: Oxford University Press.

Chapman, A. R. and Sussman, R. W., Eds. (2004). *The Origins and Nature of Sociality.* New York: Aldine de Gruyter.

Chapman, C. A., Balcomb, S. R., Gillespie, T. R., Skorupa, J. P., and Struhsaker, T. T. (2000). Long-term effects of logging on African primate communities: A 28-year comparison from Kibale National Park, Uganda. *Conservation Biology, 14,* 207–217.

Chapman, C. A., Struhsaker, T. T., and Lambert, J. E. (2005). Thirty years of research in Kibale National Park, Uganda, reveals a complex picture for conservation. *International Journal of Primatology, 26,* 539–555.

Cohen, M., and Nagel, E. (1934). *An Introduction to Logic and Scientific Method.* New York: Harcourt Brace.

Collard, M., and Wood, B. (2000). How reliable are human phylogenetic hypotheses? *Proceedings of the National Academy of Sciences, USA 97,* 5003–5006.

Darwin, C. (1859). *On The Origin of the Species by Means of Natural Selection, or the Preservation of Favoured Races in the Struggle of Life.* Cambridge, MA: Harvard University Press.

Dobzhansky T. (1973). Nothing in biology makes sense except in the light of evolution. *American Biology Teacher, 35,* 125–129.

Fleagle, J. G. (1999). *Primate Adaptation and Evolution.* San Diego: Academic Press.

Futuyma, D. J. (1982). *Science on Trial: The Case for Evolution.* New York: Pantheon Books.

Futuyma, D. J. (1998). *Evolutionary Biology.* Sunderland, MA: Sinauer Associates.

Green, C., Hoppa, R., Young, T., and Blanchard, J. (2003). Geographic analysis of diabetes prevalence in an urban area. *Social Science & Medicine, 57,* 551–560.

Groen, J., Smit, E., and Eijsvoogel, J., Eds. (1990). *The Discipline of Curiosity: Science in the World.* Amsterdam: Elsevier Science & Technology.

Hoppa, R. (2000). Population variation in osteological aging criteria: An example from the pubic symphysis. *American Journal of Physical Anthropology, 111,* 185–191.

Jobling, M., Hurles, M., and Tyler-Smith, C. (2004). *Human Evolutionary Genetics: Origins, Peoples & Disease.* London/New York: Garland Science.

Klepinger, L. (2006). *Fundamentals of Forensic Anthropology.* New York: John Wiley & Sons.

Lycett, S., Collard, M., and McGrew, W. (2007). Phylogenetic analyses of behavior support existence of culture among wild chimpanzees. *Proceedings of the National Academy of Sciences, USA, 104,* 17588.

Miller, D., and Salkind, N. (2002). *Handbook of Research Design and Social Measurement.* Thousand Oaks, CA: Sage Publications Inc.

Parra, E., Kittles, R., Argyropoulos, G., Pfaff, C., Hiester, K., Bonilla, C., Sylvester, N., Parrish-Gause, D., Garvey, W., and Jin, L. (2001). Ancestral proportions and admixture dynamics in geographically defined African Americans living in South Carolina. *American Journal of Physical Anthropology, 114,* 18–29.

Shriver, M., Parra, E., Dios, S., Bonilla, C., Norton, H., Jovel, C., Pfaff, C., Jones, C., Massac, A., and Cameron, N. (2003). Skin pigmentation, biogeographical ancestry and admixture mapping. *Human Genetics, 112,* 387–399.

Skinner, M. (1987). Planning the archaeological recovery of evidence from recent mass graves. *Forensic Science International, 34,* 267–287.

Spencer, H. (1864). *Principles of Biology.* London: Williams and Norgate.

CHAPTER 2

Microevolution and Evolutionary Anthropology

GOALS

By the end of this chapter you should understand:

1. How genetic information is transmitted between generations in sexually reproducing organisms.
2. Patterns of genetic variation at the population level.
3. Mutation, genetic drift, gene flow, and natural selection.

CHAPTER OUTLINE

Genetic Basis of Inheritance and Biological Evolution

Population Genetics

Natural Selection and Adaptation

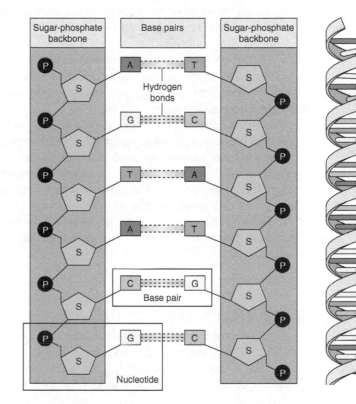

Introduction

As a fan of science fiction, I'd read plenty of stories about the use of genetic techniques to understand human history. Even more fascinating are comics and movies that describe mutants who acquire super powers by some alteration of their genetic code. Although fascinating, applying genetics in my world seemed more fiction than fact. It's not like anyone can just send some of their DNA in the mail to a local genetic company, right? If you could do this, it would have to be exorbitantly expensive. My appreciation for the rapid changes in consumer access to genetic products all changed while perusing the weekend collection of fliers. In one flier from a local electronic chain, I came across a rather stunning advertisement for something other than MP3 players or laptops. Prominently displayed on one page was a full-colour ad for a home kit to determine a person's genetic ancestry! The company offered simple, powerful, and affordable solutions to determine a client's genetic connections to individual ethnic groups. The company also provided detailed world maps showing regional patterns associated with each client's genetic profile. A simple search for genetic testing on the internet revealed multiple companies offering similar services. Each offered loads of information on how genetics can be used to determine a person's ancestry. Clearly, I was behind the times with genetic testing!

In this chapter, we review the main biological processes and patterns in modern evolutionary theory as they pertain to **microevolution**. What's microevolution? Put simply, it refers to small changes in biological evolution, such as a change in a population's gene pool over a succession of generations (Futuyma, 1998). Thus, we begin our review by looking at the genetic basis of inheritance. This information allows us to better understand what exactly was going on at the genetic level in Mendel's experiments, which we discussed in Chapter 1. From there, we delve into genetic changes at the population level. Finally, we review the four mechanisms of biological evolution: mutation, genetic drift, gene flow, and natural selection.

Microevolution ■ Evolutionary changes within populations.

Genetic Basis of Inheritance and Biological Evolution

Modern evolutionary biology is based on genetics. Although genetics is often mentioned in magazines and newspapers, few of the writers seem to know what it is or what it does. For example, Sony advertises that the superior quality of its high-definition televisions is "in our DNA," and an advertisement for Wal-Mart claims that its financial services "play to our DNA." As we'll see, neither companies nor machines have DNA, and they do not evolve! Consequently, many people are confused about the genetic basis of biological evolution. In this section, we focus on genetic principles and description of the sources of genetic variation and its effects on populations.

Chromosomes and Genetic Materials

There are two types of cells in any living organism: prokaryotic and eukaryotic. The main differences between prokaryotic cells and eukaryotic cells is that prokaryotic cells, such as bacteria, lack a cell **nucleus** and are unicellular, while eukaryotic cells have a nucleus and can be unicellular or multicellular. This distinction between nucleated (eukaryotic) and non-nucleated (prokaryotic) cells is a major, fundamental difference in terms of life forms on Earth. Why? Because eukaryotic cells can form complex systems in multicellular organisms, such as humans. Prokaryotic cells cannot form multicellular organisms. We're going to focus on eukaryotic cells, which are found in "complex" organisms, such as plants and animals.

Nucleus ■ Part of a eukaryotic cell containing genetic material.

Within the nucleus of eukaryotic cells are **chromosomes**. Chromosomes are DNA molecules that contain hereditary information. Each eukaryotic cell can duplicate itself and its chromosomes in a complex process known as **mitosis** (Figure 2.1), in which cells divide into two identical daughter cells with the same number of chromosomes as the parent cell. More important to inheritance, and therefore evolutionary processes, is **meiosis,** in which cellular divisions result in daughter cells with half the chromosomes of the parent cell and which also results in the formation of haploid cells that determine an organism's sex (i.e., sex cells or **gametes**). Meiosis provides the hereditary material passed between generations in sexually reproducing species, like humans.

Humans typically have 23 pairs of chromosomes (i.e., 46 chromosomes) in a diploid cell. A diploid cell is, quite simply, a cell containing two sets of chromosomes, or one set inherited from each parent. Put differently, in mammals, each set of chromosomes is inherited from the mother, and the other, from the father. Of these 23 pairs, two determine sex, which you may know as the X and Y chromosomes. Females have an XX set of sex chromosomes and males have an XY set of sex chromosomes. One member of each pair of chromosomes is inherited from the biological mother and the

Chromosome ■ Double-stranded DNA molecule in nucleus of eukaryotic cells that carries genes and functions in the transmission of hereditary information.

Mitosis ■ Cellular division resulting in two identical daughter cells with the <u>same</u> <u>number</u> of chromosomes as the parent cell.

Meiosis ■ Cellular division resulting in each daughter cell receiving <u>half</u> the amount of DNA as the parent cell. Meiosis occurs during formation of egg and sperm cells in mammals.

Gamete ■ A sex cell; a sperm or egg.

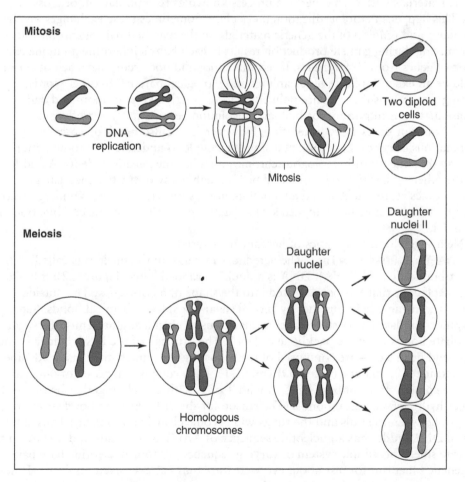

Figure 2.1

Mitosis and meiosis. Mitosis is how most cells make copies of themselves, whereas meiosis produces sex cells. In meiosis, the daughter cells contain only a single set of chromosomes (i.e., half the normal number of chromosomes). The red and blue colours indicate differing alleles. During meiosis, genetic material may cross over from one section of a chromosome to another.

other member is inherited from the biological father. Consequently, each human has two versions of every gene, one from the biological mother and one from the biological father. Humans don't reproduce by passing on 23 pairs of chromosomes from the biological mother and 23 pairs of chromosomes from the father. If they did, then the baby would have too many chromosomes (46 pairs). What actually happens is that each gamete (egg or sperm) has only half the total number of chromosomes (23 unpaired chromosomes in humans), known as the haploid number. When the egg and sperm are joined, the baby receives the normal 23 matched pairs. In other words, each gamete contains 22 **autosomes**, chromosomes that are not involved in determining sex, and one sex chromosome (X or Y), except in rare cases where extra chromosomes are passed on to offspring. The total number of chromosomes can vary between species, and can, in a few cases, vary within species. For example, chimpanzees have 48 chromosomes and the common goldfish has anywhere from 100 to 104 chromosomes.

Autosome ■ Chromosome(s) not involved in determining an organism's sex.

Other cool and important stuff happens during the production of sex cells! When a gamete is made, the chromosomes first find their matched partners and exchange some genetic materials with each other in a process known as **recombination**, or crossing over. This happens before fertilization takes place. Sometimes these exchanges involve a breakage and reunion of the genetic materials on the matched pair of chromosomes. Gene mixing during gamete production results in each baby's inheriting a unique combination of genes from its forebears. If recombination did not occur, then each offspring would be an exact duplicate of its siblings and biological parents. In other words, crossing over means that you are unlikely to look exactly like your mom and dad. Recombination is important for biological evolution because it can introduce new combinations of genes every generation. However, it can also break up so-called good combinations of genes. Let's look at a simple example to understand recombination. Let's say that one set of homologous chromosomes has the genetic code for A and B and the other set has the code for a and b. Although many of the matched pairs of chromosomes retain the A,B and a,b combinations, some chromosomes undergo recombination, which results in a matched set having, for example, a unique combination of A,b and a,B.

Recombination ■ The process by which two homologous chromosomes exchange genetic material during gamete formation.

Next, we'll look at specifics of hereditary material.

DNA: THE BLUEPRINT FOR LIFE The hereditary material in the nucleus is called deoxyribonucleic acid (DNA). DNA is a double-stranded helix (Figure 2.2); it looks like a stepladder that has been twisted into the shape of a corkscrew. The outside "rails" are strongly held together by special sugar-phosphate chemical bonds. Sugar-phosphate bonds are very strong, being analogous to chemical glue. Thus, the sugar-phosphate bonds form the backbone of DNA. The "rungs" of the DNA ladder—where feet would be placed—are composed of the following four **nucleotide** bases: adenine (A), cytosine (C), guanine (G), and thymine (T). Each rung is composed of only two possible combinations of base pairs, A with T or C with G, held together by relatively weaker hydrogen chemical bonds. (The reason for the differences in bond structure and strength between the rails and the rungs will become clear in a moment.) Thus, a hypothetical DNA ladder has a nucleotide sequence of AACT on one side and TTGA on the opposite side. This simple system of varying sequences of four nucleotide base pairs is the genetic blueprint for just about every creature that has ever lived on Earth. That's it, just those four bases. Amazing stuff!

Nucleotide ■ A building block of DNA, consisting of a base, sugar, and phosphate group.

Now we can piece together all this stuff to understand the fine structure of heritable materials in eukaryotic cells (Figure 2.3). In these cells, DNA doesn't just float around in the nucleus. Rather, a DNA strand is tightly wrapped around spool-like proteins, called histones, to form a chromosome. The centre of each chromosome contains a centromere. This structure plays a critical role in how cells divide and in gene

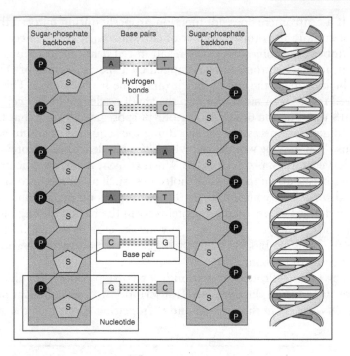

Figure 2.2

Basic structure of DNA. Note the differences in bonds between the backbone
and base pairs. In the figure, the four nucleotide bases are each uniquely
coloured to ease identification of each base pair. Note that A bonds only with
T and that C bonds only with G.

Courtesy: National Human Genome Research Institute.

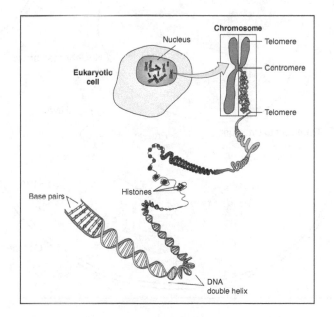

Figure 2.3

Fine structure of a chromosome in a eukaryotic cell. So, just how long is the
DNA in your cells? If all of the DNA molecules in just one of your cells was
unwound and then placed end to end, they would stretch to two metres!

Courtesy: National Human Genome Research Institute.

expression. If a centromere does not function properly during mitosis, then daughter cells may not contain the proper number of chromosomes. Any cell containing an improper number of chromosomes may result in cell death or in serious abnormalities for the organism. Each chromosome is capped by a special section of DNA, called a telomere, which protects the end of the chromosome from damage. This tight packaging is required to fit DNA molecules into the small nucleus within a cell.

So, what's the function of DNA? For our purposes, we'll state that DNA contains the genetic "blueprint" necessary for specifying the sequence of **amino acids** that comprise **proteins**. You may be wondering, what's the big deal about proteins? Well, do you like fruit, vegetables, pizza, or cake? When you eat them, specific proteins in your digestive tract break down the various molecules, such as starch, into smaller ones, so they can be absorbed by your intestines. These proteins do much, much more than just enable you to digest food. Structural proteins form the basic building blocks of every part of your body, from your brain cells to your skeleton to your skin. In other words, proteins are the building blocks of life! Now let's look at how DNA and other cellular stuff interact to form proteins.

PROTEIN FORMATION   Protein formation is a two-step process involving *transcription* and then *translation* (Figure 2.4). **Transcription** is the biological means of copying the DNA code in the nucleus and then getting it out into the cytoplasm,

Amino acid ▪ One of a class of 20 molecules that are combined to form proteins in living things.

Protein ▪ A large molecule composed of a specific sequence of amino acids.

Transcription ▪ Process by which genetic information from DNA is transferred into RNA.

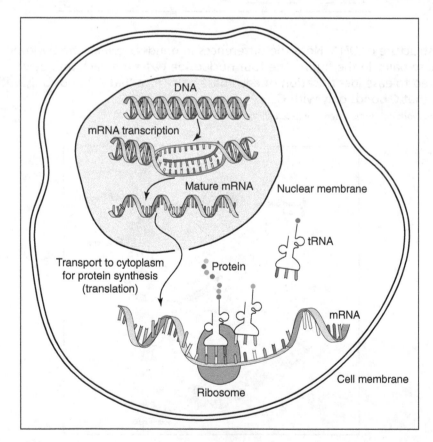

Figure 2.4

A graphical representation of transcription and translation in a eukaryotic cell. The solid dots represent specific amino acids located at the end of each tRNA molecule. The longer string of these joined amino acids forms part of the protein.

where protein formation takes place. Think of the nucleus as the "head office" for a protein-building contract, and the DNA as the "blueprint" for producing the protein. DNA cannot leave the head office (nucleus), and therefore the cell needs a "copy" made of the blueprint (nucleotide sequence) on one side of the DNA strand. Through the complicated transcription process, the rungs (nucleotides) of the DNA molecule "unzip," exposing the nucleotide sequences along one side. A special form of **RNA** (ribonucleic acid), often called messenger or mRNA, makes a "mirror image" of the blueprint (nucleotide sequence), though the thymines (T) on DNA are replaced with uracils (U) on the mRNA. Although there are complex reasons for the replacement of thymine on DNA with uracil on mRNA, what we can say here is that this replacement serves principally to protect the DNA from errors during protein formation. Thus, a nucleotide sequence of AATTGC on one side of the DNA results in a corresponding mRNA sequence of UUAACG. Consequently, the genetic information encoded in the DNA is transferred to mRNA, which acts as a "messenger" carrying the genetic blueprint (nucleotide sequence) out of head office (nucleus) and into the **cytoplasm** of the cell, where translation occurs. If the above is your first experience with protein formation, then take a deep breath. Now let it out slowly. You're going to be okay! If you're still confused, then check out the associated links at the end of the chapter. Some of these may assist you in understanding transcription.

Translation, the process during which the information in mRNA molecules is used to construct proteins, is the second step of protein formation. This process involves mRNA (messenger), ribosomes (factories), tRNA (factory workers), and amino acids. **Ribosomes** are the "factories" in the cell. Within a factory, the amino acids that constitute each protein are specified by a sequence of three nucleotides in mRNA, known as a **codon**, which is a sequence of three base pairs that codes for a specific amino acid. There are multiple codons for each of the 20 standard amino acids in proteins. For example, GGU, GGG, or GGC are some of the mRNA codons for the amino acid glycine. A final RNA molecule is needed to transfer a specific amino acid to the growing protein; this RNA molecule is typically called transfer RNA or tRNA. You can think of tRNA as the "factory worker" who reads the blueprint (nucleotide sequence) provided by the messenger (mRNA) and assembles the "building materials" (amino acids) in the factory (ribosome). Each factory worker (tRNA) has an **anticodon**, which is a unit made up of three nucleotides that correspond to the sequence of three bases of the codon on the mRNA. Thus, the anticodon decodes the genetic information on the messenger (mRNA).

In our hypothetical example, the DNA template was AATTGC and the mRNA copy was UUAACG. The tRNA translation would be AATTGC, thereby returning the genetic information back to the original pattern in the DNA. Each factory worker (tRNA) also has a receptor site for one amino acid specific to an anticodon. Thus, our hypothetical tRNA with the code AATTGC has the following two anticodons: AAT and TGC. The protein factory (ribosome) moves along the blueprint (nucleotide sequence) provided by the messenger (mRNA). The worker (tRNA) then "reads" (translates) this information and brings in the correct "building materials" (amino acids). The building materials (amino acids) are joined together at the factory (ribosome) to form a protein. Although our hypothetical protein is composed of only two amino acids, real proteins range in size from 466 to 27 000 amino acids. That's how proteins are made!

The above description of protein formation is a highly simplified look at some of the most complex processes in the natural world. We have purposely avoided discussing important stuff like the various genetic switches that operate transcription and translation, the evolutionary source and significance of different amounts of DNA in various organisms, genetic errors and diseases, and gene expression. Each topic is invaluable for a more informed understanding of modern evolutionary biology. You

RNA ▪ Single-stranded nucleic acid. The primary function of RNA in a cell is the step between DNA and protein synthesis.

Cytoplasm ▪ Internal fluid (called cytosol), dissolved materials, and cellular organelles in a cell, except for the nucleus. The cytoplasm is the primary site for chemical activity in the cell.

Translation ▪ Process by which information coded in sequence of mRNA is translated into sequence of amino acids in a protein.

Ribosome ▪ A structure within cells that manufactures proteins by linking together amino acids according to the coded sequence on a strand of mRNA.

Codon ▪ Genetic information encoded in a sequence of three nucleotides.

Anticodon ▪ A complementary three-nucleotide site on the tRNA that recognizes and binds to a specific codon on the mRNA during protein synthesis.

are strongly encouraged to seek out this additional information if you plan to pursue advanced studies in evolutionary anthropology. Our simplified review of chromosomes and genetic materials also serves to introduce the concept of genetic mutation, which represents one of the four mechanisms of biological evolution.

Mutation: The Ultimate Source of Genetic Variation

Mutation ■ An error or alteration of a nucleotide sequence, which represents the ultimate source of new genetic material in populations.

Perhaps no other evolutionary concept is as attractive to movie and television producers as **mutation**. Famous fictional mutants include the X-Men, the Fantastic Four, and Spiderman. My personal favourite is Spiderman, who received his incredible powers after being bitten by a radioactive spider. Who hasn't dreamed of being able to climb walls and swing through the air like Spiderman? Unfortunately for the legions of Spiderman fans, the reality of mutation is quite different from that portrayed in comics and movies (Figure 2.5). In evolutionary anthropology, *mutation* refers to a change in an organism's DNA. We know that an organism's DNA influences its biological structure, physiology, and reproduction. Any change in an organism's DNA can cause concomitant changes in its life history and fitness. Despite the rarity of mutations that affect an organism's phenotype, they have a potentially enormous impact on biological evolution. Why? Because mutations represent the ultimate source of genetic variation, thereby increasing variations within and between populations.

So, what causes a mutation? Mutations result from any of the following four things: copying errors in the genetic material during cell division, exposure to ultraviolet or ionizing radiation, chemical mutagens, and viruses. Of these four mutagens, ultraviolet radiation produced by the sun—or tanning beds—is most related to human health. Some potentially lethal forms of skin cancer result, in part, from overexposure to ultraviolet radiation. Not all mutations are directly relevant to evolutionary

Somatic cells ■ Any cells in the body that are not sperm or egg cells.

Germ cells ■ Sex cells (sperm or egg).

processes in populations. In fact, there are two classes of mutation: **somatic cell** and **germ cell** mutations. Somatic cell mutations, which are changes to the nucleotide sequence of the genetic material in body cells except those in the sperm or egg, cannot pass from one generation to the next, so these genetic changes have little relevance to evolutionary processes. Germ cell mutations, which are changes to the nucleotide sequence of the genetic material in sex cells, involve heritable materials and can therefore be passed on to descendants. Thus, germ line mutations have the potential to influence evolutionary processes, such as fitness.

An important thing to understand about mutations is that they do not serve the needs of an organism; mutations are random. For example, there has been considerable media coverage of so-called mutant bacteria in hospitals. These potentially lethal bacteria are not directed mutations resulting from recent exposure to antibacterial medication. Rather, the combined effects of over-prescription of antibiotics and people failing to complete taking their medication have resulted in selection for antibiotic resistance in bacteria. As the antibiotics destroy most of the relatively susceptible bacteria, other bacteria either survive due to natural resistance or have a mutation enabling them to survive (Figure 2.6). In either case, the bacteria pass this trait on to the next generation. In other words, a relatively benign strain of bacteria didn't "force itself" to mutate into a new, virulent strain just to overcome very recent exposure to penicillin. Similar patterns of random mutations for drug resistance are seen in malaria and tuberculosis. The question arises, then, whether mutations are always beneficial.

Mutations can be neutral, harmful, or beneficial for an organism. Most mutations are neutral and typically result from a change in the nucleotide sequence of a DNA strand, but do not alter the genetic code for an amino acid. For example, the amino acid alanine is produced by a variety of codons, such as GCU or GCG. A mutation that changes one nucleotide sequence from GCU to GCG in the DNA still produces

Figure 2.5
Mutations are not directed, and cannot be induced, to produce a "super" organism, such as those often portrayed in comic books and movies.

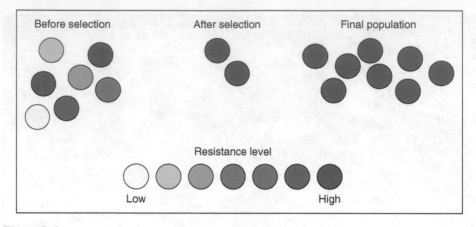

Figure 2.6

Hypothetical evolution by natural selection for antiobiotic resistance in bacteria. Bacteria with natural immunity or mutations for antibiotic resistance survive after selection. The population recovers, but with resistance to previously viable antibiotics.

Point mutation ▪ Mutation resulting from a change in a single base pair in the DNA molecule.

Hemoglobin ▪ The iron-protein component in the red blood cells that carries oxygen to the tissues.

alanine, and if there are no other mutations, the resulting protein serves its intended purpose. However, a mutation in one nucleotide sequence can also produce a different amino acid code and protein, such as AGA (arginine) mutating to AAA (lysine). In some cases, this new protein can be harmful to the host. Most harmful mutations are quickly eliminated from populations by the death of a fetus or by natural selection.

An even smaller proportion of mutations can, depending on the environment, be both harmful and beneficial to an organism. One example is sickle-cell anemia, which is caused by a **point mutation**, the exchange of a single nucleotide for another, due to one change in the nucleotide sequence of the DNA that codes for the **hemoglobin** protein. The change to the genetic code results in the production of an abnormally shaped red blood cell. Sickle-shaped cells can block blood vessels, resulting in potentially life-threatening health issues. For example, sickle-cell disease can result in serious damage to the spleen, which is an organ vital for fighting infections. The disease is expressed phenotypically only if a person has two copies of the sickle-cell gene. Persons carrying only one copy of the sickle-cell gene do not have the disease, although they can pass the gene on to their children. Sickle-cell anemia causes many health issues, including an inability of hemoglobin to carry oxygen. Complications due to sickle-cell anemia are particularly dangerous at high altitudes, where oxygen levels are low. The beneficial aspect of sickle-cell anemia is that it provides afflicted people with a resistance to malaria, a potentially fatal parasitic illness common to equatorial regions.

Only a very small percentage of mutations are beneficial to an organism. One of the few beneficial mutations discovered in humans involves a change in a small nucleotide sequence of a gene (CKR5) on human chromosome 3. This mutation results in the production of a protein that provides varying degrees of resistance to the human immunodeficiency virus (HIV). Although the reasons for the low rate of beneficial mutations are poorly understood, geneticists hypothesize that populations eventually run out of new ways to maximize their fitness. In other words, beneficial mutations are more likely to pop up in individuals in populations characterized by low overall fitness levels (Betancourt, 2007). However, natural selection has selected against most low-fitness individuals, making it extremely unlikely for researchers to find a rare, random thing (mutation) in a population. In other words, low-fitness individuals disappear quicker than researchers can measure their genotypes. Mutations also have certain dynamic aspects, discussed below, that make it unlikely that DNA changes will result in a positive outcome for an organism.

There are few direct relationships among a gene, a mutation, or a trait. **Discontinuous variation** refers to genetic characters that are either displayed or not displayed in terms of the physical appearance of organisms. Wait a second, you may be thinking: didn't Mendel's pea plants exhibit discontinuous variation? In this case, there can be no intermediate forms. In fact, pea plants do exhibit phenotypic traits that result from the presence or absence of a single dominant gene. However, most mammals exhibit something called **continuous variation,** which means that there is a range of differences between two physical extremes. For example, body mass operates along a continuum from small to large in each mammal species: domestic dogs range in size from tiny chihuahuas weighing 1.5 kg through medium-sized Labrador retrievers (25 kg) to relatively huge Great Danes, topping the scale at 90 kg! The usual case is for genes and traits to reflect both **polygenic** (multiple genes) and **pleiotropic** (single gene) effects. In other words, multiple traits result from the interactions of multiple genes and the environment. For example, multiple genes code for things like height and skin colour in humans. Using **genetic engineering,** or human-caused changes in the genotype of an organism, to attempt to alter a phenotype would likely have collateral pleiotropic effects that could be detrimental to the health and evolutionary fitness of the individual.

Now that we've identified genetic mutations as a mechanism of biological evolution, how they come about, and their consequences for individuals, we can turn our attention to how genetic variation influences populations.

Population Genetics

Population genetics represent statistical effects, and are best investigated by using complex mathematical models. Yikes, complex mathematical models? Take a deep breath and relax! This text is not associated with either statistics or mathematics. We limit ourselves to a descriptive review of population genetics. The term *population* has various meanings and applications. In evolutionary anthropology, a population represents all the individuals of a particular species within a defined area. When population analysis is combined with genetics, we get **population genetics,** which is the scientific study of genes in populations. Next, we cover two aspects of population genetics: genetic drift and gene flow. These mechanisms of biological evolution impact how species evolve and patterns of species diversity through time and space.

Genetic Drift

Genetic drift, one of the mechanisms of biological evolution, is random changes in a gene pool over time. It results from chance alone, not from natural selection or mutations. So how does genetic drift happen? Because of the work of Malthus and Darwin, we know that all populations are limited in terms of their size and geographic distribution. What you may not know is that mating is not entirely a random process in sexually reproducing species because there are always individuals that do not or cannot produce offspring. Due to the combined effects of finite population size and non-random mating patterns, chance determines which alleles within a population are maintained and which are lost. In humans, for example, there are individuals who, whether by choice or circumstance, do not reproduce (e.g., clergy in some religious denominations). In many animal species, only a few males have the opportunity to reproduce. For example, some primate species live in groups composed of one male

Discontinuous variation ▓ Phenotypic variation that falls into discrete categories (e.g., yellow or green seeds in Mendel's pea plants).

Continuous variation ▓ Phenotypic variation that falls along a continuum rather than in discrete units or categories (e.g., body mass in modern humans).

Polygenic ▓ A trait that results from the interaction of multiple genes.

Pleiotropic ▓ The phenotypic effect of a single gene on more than one trait.

Genetic engineering ▓ Removing, modifying, or adding genes to a DNA molecule to change the information it contains.

Population genetics ▓ The study of distribution of allele frequencies and changes under the influence of the four main mechanisms of evolution: mutation, genetic drift, gene flow, and natural selection.

and multiple females and their offspring. The other adult males are nearby, either alone or in all-male groups. Only a few of these males have the opportunity and ability to displace the resident male and, hopefully, have time to mate with the females.

Based on these principles, biological evolution by genetic drift has three important outcomes. First, genetic drift ultimately reduces genetic variation within a population. Populations experiencing drift have a reduced ability to respond to new selective pressures in the ever-changing environment. Second, evolution by genetic drift is more likely to occur and proceeds faster in smaller populations, such as rare species. Finally, genetic drift can lead to increased variation between populations, which we soon see can result in speciation by the formation of small, isolated populations. In other words, genetic drift results from something very similar to **sampling error**, which is simply a mistake that can creep into studies when only a limited number of individuals are studied or surveyed. For example, many political surveys in Canada and the U.S. are based on responses from a limited number of individuals. When elections are finally completed, the electoral response is often very different from the numbers produced by limited survey sampling.

Sampling error ■ An error that results from a mistake in sampling procedure.

A simple example with jellybeans can help you understand the basic principles of biological evolution by genetic drift and sampling error. Let's say that I bought a bag of 100 jellybeans (the species) composed only of my favourite flavours (alleles), orange and cherry. Thus, the starting population is 50 orange jellybeans and 50 cherry jellybeans, which is a ratio of 50:50. I love eating jellybeans, so I consume 10 randomly selected candies before I get home. Because I'm picky, I dump out my old bag and go back to the store to get a brand new batch of 100 jellybeans. The catch is that I always fill my new bag with the same proportion of orange and red jellybeans that I just ate. The first random selection was 6 orange and 4 cherry jellybeans (i.e., ratio of 6:4). So I got a new bag with 60 orange and 40 red jellybeans, which produces a ratio in the second generation of 60:40. I then ate 10 randomly selected candies in a ratio of 7:3 (orange:cherry ratio), so my third-generation bag must have a ratio of 70:30. Theoretically, I could continue eating and restocking my bag until I either ran out of money or got sick from all the candy. As you can see, the ratio of orange to cherry flavours (alleles) of jellybeans (the species) drifted from one generation to the next as follows: 50:50, 60:40, and 70:30. This methodology reflects the non-random mating and therefore reproductive processes inherent in sexually reproducing species. Put differently, only some of the jellybeans successfully "reproduce." Therefore, genetic drift is the random change in gene frequencies in populations. Next we'll look at some specific examples of how genetic drift influences small populations in the natural world.

FOUNDER EFFECTS AND POPULATION BOTTLENECKS   Two forms of genetic drift are directly associated with small populations: founder effects and bottlenecks. Founder effects occur when a new subpopulation is composed of only a few individuals from the original population. This can have two consequences. First, individuals may have reduced genetic variation from the original population. Second, these individuals may have a non-random sample of genes in the original population. If both consequences occur then the founder population may "fix" a potentially deleterious gene in a large proportion of individuals. For example, the Afrikaners of South Africa are descended mainly from a few Dutch colonists, who happened to have a high frequency of the gene that causes Huntington's disease. Consequently, modern Afrikaners suffer from an unusually high frequency of Huntington's disease.

The other form of genetic drift, population bottlenecks, occurs when there is a drastic reduction in a population's size for at least one generation. Allele frequencies can change dramatically as the population size increases after the bottleneck event.

Figure 2.7
Northern elephant seal. This species was pushed close to extinction by over-hunting. Despite making a remarkable recovery, the population now has reduced genetic variation compared to elephant seal species not subject to such extreme hunting pressures.
© Robert Schwemmer NOAA, USA

In other words, the frequencies of some alleles are relatively higher or lower between the pre-bottleneck and post-bottleneck populations. One of the best known examples of population bottlenecks involves the northern elephant seal (*Mirounga angustirostris;* Figure 2.7). Hunting by humans reduced the elephant seal population down to between 100 and 1000 individuals. Due to conservation awareness and protection in the early part of the 20th century, the population of northern elephant seals now numbers approximately 100 000 individuals. However, these northern elephant seals have greatly reduced genetic diversity compared to populations of southern elephant seals (*Mirounga leonina*) that have rarely been hunted. Consequently, the heavily hunted populations are less likely to have the necessary genetic variation to deal with differing types of natural selection. The question arises then as to what the evolutionary consequences are for organisms that move or rarely move between populations.

Gene Flow

Few populations of a species are completely isolated from each other. Many populations experience **gene flow**, the movements of individuals, and genes, between populations. Initially, gene flow can introduce or reintroduce alleles, thereby increasing the genetic variation within a population. In time, gene flow between populations reduces

Gene flow ∎ The movement of individuals, and therefore genes, between populations.

genetic variation between populations. How much gene flow reduces genetic variation between populations depends on the rate of gene flow. Species with a low rate of gene flow tend to be more isolated from each other. For example, some sedentary plant species are limited by their pollination system to a low rate of gene flow that operates over a distance of less than 25 m. Conversely, mobile species tend to have much higher rates of gene flow. In most species, the average level of gene flow is very low. The combined effects of reduced gene flow and increased genetic drift can lead to new species. Thus, gene flow is seen as one of the main mechanisms of biological evolution. Before we can delve deeper into the fascinating implications of gene flow and genetic drift for species evolution, we need to reinterpret natural selection in light of modern population genetics.

Natural Selection and Adaptation

Natural selection is the final mechanism of biological evolution that we cover. At its most basic level, natural selection is a deterministic process involving differential reproductive success. In other words, it's not a random evolutionary process, like others we have discussed. Below, we investigate fitness concepts and how various modes of selection affect individuals and populations. With these concepts in mind, we look at differences between natural selection and biological evolution. Finally, we review some of the controversies surrounding the concept of adaptation. Just as we debunked the naive concept of natural selection as "survival of the fittest," we also dispel the notion that adaptations evolve only to ensure the survival of species.

Natural Selection Revisited

Natural selection acts only on existing variation in a population. For example, increased predation pressures have resulted in some male guppies, which are small fish common in North American coastal waters, to lose their bright colours. In this case, there must have been existing variation in the male guppies such that those individuals with genes for inconspicuous colours could be selected for and then thrive and reproduce. Natural selection does not create variation; rather, this mechanism of biological evolution selects for specific physical features. Natural selection determines how phenotypes and, by association, alleles vary in expression and frequency in populations. Thus, natural selection can increase or decrease variations within and between populations. Before we get into the specifics of this selection process, we need to understand the difference between selection *of* organisms and genes and selection *for* features. This isn't just some kind of semantic argument. Perhaps a simple example can assist you in understanding what I mean.

While shopping for a birthday present for my young son, I came across a fascinating child's selection toy, a large, clear tube with various levels within its body. Each level had different sized holes. The child drops marbles of different sizes and colours into the top of the tube and watches them fall through. The smallest marbles fall through all levels to the bottom, with progressively larger marbles being intercepted along the way. This toy was nearly identical to the one used by Elliot Sober (1993) to illustrate differences between "selection of" and "selection for." The toy involves selection *of* marbles and *for* marble size. Totally obvious, right? Just hold on a minute! I also observed that each marble size differed by colour (e.g., the smallest marbles were blue). When I showed this toy to my son, he reasoned that the toy picked marbles based on colour differences (i.e., selection *for* marble colour). In a sense, he was correct. Marble colour "piggybacked" on marble size in response to selection pressure (i.e., hole size). In other words, the toy was not selecting for colour, although that was a trait that did show differing patterns of selection. This simple experiment becomes more relevant to evolutionary anthropology if we consider the selective pressures for **bipedal locomotion**—walking upright on two legs—in our earliest ancestors. Put another way, was bipedal locomotion the feature that was originally selected *for,* or was it simply piggybacking on some other feature? As we'll see in Chapter 6, there are few definitive answers to this question. By the way, my son did eventually figure out what the selection toy was really selecting for.

Bipedal locomotion ▪ Moving upright using two legs.

A modern definition of natural selection must incorporate descriptions of a trait that varies between biological entities and the relationship between this trait and some aspect of reproductive success. The term *entities* is used because the unit of selection can be an individual, gene, or kin group. Therefore, we define *natural selection* as follows: any consistent difference in fitness among phenotypically different biological entities (Futuyma, 1998). We can now turn our attention to an examination of fitness as it applies to natural selection.

FITNESS   *Fitness* is a term that applies to a variety of things, depending on the situation. Physical fitness, for example, relates to achieving a general state of good health, usually due to exercise and proper nutrition. In evolutionary anthropology and biology, fitness involves selection for heritable traits. Fitness has the following two interrelated properties: it involves the success of a biological entity in producing offspring, and it represents the **average** contribution of an allele or genotype to the next generation or to succeeding generations. The fitness of different individuals with the same genotype is not necessarily equal because of environmental differences. In other words, individuals with the same genotype have different reproductive success if their environments have different selective pressures. Consequently, evolutionary anthropologists and biologists employ the average fitness contribution for a genotype.

Average ▪ The middle or most common value in a set of data.

MODES OF SELECTION   Now we can look at the effects of different modes of natural selection on the frequency of heritable traits in a population. Understanding these modes of selection is important because they help explain the incredible levels of phenotypic diversity seen in nature (Rieseberg et al., 2002). Typically, there are three modes of natural selection: directional, stabilizing, and disruptive (Figure 2.8). First, *directional selection* is an evolutionary process that tends to favour either higher or lower values of a character than its current average value. Directional selection promotes phenotypic variation, and it has been suggested to be a primary cause of speciation (Schluter, 2000).

Second, *stabilizing selection* occurs when an average phenotype within a population is fittest. In other words, extreme values of a character are selected against. Stabilizing selection acts to reduce variations in form, which keeps the phenotypic aspects of individuals in a population constant through time. Longitudinal field studies have revealed that stabilizing selection is the most common form of natural selection in animals.

Finally, *disruptive selection* occurs when individuals at both extremes of a range of phenotypes are favoured against those intermediate between them. The evolutionary significance of disruptive selection lies in the possibility that the gene pool may become split into two distinct gene pools. Thus, sustained disruptive selection can increase genetic variance, which as we recently discussed is a prerequisite for speciation. Although directional selection and disruptive selection increase variation in a population, these selection modes are rarely sustained long enough for speciation to occur.

You should recall that the environment is constantly changing, which can result in fluctuating selection pressures. For example, a multi-year drought caused increased overall beak size in ground finches (*Geospiza fortis*) in the Galapagos Islands (Grant,

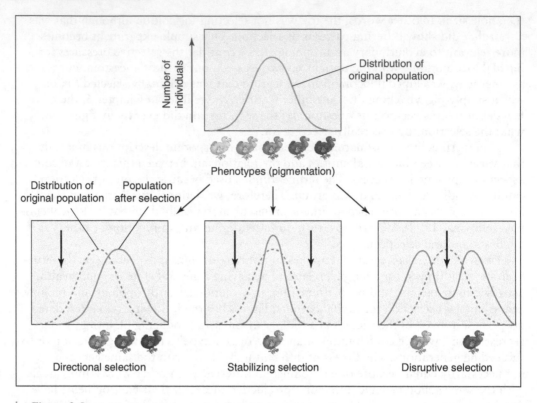

Figure 2.8

A hypothetical example of the effects of differing forms of selection on dodo phenotypes (pigmentation of the feathers, skin, and beak). The heavy vertical arrows indicate the part(s) of the population selected against.

1999). Beak size increased because only individuals with the largest beaks could crack open the hard seeds produced by the few plant species able to seed during the drought. Many birds with small beaks died from starvation. Here is a clear case of directional selection for larger beak size. However, in following years the island received excessive rains, which favoured individuals with small beaks. Small-beaked birds were favoured, in part, because they could exploit abundant small seeds and thereby experienced reduced competition for the few available large seeds. Consequently, fluctuating or even conflicting selection pressures tend to result in a pattern of stabilizing selection over the long term.

BIOLOGICAL EVOLUTION BY NATURAL SELECTION   Now that we've covered population genetics and some details of natural selection, we need to consider a seemingly contradictory aspect of natural selection and biological evolution by natural selection. In fact, here's where things tend to get a little confusing: Biological evolution and natural selection are not necessarily the same thing. Biological evolution is a process that starts with genetic variation by recombination or mutation. Subsequently, there must be a change in the proportion of heritable traits from one generation to the next, which results from either non-random natural selection or random genetic drift. Thus, recombination and mutation produce genetic variations whereas natural selection and genetic drift are responsible for heritable differences becoming more common or rare in a population. Biological evolution can occur without natural selection, and vice versa, so natural selection is not the same thing as biological evolution *by* natural selection.

What's an Adaptation?

In evolutionary anthropology, adaptation refers to both a process and a feature. Adaptation is a process in which any change in the structure or function of an organism allows it to survive and reproduce more effectively in its environment. Adaptation also represents a characteristic that performs a function that is of utility to the organisms possessing it.

We also need to deal with a common misunderstanding involving adaptation and **acclimatization**. Tourists travelling from temperate countries to hot, humid resorts often sweat profusely and need to drink considerable amounts of water. In two to four weeks, their bodies acclimate to the heat and humidity, which drastically reduces sweating and water intake. This acclimatization is neither permanent nor heritable. The tourists lose their acclimated features shortly after they return home.

In both the process and feature aspects of adaptation, a characteristic must have evolved over many generations by natural selection for that particular function (Larson and Losos, 1996). Genetic drift does not produce adaptations. The adaptive significance of a trait is directly related to its function. A species is not required to constantly adapt to a changing environment in order to survive. Furthermore, an adaptation can arise as a consequence of mutations in unchanging (static) environments. Thus, adaptations are not a requirement for species survival.

Parasites provide some of the best examples of amazing adaptations. Two of the most fascinating parasites are liver flukes and parasitic wasps. The lancet liver fluke (*Dicrocoelium dendriticum*) is a parasite that spends its adult life inside grazing mammals, such as cattle. Adult flukes produce eggs, which the grazers then excrete into pastures. Land snails love to eat these feces, and thereby become infected by the larvae of the liver fluke. In time, a snail also excretes the maturing parasites onto grass stems. Local ants use the snail slime as a source of moisture, thereby becoming infected by the larvae. Now comes the truly amazing stuff! Some of the maturing larvae infect special nerve bundles associated with movement control in the ant host. Each night, these tiny parasites force the infected ant to leave its colony, climb a blade of grass, and clamp down on the very top part of the grass stem. In the morning, the parasite releases its control of the ant, which returns to the colony. Eventually, a grazer comes along one night, eats the grass stem and ant, and thereby starts the entire liver fluke life cycle all over again. This parasite evolved a suite of adaptive characters, such as eggs that can survive and grow inside the digestive tracts of multiple species and specific larvae that can locate, infiltrate, and control motor functions in ants. This adaptive process just blows my mind!

My other favourite parasite, parasitic wasps (suborder Apocrita), has caught the attention of moviemakers. An adult female parasitic wasp seeks out spiders and caterpillars as hosts for her offspring. The wasp's sting renders the host incapable of movement. The female then injects one or more eggs inside the host. In some wasp species, the host recovers from the sting and proceeds to engorge itself, and its new parasite, on local foods. The parasite eventually matures and bursts out from the host's body! The suite of adaptive characters here involves sublethal venom, special egg-deploying parts in the female wasp, and the ability of the parasite to know when and how to exit the host. Sound familiar? Have you seen one of the science fiction horror films in the *Alien* series? In each of these movies, a spider-like alien immobilizes a human and then transfers an egg into the host's chest. Shortly thereafter, the parasite bursts from the chest of the infected human. The alien morphs quickly into a large, predatory adult form. Hollywood loves evolutionary concepts!

We'll now cover the reasons for invoking natural selection and specific functions when defining adaptation.

NON-ADAPTIVE TRAITS Because each environment eventually changes, past selective pressures may produce an adaptation that does not fit its current use. Some adaptations

Acclimatization ■ The short-term process of an organism adjusting to chronic change in its environment (i.e., within one organism's lifetime).

Parasite ■ An organism living upon or in, and at the expense of, another organism.

are a by-product of development and therefore have no original function at all. The red coloration of blood is not in itself an adaptation but, rather, a by-product of the basic structure of hemoglobin. Non-adaptive traits, though they may once have served a function, no longer do, but have not yet been selected against or replaced by another adaptation. For example, the beautiful guanacaste trees of Central America are renowned not only for the wonderful shade they provide along local beaches, but also for their incredibly hard seeds. In fact, the seeds are so hard that it's almost impossible for them to **germinate**. Researchers hypothesize that the seeds adapted to be germinated by horses and giant ground sloths that went extinct approximately 10 000 years ago! Consequently, there has been a major shift in the historical distribution of the tree from dry interior forests to the wetter coastline of Central America. In these areas, the seeds germinate either by falling in large pools of water or by being chewed by local livestock. Therefore, a very hard seed represents a non-adaptive trait in guanacaste trees in their natural environment.

Germinate ■ To grow from a seed.

Behavioural Adaptations and Biological Evolution

Genetic behaviour is often described as hard-wired or instinctive, and non-genetic behaviour is often described as learned. For example, many insects, such as honeybees, are born with the instinctual ability to carry out complex social and ecological functions in a colony. Observations of such hard-wired behaviour led to the theory of **sociobiology**, the study of animal and human behaviour based on the assumption that it is controlled by the genes. Despite the value of insights gained from applying a genetic basis of behaviour to insects, there has been considerable controversy in applying sociobiology to humans. Why? Because modern humans are the most complex social beings on the planet. Although some researchers argue that we are born with no instinctual behaviour, others suggest that sleeping and sex represent hard-wired aspects of human behaviour. This debate focuses on subtle, semantic definitions of instinct. The distinction between nature and nurture is a gross simplification of how many evolutionary anthropologists see behaviour, which is a continuum of phenotypic variation within and between species.

Sociobiology ■ The study of animal (and human) behaviour based on the assumption that behaviour is controlled by the genes.

Recent news reports describe the discovery of various genes associated with serious health issues in humans, such as Alzheimer's disease. You may wonder, then, is there a gene that codes for behaviour, such as intelligence? If so, then might it be possible to use genetic engineering to alter something like a person's intelligence? The answers to these intriguing questions are complex, but what we can say here is that behaviour has both genetic and non-genetic components. There is no evidence that a specific gene controls for any human behaviour. Many genes influence many traits, such as intelligence and personality. Numerous cultural and societal issues are associated with measuring intelligence, which is typically done using standardized IQ (intelligence quotient) tests. Put differently, anthropologists have serious concerns about whether so-called IQ tests measure intelligence or measure an ability to take tests specific to a cultural or socio-economic group. Therefore, behaviour is just another trait, like body mass, that has genetic and phenotypic components and responds to the varying selection pressures in different environments.

Misconceptions about Natural Selection and Adaptation

There are common misconceptions regarding perfection and goal in natural selection and adaptation. First, natural selection and adaptation do not produce perfect entities. There is no "perfect design" for a biological entity, including humans, to achieve. In *On the Origin of Species,* Darwin stated, "Natural selection will not produce absolute

Figure 2.9

Satirical view of the futility of trying to avoid natural selection.

perfection, nor do we always meet, as far as we can judge, with this high standard under nature" (page 163). The environment is always changing such that no perfect blend of genetic and phenotypic variants has been or will be achieved. Second, it is very important to understand that natural selection and adaptation have no goal— they aren't trying to produce anything in particular. Just as there is no perfect organic being, there is no "finish line" for the evolutionary process (Figure 2.9). Contrary to a

Great chain of being ■ The belief that all things and creatures in nature are organized in a hierarchy from inanimate objects at the bottom to God at the top.

Western medieval concept, there is no **great chain of being** or *scala naturæ* for any biological entity. A monkey living in Africa is just as important a biological entity as either a so-called great ape or a human.

Moreover, you should not assume that improvements in reproduction and survival within a lineage represent progress. Why? Because the random and non-random aspects of biological evolution are completely lacking in foresight. Without foresight, there can be no goal. The origin of the first primate species resulted from a purely random series of geological and environmental events. What do you think present-day Earth would be like if the dinosaurs had not gone extinct, and what would the effect of this change have on the biological evolution of our species, *Homo sapiens*? As we'll see in the following chapter, dinosaurs were the dominant terrestrial life form for millions of years on our planet. Early mammals were rather small-bodied and likely had coats and behavioural patterns that provided camouflage. Researchers theorize that mammals and early primates underwent an adaptive radiation, which is an increase in species diversity within a lineage. The adaptive radiation in question was due, in part, to the mass extinction of dinosaur lineages. If the dinosaurs had survived, then it is likely that primates would have evolved differently, or not at all, for many extant species, such as humans! With this fun but purely hypothetical thought in mind, in the following chapter we will discuss what a species is and how species evolve.

Summary

1. Genetic information is stored and transmitted in DNA, which form chromosomes inside a cell nucleus. Protein formation occurs through a two-step process involving transcription and translation. Randomly occurring germ line mutations represent the ultimate source of genetic variation.
2. Genetic drift and gene flow are two mechanisms of biological evolution that operate at the population level. Founder effects and bottlenecks represent two forms of genetic drift that are directly associated with evolutionary processes in small populations.
3. Natural selection determines how phenotypes and, by association, alleles vary in expression and frequency in populations. There are three modes of natural selection: directional, stabilizing, and disruptive. Natural selection is not the same thing as biological evolution by natural selection. Adaptation represents both an evolutionary process and an organismal character, provided they evolved due to natural selection.

INTERNET RESOURCES

1. See some cool animation on protein formation:

   St. Olaf College Biology Department
   www.stolaf.edu/people/giannini/flashanimat/molgenetics/transcription.swf
   On transcription.

   St. Olaf College Biology Department
   www.stolaf.edu/people/giannini/flashanimat/molgenetics/translation.swf
   On translation.

The University of Utah Genetic Science Learning Center
http://learn.genetics.utah.edu/units/basics/transcribe/
Build your own protein!

Biovisions at Harvard University: Inner Life
http://multimedia.mcb.harvard.edu/
An amazing video on cellular processes called Inner Life!

YouTube
www.youtube.com/watch?v=u9dhO0iCLww&feature=related
An outdated, but unintentionally hilarious, 1970s video of the then current knowledge of protein synthesis.

2. See some cool videos on mutations:

PBS: A Mutation Story
www.pbs.org/wgbh/evolution/library/01/2/l_012_02.html
Watch this PBS video describing the effects of the sickle cell mutation on humans.

PBS: Evolution in Action
www.pbs.org/wgbh/nova/link/evolution.html
See evolution in action by creating mutations in a simulated population.

PBS: Evolution of Antibiotic Resistance
www.pbs.org/wgbh/evolution/library/10/4/l_104_03.html
Learn about random mutations as they apply to antibiotic resistance in bacteria.

3. Learn about the Human Genome Project:

Human Genome Project Information
www.ornl.gov/sci/techresources/Human_Genome/home.shtml
This site describes the Human Genome Project, which identified all the genes in human DNA.

4. Learn about one person's genome sequence:

The Diploid Genome Sequence of an Individual Human
http://journals.plos.org/plosbiology/article?id=10.1371/journal.pbio.0050254

An amazing publication describing the entire genome sequence (6 billion letters) of a famous geneticist, J. Craig Venter.

LITERATURE CITED

Betancourt, A. (2007). Mutation rates: When the going gets tough, beneficial mutations get going. *Heredity, 99*(4), 359–360.

Futuyma, D. J. (1998). *Evolutionary Biology.* Sunderland, MA: Sinauer Associates.

Grant, P. (1999). *Ecology and Evolution of Darwin's Finches.* Princeton, NJ: Princeton University Press.

Larson, A., and Losos, J. B. (1996). Phylogenetic systematics of adaptation. *Adaptation* (ed. by M. R. Rose and G. V. Lauder), pp. 187–220. San Diego: Academic Press.

Rieseberg, L., Widmer, A., Arntz, A., and Burke, J. (2002). Directional selection is the primary cause of phenotypic diversification. *Proceedings of the National Academy of Sciences, USA, 99*(19), 12242–12245.

Schluter, D. (2000). *The Ecology of Adaptive Radiation.* Oxford: Oxford University Press.

Sober, E. (1993). *The Nature of Selection: Evolutionary Theory in Philosophical Focus.* Chicago: University of Chicago Press.

CHAPTER 3

Macroevolution and Evolutionary Anthropology

GOALS

By the end of this chapter you should understand:

1. The main species and speciation concepts as they apply to animals.
2. How to interpret a cladogram.
3. Macroevolutionary processes.
4. The evolutionary synthesis.

CHAPTER OUTLINE

Species and Speciation

An Introduction to Cladistics

Macroevolution: Species Diversity on a Grand Scale

The Modern Synthesis: Putting All This Stuff Together

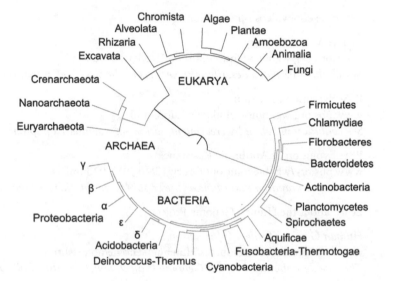

Introduction

As an undergraduate student sitting in class, I often daydreamed about discovering a new animal species in some exotic equatorial forest. Although I eventually participated in many expeditions to unexplored regions of the world, none of my trips provided an opportunity to discover new species. In fact, all my preconceived notions on discovering a new species changed in one moment! That moment came about as I led a team of researchers and local guides to document species diversity in a remote part of Madagascar. I had just returned from the forest to our main camp of tents and thatch-roofed labs. Everyone was crowded around a small bush jammed into one of our lab benches. Perched on a branch of this bush was a beautiful chameleon (Figure 3.1). Our resident reptile expert excitedly paged through a guidebook on chameleons, unable to find a picture of anything similar to this small creature. We felt confident that it was a new species; at last, one of my dreams seemed to be coming true! Various scientific questions crashed through my mind. Was it simply a colour variant of an existing species? Why was this particular creature here? How did its genes differ from those of other nearby chameleons? Could there be other unknown species lurking nearby? My scientific reverie was cut off abruptly when one of the researchers noted

Figure 3.1

Possible new species of chameleon discovered in the Fandriana-Marolambo forest corridor in eastern Madagascar.

Note the slight bumpiness in the torso region, which indicates that this female is carrying eggs.

© S. M. Lehman

that the chameleon was a pregnant female. We decided that it would be wrong to collect (kill) the chameleon for further study, thereby shattering my dream of participating in the discovery of a new species. As we released the very angry and pregnant chameleon back into her forest home, I wondered what would become of her and her offspring. Just then, one of our local guides expressed considerable knowledge of this chameleon, indicating that we were clearly not the first humans to see this creature. As an anthropologist, I suddenly understood issues with the so-called discovery of a new species when local people had known of the creature long before my scientific colleagues and I ever visited the forest. Put differently, it seemed presumptuous of us to "discover" a creature that local people had long known about and seen. Nonetheless, it was a heady experience to be one of the first scientists, but not the first person, to see a potentially new animal species.

In this chapter, we review the main processes and patterns in modern evolutionary theory as they pertain to macroevolution. *Macroevolution* refers to large-scale changes at or above the species level, extending over a geologic era, and resulting in the formation of new taxonomic groups. We explore fundamental issues on species concepts and how species evolve. We then expand our review of modern evolutionary theory from the species level to that of a community of different species in space and time. Finally, we review the modern synthesis, which establishes the primacy of evolutionary theory for understanding the history of life on our planet.

Species and Speciation

Speciation ■ Evolutionary process involving the formation of a new species.

Two fundamental issues in evolutionary anthropology are defining species and understanding **speciation**, which encompasses the various evolutionary processes that result in new species. Resolving these seemingly simple issues is more complex than it appears. Consider, for example, species designations in domestic dogs and wild birds. Dogs come in a variety of shapes and sizes, ranging from the 1.5 kg chihuahua up to the impressive 90 kg Great Dane (Figure 3.2)! Despite this considerable phenotypic variation, all domestic dogs belong to one species (*Canis lupus*). Conversely, numerous birds, such as some species of macaw, are nearly identical in physical form yet represent unique species (Figure 3.2). In fact, different bird species are often so similar in form that non-ornithologists, like me, jokingly refer to them as LBJs (i.e., little brown jobs, little blue jobs, little beige jobs, etc.). Thus, how is it possible that in some **taxa** phenotypically variable individuals represent one species whereas in other taxa, phenotypically identical individuals represent different species?

Taxa ■ Groupings of organisms given a formal scientific name such as species, genus, family, etc. (singular is taxon).

What's a Species?

Typological ■ The study or systematic classification of types that have characteristics or traits in common.

In Chapter 1, we defined a species as a single, distinct class of living creature with features that distinguish it from other species. This **typological** definition, in which a scientist simply lumps similar-looking individuals into discrete categories, is similar to what Linnaeus and his contemporary taxonomists used in their work. These taxonomists held the view that each species can be defined by discrete properties, such as beak length and feather colours in birds. However, as discussed above, individuals that vary morphologically can be members of the same species (Futuyma, 1998). In response to Darwin's ideas on common descent, the definition of *typological species* was modified

Figure 3.2

Species concepts in dogs and birds.

The chihuahua and Great Dane in the top panel are members of the same species of domestic dog, despite major differences in shape and appearance. Although the birds in the bottom panels are nearly identical, they represent different species: two green-winged macaws on the left and a scarlet macaw on the right. Thus, how do we define a species?

Courtesy of Pixbuilder/Dreamstime; Courtesy of Stepanjezek/Dreamstime; Courtesy of Daniel Budiman/Dreamstime.

as follows: Individuals are the same species if they can successfully produce fertile offspring. However, the modified typological species concept is no longer favoured, for three reasons. First, it fails to account for geographic variations within species. Second, strict application of the concept can lead to the erroneous conclusion that males of the same species, or **conspecific** males, represent separate species. Because two male mammals cannot sexually reproduce, then a typological definition of *species* would imply that they represent different species. Finally, this concept cannot account for instances in which distinct species mate and produce a fertile **hybrid**. For example, there is a **hybrid zone** that involves hamadryas baboons (*Papio hamadryas*) and olive baboons (*Papio anubis*) in eastern Africa. These two species look and act very differently, as do their hybrid offspring. Hybrids typically exhibit various physical and behavioural features that are a strange mishmash of those from each parent species. One of the many cool primatological studies conducted just outside this zone looked at mate selection in purebred females. Away from the hybrid zone, hybrid males seem to have little sex appeal (Weiss, 2004)!

Conspecifics ▪ Members of the same species.

Hybrid ▪ Offspring produced from mating plants or animals from different species, varieties, or genotypes.

Hybrid zone ▪ A region in which genetically distinct populations come into contact and produce at least some offspring of mixed ancestry.

Although there are at least 12 modern definitions of species, we'll focus on the two with the strongest relevance to evolutionary anthropology: the biological and phylogenetic species concepts. Each of these species concepts represents a testable scientific hypothesis.

BIOLOGICAL SPECIES CONCEPT (BSC)   The BSC resulted from the work of 20th-century geneticists and other researchers who study the diversity of life on Earth. These researchers noted that any one feature rarely defines a species. Many different species share some features because of their common descent. The researchers observed that a species represents a population of individuals that varies from other species in a variety of ways and that individuals in a population exchange genes by interbreeding. Moreover, biological features prevent one species from breeding with another species. Based on these suggestions and his own groundbreaking studies in evolutionary biology, Ernst Mayr (1942) defined biological species as actually or potentially interbreeding populations, which are reproductively isolated from other such groups.

Implicit in the BSC is that increased species diversity can occur within a geographic region if the species involved are reproductively isolated from each other. However, applying the "potentially interbreeding" aspect of the BSC in evolutionary anthropology is problematic. A strict application of the BSC could lead a researcher to spend considerable time and effort trying to get two potentially different species to interbreed, which can be a particularly serious issue if they are large, dangerous animals, such as wild chimpanzees (Figure 3.3). But that's not what happens when researchers seek to distinguish species. Instead, researchers employing the BSC collect and analyze as much morphological, behavioural, and ecological data as they can on a potential new species. The assumption is that the conservative application of these data provides deductive proof of reproductive isolation.

Despite the importance of the BSC for understanding species evolution, this concept cannot be applied to fossilized species, and collecting data on rare, extant species is not always possible. Thus, an alternative species definition is needed.

PHYLOGENETIC SPECIES CONCEPT (PSC)   Many evolutionary anthropologists, particularly paleoanthropologists, employ various forms of the phylogenetic species concept. Although there are at least three versions of the PSC, we'll review a slightly modified version that is most relevant to evolutionary anthropology. This modified PSC states that a species is the smallest aggregation of (sexual) populations diagnosable by a unique combination of **character states** (Wheeler and Platnick, 2000). You may be thinking, "What the heck does that mean?" It means that use of the PSC requires a researcher to measure and analyze character states of a sample of individuals in and between populations. These data are then analyzed using **cladistics,** which is the study of evolutionary relationships within and between organisms on our planet. Although a detailed examination of cladistics is beyond the scope of this book, we can state that this method emphasizes the phylogenetic history of the organisms in question, rather than present or future biological processes, such as interbreeding. We'll go into cladistics in more depth later in the chapter.

Cladistics came about in response to weaknesses with **phenetics,** the process of classifying organisms based on their overall patterns of shape and appearance. Specifically, phenetics has no evolutionary component and it assumes that phenotypic variation alone is sufficient to determine species differences. Thinking back to our example of species designations in dogs (high phenotypic variation) and some tropical birds (low phenotypic variation), a purely phenotypic approach would fail to distinguish species-level differences in either taxa. Thus, the relevance of the PSC to evolutionary anthropology is that this concept can be applied to both fossilized organisms, such as extinct humans, and to rare, extant primates. For example, the advent of non-invasive

Character state ■ Alternative expressions of a character. For example, each character is described in terms of its states, such as "hair present" or "hair absent," where "hair" is the character, and "present" and "absent" are its states.

Cladistics ■ A system of biological taxonomy based on the quantitative analysis of comparative data that is used to reconstruct the (assumed) phylogenetic relationships and evolutionary history of groups of organisms.

Phenetics ■ The classification of organisms based on their overall phenotypic similarities, regardless of their evolutionary relationships.

Figure 3.3
Satirical view of what is implied in any attempt to apply the biological species concept to the millions of living organisms on our planet.

methods for collecting genetic samples from feces and hair has greatly accelerated use of the PSC in studies of the conservation biology of rare primates. Before these collecting methods, researchers were forced to "collect" (kill) a few individuals to obtain the necessary phenotypic and genotypic data for species diagnosis.

Now that we've defined a species, we can look at how species evolve.

What's Speciation?

Speciation is one of the most controversial and, therefore, exciting research topics in evolutionary anthropology and biology. The controversy exists because scientists are still trying to determine whether speciation is an adaptive or non-adaptive process, how natural selection and genetic drift influence speciation, and what factors influence differing speciation rates in taxa. Perhaps the most fundamental issue in speciation research is determining how different populations can be formed without gradually evolving forms that are intermediate in shape and appearance from the original species (Futuyma, 1998). Although there are at least four speciation models, we review only the one that is most relevant to evolutionary anthropology.

In **allopatric speciation**, some form of physical barrier causes geographic isolation and reduced gene flow between populations. The barrier only has to limit gene flow; complete isolation is not necessary. Thus, a barrier can operate in very small geographic scales for some organisms. For primates, a barrier is most likely to be something large, such as a body of water (ocean, river), mountain range, or an expansive,

Allopatric speciation
■ Species formation that occurs following the geographic isolation of populations.

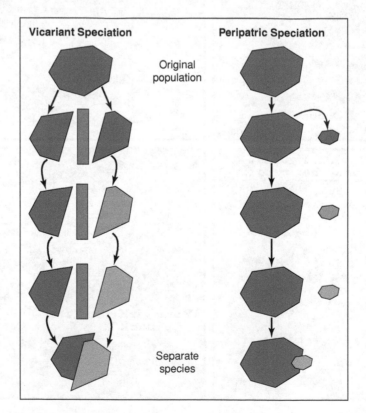

Figure 3.4

Vicariant and peripatric speciation modes.
In the vicariant mode, the purple bar represents a barrier to gene flow.

unsuitable habitat. Isolation is typically related to reduced movement of individuals between populations rather than geographic distance between populations. Allopatric speciation is considered by many evolutionary anthropologists and biologists to be the most common mode of species formation in animals (Coyne and Orr, 2004).

There are two major models of allopatric speciation: vicariant speciation and peripatric speciation (Figure 3.4). Vicariant speciation occurs when a physical barrier creates large, geographically separated populations, which then diverge from each other and can no longer interbreed. Peripatric speciation occurs when a small, peripherally isolated colony of the main population diverges to become a new species (Losos and Glor, 2003). The key differences between the two models are population size after the split (large vs. small) and the extent of the separation between the populations (major split vs. peripheral isolation). In both models, species can become sympatric if the physical barrier no longer exists, the niche expands into the original range of the parent population, or a species disperses around the physical barrier. Although speciation rates are highly variable, the time required for new species to evolve is roughly 3 million years (Futuyma, 1998). With these concepts, modes, and models in mind, we can now turn our attention to patterns of diversity above those at the species level.

An Introduction to Cladistics

All life forms on Earth are united by evolutionary history, which means that each organism is related in some way to all other organisms, creating a vast tree of life. As noted earlier in this chapter, cladistics is the study of evolutionary relationships within and between organisms on our planet. A **cladogram**, also known as a phylogeny or evolutionary tree, is a graph used to visualize hypothesized evolutionary relationships. Thus, a cladogram is a graphical representation of the evolutionary relationships among organisms, whether extinct or extant. In many ways, a cladogram looks similar to a family genealogy. The main difference between the two is that cladograms refer to taxa whereas genealogies refer to related individuals within a family.

Cladogram ■ A branching diagram used to illustrate phylogenetic relationships.

Cladistics comprises three main assumptions about the relationships among the organisms. First, there are changes in characteristics, which are the genetic or physical features of the organisms, within lineages over time. In fact, researchers are particularly interested in the character changes that occur in organisms within lineages, because it is these changes that provide information on evolutionary relationships. Second, all organisms are descended from a common ancestor. This assumption implies that we should be able to construct ancestor–descendant relationships between every life form that has ever existed on the planet. The final assumption is that when a lineage splits, it divides into exactly two groups. This last assumption is a real issue because there are cases where one species evolved rapidly, in terms of geologic time frames, into multiple species. For example, many evolutionary biologists hold that the original finch that arrived on the Galapagos Islands evolved into multiple lineages. Below, we'll undertake a brief introduction to cladistic analysis and visual interpretation of cladistic trees.

DATA USED TO CREATE CLADISTIC TREES   Under ideal circumstances, a researcher employs a complete set of morphological and molecular data, which is sometimes called total evidence. Put differently, all data should be used to determine phylogenetic relationships. The issue of total evidence is particularly relevant to fossils. Why? Because fossils are often represented only by a few scraps of bones and teeth. As we'll see in Chapter 5, most phylogenetic analyses of fossils are based primarily on teeth and a few cranial features. It's very rare to find postcranial materials for early primates. However, experimental research has shown that conflicting cladograms can result from the use of differing datasets on the same species. For example, although we can sample just about every biological and genetic feature of extant primates, very complex statistical procedures are needed to resolve differences between cladograms derived from each data type (Gilbert and Rossie, 2007). In other words, until these statistical procedures were developed, a cladogram based on morphological data often looked different from one based on molecular data for the same taxa. For example, Collard and Wood (2000) compared cladistic trees based on the craniodental and genetic data in extant baboons. They found that the two cladograms, one based on genetics and the other on the skull and teeth, were very different from one another. Moreover, biological evolution can be tricky in that it can produce a **homoplastic character**, a trait shared between differing taxa but not because of inheritance from a common ancestor. If unaccounted for, homoplasy, the independent evolution of a similar character in two lineages, confounds our understanding of evolutionary relationships. What all this means is that we need to view phylogenetic analyses as hypotheses—not as facts. We should be cautious of a phylogenetic tree spanning the complete primate fossil record over 65 million years when this tree is based on data from different morphological systems, such as teeth and postcrania. Thus, our phylogenetic review of fossil primates will be focused primarily on taxa within each epoch. Before we get to that, we need to undertake a primer on reading and interpreting cladistic trees.

READING AND INTERPRETING CLADISTIC TREES   Cladograms come in a variety of shapes and sizes, depending on the number of taxa and the question being pursued by the researcher. We're going to use two of the most commonly used cladograms: diagonal cladograms and rectangular cladograms (Figure 3.5). Diagonal cladograms show evolutionary relationships based on angled lines. Rectangular cladograms also show evolutionary relationships, except this type of cladogram employs rectangular bifurcations. Irrespective of the type of cladogram being used, each describes hypothetical evolutionary relationships. Because you are unlikely to be conducting cladistics, what we need to focus on is how to read and understand cladistic trees in this book and any supplemental readings.

The diagonal and rectangular cladograms in Figure 3.5 show the relationships among six hypothetical taxa (A, B, C, D, E, and F). Each letter refers to a species, just to make things simple. Although the cladograms are shaped differently, they

Homoplastic character ■ A feature in two or more taxa whose similarity is not due to common descent (e.g., body forms in whales and fish, or eyeball morphology in an octopus and primate).

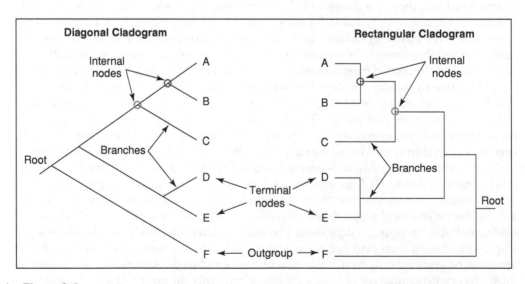

Figure 3.5

Two cladograms showing evolutionary relationships among six hypothetical taxa.

Note that despite the differences in form, each cladogram shows the same evolutionary hypotheses.

show the same phylogenetic patterns. Each upper-case letter is referred to as a terminal **node** or "tip" within a tree. Each terminal node is connected to another by a series of branches or lines that join at internal nodes. Each internal node represents a speciation event (lineage splitting) that resulted in the evolution of a descendant sister group. Put differently, a node represents a recent common ancestor. Researchers are specifically interested in **tree topology**, the branching patterns of lines connecting nodes and organisms in a cladogram. Why? Because these branching patterns provide information on ancestor–descendant relationships among taxa. Thus, the placement of the terminal nodes or tips is largely arbitrary.

So how do you interpret the evolutionary hypotheses implicit in a cladogram? In our hypothetical cladogram (Figure 3.5), there is much more biological evolution at work than meets the eye! Within the cladogram are a number of **clades**, a related group of animals with their common ancestor, such as the one formed by species A, B, and their common ancestor (red circle). Another clade is formed by species A, B, and C and their common ancestor (green circle). Thus, species A and B in our hypothetical tree (Figure 3.5) are referred to as "sister taxa," as are species D and E. Species F is listed as the outgroup. That doesn't mean species F is uncool or bizarre in some way. Rather, species F shows the last common ancestor shared by the entire group of species under review—the "root" of our tree. By reviewing the tree topology, we can state that species D is most closely related to species E. Why? Because they share a unique common ancestor. However, it's important to recognize that species A, B, and C are equally related to species D and E. Why? Because they share a common ancestor at the node joining the branch to D and E with the branch leading to A, B, and C. Species A through E are equally related to the outgroup (species F). The reasoning behind these phylogenetic relationships will be clearer below as we go over an example of internal branching patterns.

Understanding the precedence of internal branching patterns over external nodes can be most easily understood by looking at a cladogram of humans, chimpanzees, and gorillas (Figure 3.6). In this cladogram, chimpanzees and humans share a more recent common ancestor than either does with gorillas. Thus, chimpanzees and humans form one distinct clade composed of two taxa. Similarly, chimpanzees, humans, and gorillas form a different clade. It would be incorrect to interpret this cladogram as showing that chimpanzees evolved from humans, as it would be incorrect to assume that humans are "more evolved" than gorillas, or any other extant ape. Specifically, the node connecting chimpanzees and humans does not represent either a chimpanzee or

Node ▪ The start point (internal) or end point (terminal) of a line segment in a cladogram.

Tree topology ▪ Patterns of evolutionary relatedness among the taxa within a cladogram.

Clade ▪ A group of organisms that contains an ancestral taxon and all of its descendants.

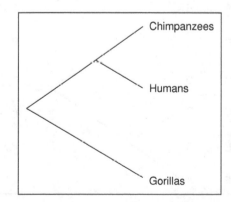

Figure 3.6

Cladogram of chimpanzees, gorillas, and humans.
Human did *not* evolve from chimpanzees, or vice versa.

human. Rather, this node represents some hypothetical common ancestor that resulted in the two descendent lineages (chimpanzees and humans). What we can learn from this cladogram is that humans and chimpanzees share a common ancestor, which was not a chimpanzee or human. This means that we did not evolve from any extant ape, or for that matter, monkeys. The most recent common ancestor shared between apes and humans has been extinct for millions of years.

We need to resolve three common misconceptions about cladograms. First, evolution produces patterns of relationships among organisms that are like a tree and not like a ladder. In other words, the "ladder" in Figure 3.7 does not show the same evolutionary relationships as in the cladogram. Cladograms do not show levels of advancement. Second, although most cladograms are organized from left to right, you should not assume that those taxa on the right are more advanced than those taxa on the left. In fact, you can flip the cladogram without altering any of the relationships between the taxa (Figure 3.8). Each of the cladograms in Figure 3.8 shows the same phylogenetic

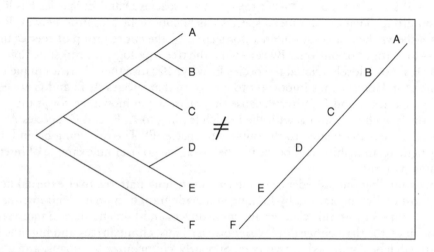

Figure 3.7

Cladograms are evolutionary trees, not evolutionary ladders. Do not assume any implicit progression in a cladogram.

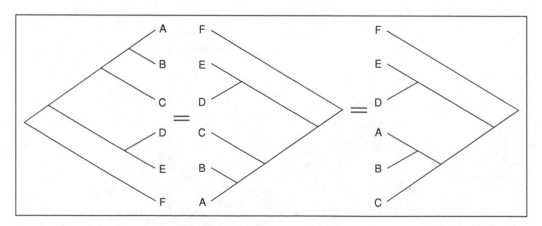

Figure 3.8

Three cladograms showing the same evolutionary relationships among six hypothetical taxa, despite differences in branch orientation.

relationships between species A to F. Third, avoid reading across the terminal nodes (tips), the order of which has no meaning; thus, you should look at the internal branching patterns. Evolutionary patterns are evident only in the internal branches. In Figure 3.8, species C is not more closely related than species B to species D and E. Instead, each is equally related to species D and E. Similarly, species C did not evolve from species D and E; rather, they share a common ancestor.

If you're still confused about cladograms, check out some of the associated links at the end of this chapter. Once you're confident in what a cladogram shows and does not show, then you can proceed to the following sections on macroevolutionary processes.

Macroevolution: Species Diversity on a Grand Scale

Macroevolution focuses on patterns of evolutionary changes in complex, integrated natural systems (Simpson, 1984). Research on macroevolution focuses on the massive tableau of life as new life forms evolve, expand in species diversity and range, and then ultimately go extinct. A macroevolutionary study of dogs encompasses the origins of the earliest ancestor of canids far back in geological time (i.e., millions of years ago), their divergence into various lineages and places, and the inevitable extinction of some of these lineages. The researcher asks questions on what evolutionary mechanisms (mutation, genetic drift, gene flow, and natural selection) influenced taxa in each canid lineage. Other questions follow regarding when and how these mechanisms of biological evolution influenced canids and their prey.

Macroevolutionary Patterns and Processes

Evolutionary anthropologists and biologists observe patterns of evolutionary change by investigating lineage **stasis**, typified by no changes in the shape or appearance of a species over geological time, as well as character changes, lineage splitting, and extinction. Although many lineages exhibit remarkable morphological changes, some have changed little over millions of years. Species within these static lineages are sometimes referred to as "living fossils." One of best examples of a living fossil is a fish, the coelacanth (*Latimeria chalumnae*). Coelacanths were thought to have gone extinct approximately 70 million years ago. However, a living coelacanth was captured in 1938 off the coast of South Africa. Since then, numerous coelacanth species have been caught in waters near Indonesia, Kenya, and Madagascar. These extant coelacanth species are essentially the same in form to the fossil coelacanth.

Character change reflects the kind and number of morphological changes in a lineage or lineages over time. This change can result from the accumulation of new characters, or from character reversal where an organism regains a character trait that had been lost earlier in the lineage. For example, modern whales represent a fascinating example of character reversal (Thewissen, 1998). The general trend for vertebrate evolution is for taxa within lineages to have moved from the sea to land. Whale evolution is backwards, in that over the course of millions of years they moved from land back to the sea!

A researcher spots lineage splitting by analyzing a **phylogenetic tree** (Figure 3.9), a chart showing the relationships among ancestors and their descendants. Specifically, the researcher looks for bifurcating patterns in the frequency and rate of lineage splitting, such as an **evolutionary radiation**, the rapid formation of a new species within a geological time period. Extinction is an important aspect of macroevolution. Earth would be an incredibly crowded place if every species that ever evolved still existed! Although there are numerous reasons why a species goes extinct, the theory of biological evolution holds that all species will, in time, disappear from the planet. As species go extinct,

Stasis ▪ Reduced or non-existent morphological changes over long time periods within a lineage.

Phylogenetic tree ▪ A graphical representation of the evolutionary interrelationships among various taxa that have a common ancestor, based on paleontological, morphological, molecular, or other evidence.

Evolutionary radiation ▪ A geologically rapid diversification of members of a single lineage into a variety of forms.

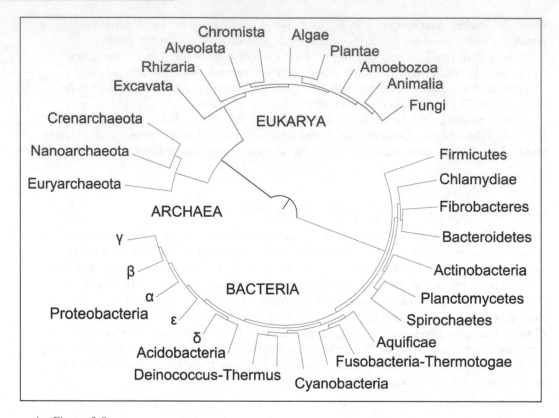

Figure 3.9

Phylogenetic tree of life at a high taxonomic level for all biological entities on Earth.

Humans represent a relatively miniscule part of the Animalia branch, which in this generalized view is closely related to fungi.

Mass extinction ■
The disappearance of numerous species over a relatively short time.

new opportunities become available for other species to diversify and adapt. There have also been so-called **mass extinctions**, the extinction of large numbers of taxa during a geologic time frame. For example, the Cretaceous–Tertiary extinction event, which represents the loss of many species of dinosaurs, amphibians, insects, and plants, happened 65 million years ago. Although the cause of this event is hotly debated, the consequences for species diversity are not. Conversely, some mammal lineages survived relatively unchanged. Evolutionary anthropologists and biologists have synthesized their observations on evolutionary patterns in fossils to formulate two hypotheses about evolutionary processes.

Phyletic Gradualism

The prevailing view of many scientists in the 19th and 20th centuries was that macroevolution, as they understood this concept, represented a process of gradual evolutionary change over time. Modern scientists developed and expanded this basic idea into the phyletic gradualism hypothesis (Figure 3.10). Phyletic gradualism states that biological evolution occurs at a constant rate, that new species arise by the gradual transformation of ancestral species, and that the rate of biological evolution during the origin of new species is much like that at any other time (Ridley, 2003). Thus, a review of the fossil record should reveal transitional forms linking different species within a

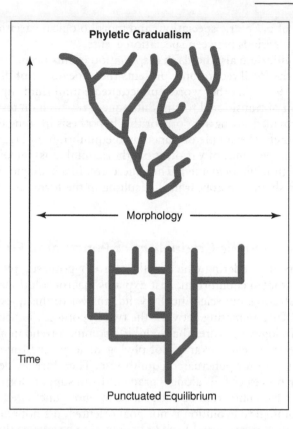

Figure 3.10

Differing rates of morphological change in two lineages.

In the phyletic gradualism lineage, there are slow, progressive changes in shape and appearance. Conversely, the lineage undergoing punctuated equilibrium experiences long periods of stasis, followed by relatively rapid changes in shape and appearance.

lineage. Contrary to misinformed claims made by creationists and advocates of intelligent design, there is ample evidence for slow, gradual rates of change and intermediate phenotypes in many lineages. However, the fossil record for most lineages is not complete, resulting in gaps. Although some of these gaps represent unfavourable conditions for fossil formation and preservation, geologic processes cannot explain others. Therefore, the question arises of whether gaps represent an incomplete fossil record or speciation events too rapid to be evident in the fossil record.

Punctuated Equilibrium

Niles Eldredge and Stephen Gould (1972) formulated a new hypothesis, punctuated equilibrium (Figure 3.10). They based their work on evolutionary processes by analyzing fossilized trilobites, an invertebrate that was abundant in Paleozoic (ca. 542 MYA to roughly 251 MYA) but is now extinct, and by reconsidering the work of a famous colleague, Ernst Mayr (1942). (In fact, Eldredge and Gould coined the term *phyletic gradualism* only to juxtapose that hypothesis with their own.) Niles Eldredge noted that the rich fossil record for trilobites revealed few transitional forms. Instead, species would seemingly appear suddenly, persist for a period, and then to go extinct. These observations led Eldredge and Gould to theorize three things: speciation events proceed rapidly in *geologic time* (i.e., over the course of a few million years), speciation events occur as the result of peripatric speciation, and morphological variation remains constant in the time periods between speciation events.

Punctuated equilibrium also holds that speciation events occur so rapidly in geologic time that the fossil record only presents the appearance of discontinuous change (Futuyma, 1998). In other words, punctuated equilibrium supports the biological evolution of transitional forms. Subsequent research on testing punctuated equilibrium has provided strong support for this hypothesis in some lineages. For example, the hypothetical example of punctuated equilibrium in Figure 3.10 shows that the shape and appearance of various taxa (horizontal axis) remains unchanged for long periods of time (vertical axis). Then there are, in a geologic time frame, a series of rapid changes in shape and appearance, resulting in the formation of new taxa in some lineages.

Which Is It: Phylogenetic Gradualism or Punctuated Equilibrium?

You may find yourself wondering which of the above hypotheses, phylogenetic gradualism or punctuated equilibrium, best explains macroevolutionary patterns and processes. The frustrating, but scientifically valid, answer to this question is one, both, or neither! What?! Discriminating between the two hypotheses sometimes fails because there are no morphological features that exhibit a common trend in all lineages. Thus, one lineage may be an excellent example of phylogenetic gradualism whereas another lineage provides support for punctuated equilibrium. Therefore, evidence for macroevolutionary processes falls along a gradient from support for pure phylogenetic gradualism through a combination of both forms to pure punctuated equilibrium. The point here is that biological evolution is not goal oriented; it's not about progress. In fact, evolutionary change has been likened to something known as the **Red Queen hypothesis,** which holds that, in tightly co-evolved interactions, evolutionary change by one species, such as a prey, could lead to extinction of other species, such as predators, and that the probability of such changes might be reasonably independent of the age of the species. The phrase "Red Queen hypothesis" derives from Lewis Carroll's book, *Through the Looking Glass* (1872). Alice, the main character in the book, wants to climb a hill to see a beautiful garden in a magical land. Although Alice follows a nice, straight path up the hill, she always ends back at her starting point. If she tries to move too quickly, she actually ends up crashing into the starting point. Eventually, Alice runs alongside another character, the Red Queen, in hopes that both can reach the top of the hill. Despite their mad dash, both fail to reach the hilltop. At this point, the Red Queen says, "Now, here, you see, it takes all the running you can do to keep in the same place." Co-evolution works in much the same way: Evolutionary change may be required just to stay in the same place. Any organisms failing to change may become extinct. Quental and Marshall (2013) tested the Red Queen hypothesis by analysing the evolutionary dynamics of 19 groups of terrestrial mammals dating back 66 million years. They compared mammal groups with living descendants, such as horses and elephants, to other mammal groups that have no modern descendants (i.e. those that went extinct). Each of their study groups started with one genus and then the number of new genera and extinct genera changed over time. They authors found that the patterns of evolutionary dynamics, that is the origination and extinction of diversity, changed over time in a way that was not random. Rather, the patterns of diversity loss indicated that groups that went extinct failed to keep pace with a deteriorating environment. The catch, however, was that the researchers could not pinpoint what elements of the environment were deteriorating, indicating the need for further work in this fascinating field of research!

Red Queen hypothesis
■ As species evolve, continuing development is required to maintain fitness in the systems with which they are co-evolving.

You should note that these ideas on macroevolutionary patterns and processes do not mean that biological evolution and natural selection are completely random processes. Although the genetic variation on which natural selection acts may occur randomly, an individual's fitness is a function of the ways its inherited traits operate in the context of its local environment. If natural selection operated randomly, then we would expect any kind of phenotype to occur within a lineage. For example, observe the birds and dogs as you walk around your campus, through a local park, or around the city. How many animals do you see with four eyes, eight appendages, or antennae? The answer to this question should be none, unless you live in the fictional world of *The Simpsons*! Although these features are common to taxa in the insect lineage, they are not part of the existing phenotype or genotype of either birds or mammals. Similarly, we cannot in any scientific or objective sense state that birds and mammals are superior in terms of biological evolution to insects, or any other organism.

The Modern Synthesis: Putting All This Stuff Together

Considerable controversy prevailed in the public and scientific communities following Darwin's publication of *On the Origin of Species*. Many contemporary religious and scientific figures mistakenly saw Darwin's ideas as an attack on religion. Despite the fact that most 19th-century scientists supported the concept of biological evolution, there was little consensus on what caused biological evolution. In other words, there was little support among scientists for natural selection as a cause of biological evolution. Consequently, numerous anti-Darwinian and neo-Lamarckian theories arose as alternatives to natural selection. Although the scientific community has rejected each alternative theory, it was not until the 1930s and 1940s that an **evolutionary synthesis** bridged the gap between laboratory findings and studies of populations in the wild. This synthesis involves the evolutionary consequences of random mutation, natural selection, genetic drift, and gene flow. Thus, it encompassed ideas from three research fields: genetics, systematics and natural history, and palaeontology. The genetic component of the evolutionary synthesis involves results drawn from laboratory and field studies. Laboratory studies firmly established the primacy of genes as the particles of hereditary variations. The combined effects of genotypic and environmental variations result in varying expression of an organism's phenotype. Field studies of natural populations revealed that environmental variations, such as radiation, result in a low rate of genetic mutations. Mutations are random and typically have a neutral effect on organisms, although there is the possibility for multiple mutations to have a positive or negative influence on an organism's fitness. Because of the low rate of mutations, genotypic variations in a population can also occur due to random (genetic drift) and non-random changes (natural selection). Consequently, there is considerable genetic variation in natural populations. Natural selection can and does occur with varying intensity in populations. Even low-intensity selection pressures can result in populations undergoing evolutionary change.

> **Evolutionary synthesis** ■ A modern theory of evolutionary processes that emphasizes the combined action of the four mechanisms of change: random mutation, natural selection, genetic drift, and gene flow.

The systematics and natural history components of the evolutionary synthesis provide information on populations and species. Reproductive and geographic isolation are key components of differences between populations, which in time can result in different gene pools and species. The resulting phenotypic differences operate on a continuum, ranging from only slight variations through to complete reproductive isolation between populations. Thus, speciation results from a gradual accumulation of small genetic differences between geographically isolated populations.

Biological Evolution ■ Change in allele frequencies within a population, or a change in the genetic makeup of a population of organisms over time, or the process by which all forms of plant and animal life change slowly over time because of slight variations in genes that one generation passes down to the next.

Adaptation ■ An organismal character that performs a function that is of utility to the organisms possessing it and that evolved by natural selection for that particular function.

Palaeontologists provided the final pieces to the puzzle on the evolutionary synthesis as it applied to macroevolutionary processes. They noted that gaps between possible ancestors and descendants represent the incompleteness of the fossil record. In other words, not everything that dies becomes fossilized, and palaeontologists have not looked everywhere for fossils (Figure 3.10). Where the fossil record is relatively complete, there is evidence for biological evolution occurring by small, gradual changes in lineages. Moreover, different evolutionary processes have occurred between lineages, indicating that gradualism does not imply a constant rate of change.

Modern evolutionary anthropologists and biologists have moved beyond demonstrating the reality of biological evolution. In this regard, there is no debate in scientific circles about the primacy of evolutionary theory for explaining the history of life on Earth. Instead, the evolutionary synthesis has led to numerous, exciting debates on things like determining the unit of selection in biological evolution. Put simply, researchers are seeking answers to questions on which biological entity, ranging from the gene through the species to the group, is subject to selective pressures. The evolutionary synthesis led to an ongoing explosion of research interest into questions on the mechanisms of biological evolution, the biological evolution of adaptation, and, in particular, the molecular basis of biological evolution. Consequently, we can finally provide modern definitions of **biological evolution**, which, simply put, is changes in gene frequencies through time, and **adaptation**, a functional change in some aspect of an organism that increases its fitness and that results directly from natural selection.

Summary

1. Evolutionary anthropologists use the biological and phylogenetic species concepts. Allopatric speciation is the most common mode of species formation in animals.
2. A cladogram illustrates patterns of shared ancestry between lineages. A cladogram is a "tree" rather than a "ladder": it does not imply advancement, and the tree topology provides the main information on evolutionary relationships.
3. Macroevolutionary patterns include lineage stasis, character changes, lineage splitting, and extinction. Phylogenetic gradualism and punctuated equilibrium are two of the most important macroevolutionary models.
4. The modern evolutionary synthesis encompasses ideas from genetics, systematics and natural history, and palaeontology.

INTERNET RESOURCES

PBS Evolution website
www.pbs.org/wgbh/evolution/educators/course/session4/explore_a.html
Check out these excellent videos on the mechanisms of evolution.

Tree of Life Web Project
http://tolweb.org/tree/phylogeny.html
Learn about the Tree of Life, which provides detailed information about the diversity of organisms on Earth, their evolutionary history, and characteristics.

Understanding Evolution
http://evolution.berkeley.edu/evolibrary/article/0_0_0/evo_03
Learn about evolutionary trees from the article "The history of life: looking at the patterns" on this website.

The Burgess Shale Geoscience Foundation
www.burgess-shale.bc.ca
Learn about the Burgess Shale, a Canadian site considered by many evolutionary biologists to be one of the world's most important fossil sites.

NOVA Online
http://www.pbs.org/wgbh/nova/evolution/brief-history-life.html
Learn about the incredible time period and diversity of life on Earth over the last 550 million years.

LITERATURE CITED

Carroll, L. (1872). *Through the Looking Glass and What Alice Found There*. London: Macmillan.

Collard, M., and Wood, B. (2000). How reliable are human phylogenetic hypotheses? *Proceedings of the National Academy of Sciences, USA, 97,* 5003–5006.

Coyne, J., and Orr, H. (2004). *Speciation*. Sunderland, MA: Sinauer Associates.

Eldredge, N., and Gould, S. (1972). Punctuated equilibria: An alternative to phyletic gradualism in models in paleobiology. *Models of Paleobiology* (ed. by T. J. M. Schopf), pp. 82–115. San Francisco: Freeman, Cooper, and Co.

Futuyma, D. J. (1998). *Evolutionary Biology*. Sunderland, MA: Sinauer Associates.

Gilbert, C. C., and Rossie, J. B. (2007). Congruence of molecules and morphology using a narrow allometric approach. *Proceedings of the National Academy of Sciences, USA,* 104, 11910–11914.

Losos, J., and Glor, R. (2003). Phylogenetic comparative methods and the geography of speciation. *Trends in Ecology & Evolution,18*(5), 220–227.

Mayr, E. (1942). *Systematics and the Origin of Species From the Viewpoint of a Zoologist*. New York: Columbia University Press.

Quental, T. B., & Marshall, C. R. (2013). How the Red Queen drives terrestrial mammals to extinction. *Science*, 341(6143), 290-292.

Ridley, M. (2003). *Evolution*. Boston: Wiley-Blackwell.

Simpson, G. G. (1984). *Tempo and Mode in Evolution*. New York: Columbia University Press.

Thewissen, J. G. M. (1998). *The Emergence of Whales: Evolutionary Patterns in the Origin of Cetacea*. New York: Plenum Publishers.

Weiss, K. (2004) Doin' what comes natur'lly. *Evolutionary Anthropology Issues News and Reviews, 13*(2), 47–52.

Wheeler, Q. D., and Platnick, N. (2000). A defense of the phylogenetic species concept (sensu Wheeler and Platnick). *Species Concepts and Phylogenetic Theory: A Debate* (ed. by Q. D. Wheeler and R. Meier), pp. 185–197. New York: Columbia University Press.

Living Primates

Introduction

For my first primate expedition, I made the naive decision to look for one of the world's most elusive monkeys, Humboldt's black head uakari. With almost no Spanish language skills and a shoestring budget, I found two local men willing to take me by canoe deep into the unexplored jungles of southern Venezuela. The river provided incredible spectacles of giant river otters playfully barking and splashing about, and flashes of scarlet macaws squawking overhead. At night, the calls made by multitudes of small frogs reached a crescendo that reverberated in my chest. Local people plied me with potent *cassava* beer and regaled me with stories of the delicious *mono chocuto,* which was their term for the black-headed uakari. This monkey was a local delicacy! In the last village along the river, hunters indicated that no uakaris had been seen—or eaten—in quite some time. My guides and I paddled for days with no uakari sightings. Our food was running out and my skin burnt to the colour of fresh blood. I despaired at the failure of my first primate expedition. I reluctantly decided to inform my guides of my decision to abandon the trip. Suddenly, the guide at the front of the canoe began excitedly yelling, *"Mono chocuto, mono chocuto!"* Approximately 25 uakaris were climbing around in the trees, right over our heads! Wagging their little tails furiously and emitting nervous chirps, the uakaris took turns retrieving fruit from a large palm tree. Although clearly agitated by our presence, the monkeys did not flee. After what seemed like moments—but was probably more like minutes—they slowly moved off into the forest. Since that initial encounter, I have been hooked on studying primates in the forest.

Primates are fascinating! Many primates are cute, some are comical looking, and a few are awe inspiring. Primates are amusing when they mimic human behaviour. Consequently, you may recognize charismatic species, such as chimpanzees and orangutans, from movies and television. However, primates represent an extraordinarily diverse order of mammals. There are between 300 and 400 species of living primates, with scientists discovering and describing new species every year. Primates range in body size from a species the size of your thumb up to animals 1.8 m in height. The world's smallest primate weighs an astonishing 33 g, which is slightly less than a typical AA battery! Some primate species have specializations unmatched by any other order of mammals. For example, one species has a potentially toxic bite, and others can detoxify plant chemicals that are lethal to humans. A few primates are incredibly colourful and dramatic in their appearance, with multicoloured faces, bodies, and limbs. Others blend so perfectly into their forest habitats that it is difficult for us to see them. Some primates make and use tools, a behaviour that not long ago scientists reserved for species in the genus *Homo.* Although the initial impetus for primate studies was to model human evolution and behaviour, primate research is now a rich and rewarding research focus. The purpose of this chapter is to introduce you to the exciting science of primate studies in evolutionary anthropology.

Primate Taxonomy and Characteristics

Understanding primate taxonomy, which involves the scientific technique of classifying organisms, is important because it enables us to make some sense of the hundreds of living primate species. The Primate order is within the class Mammalia (mammals). Mammals are defined by a number of characteristics associated with their general morphology, ability to control their body temperature (thermoregulation), and reproductive biology. They have hair or fur, a four-chambered heart, a spinal cord, and a neocortex region in the brain that controls sensory perception, spatial reasoning, and conscious thought. Mammals are also **homeothermic,** meaning they have the ability to use energy from food to produce heat and self-regulate internal body temperature (Bligh, 1973), while non-mammal animals, such as lizards and amphibians, regulate their body

Homeothermic ■ The ability to use energy from food to produce heat and self-regulate internal body temperature.

Ectothermy ■ The ability to regulate body temperature by environmental exposure.

temperature by environmental exposure (**ectothermy**). For example, ectotherms will warm themselves by lying on a warm surface, such as a rock recently exposed to sunlight. Conversely, an ectotherm that is too warm will seek a cool place, such as a space under a large rock, to reduce its core body temperature. Modern biologists avoid using the terms "cold-blooded" and, by association, "warm-blooded" because ectotherms are not cold-blooded. Indeed, ectotherms often function at body temperatures similar to those of homeothermic mammals in the same place. In other words, both ectotherms and endotherms have biological design limitations in terms of functional, internal body temperatures. Most mammals give birth to live young, although a few species retain the primitive condition of laying eggs.

Mammals use a variety of thermoregulation strategies. One strategy is to exploit local microenvironments. On a hot and sunny day, we cool ourselves faster by sitting beneath a shade tree. As well, mammals are the only animals that have sweat glands. **Sweat glands** produce sweat, which helps cool the body through evaporation. Evolutionary biologists have determined that sweat glands evolved into mammary glands, which are present in male and female mammals. However, only in female mammals do these glands produce milk.

Sweat glands ■ Sweat-producing and ear wax–producing glands.

So how do primates differ from other mammals, such as cats and dogs? Primates are distinguished by their form or structure, sensory and neural systems, and life history patterns (Fleagle, 1999). Although few of these traits are unique to primates, the overall suite of characters differentiates primates from other mammals. Primates have grasping hands and feet, which are critical for holding on to branches. They also have a clavicle (collarbone). The clavicle allows extensive shoulder motion, which is important for life in an arboreal environment. Primates have two separate bones in their forearms: the radius and ulna. This morphology enables precise movements of the forearm and hand. Primates have forward-facing eyes and **stereoscopic vision,** meaning that animals use both eyes to see, which produces overlapping fields of vision. The combination of these visual traits results in **depth perception.** Why? Because selection is strong for an arboreal animal to be capable of accurately judging distance between branches high up in the forest. To understand how depth perception works, you can try a simple experiment by gently tossing up and then attempting to catch a Popsicle stick or other blunt object, while keeping one eye closed. Now repeat the experiment with both eyes open. You will likely find it more difficult to judge distance and then catch the object with one eye closed then with both eyes open. Primates also have relatively enlarged visual and reduced olfactory centres in their brain.

Stereoscopic vision ■ Organism has overlapping fields of vision.

Depth perception ■ Visual ability to judge distance.

Primates are also characterized by long periods of infancy, childhood, and adulthood. Thus, primates have a long lifespan. These life history traits are associated with learning the necessary skills to forage for food as well as to socialize and reproduce with conspecifics, or others in the same species.

Now that we know what constitutes a primate, we can begin to define or classify different taxonomic subgroups within this order. The Primate order is subdivided into two suborders (Figure 4.1), the **Strepsirhini** (strepsirhine primates) and the **Haplorhini** (haplorhine primates). We use this taxonomic classification to provide order to our general review of living primates. We first cover the main morphological and behavioural characteristics that distinguish primates at higher taxonomic levels. We then look at general aspects of their geographic range, body size, locomotion, diet and activity patterns, and social life. So, let's meet the primates!

Strepsirhini ■ Primate suborder comprising lemurs, lorises, and galagos.

Haplorhini ■ Primate suborder comprising tarsiers, monkeys, apes, and humans.

Strepsirhini

Primitive feature ■ A trait that is old on a phylogenetic scale of development.

Strepsirhines retain **primitive features** of the dentition and skull similar to those seen in Eocene primates, meaning they have some aspects of their bones and teeth that have

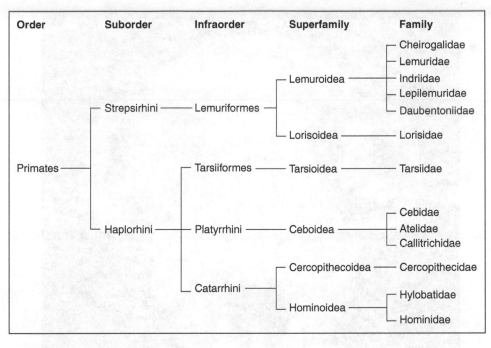

Figure 4.1

Taxonomic classification of living primates.

remained largely unchanged over millions of years. You should recall that the scientific use of the term *primitive* does not mean that the features are crude or inefficient in terms of biological evolution. Strepsirhines have a remarkable dental tooth comb, which allows them to use their lower incisors as a grooming device. Strepsirhines also have a moist rhinarium (wet nose), which is associated with an enhanced sense of smell. The upper lip of strepsirhines connects to the nose or gum, which limits the range of facial expressions. Strepsirhines also have unfused symphyses of the mandible (jawbone) and frontal bone of the skull. The mammalian jawbone is composed of two lateral bones joined in the middle (i.e., near the chin region in humans). The mammalian frontal bone, which is analogous to your forehead, is also composed of two lateral bones joined in the middle. Where the two halves meet is known as the symphysis. In adult strepsirhines, you can still see the jagged outline of the two halves of the mandible and the two halves of the frontal bone. Strepsirhines have a *tapetum lucidum,* which is a biological system improving the animal's ability to see in low light conditions, and a **postorbital bar,** a ring of bone around the eye socket (Figure 4.2). Non-primate mammals have neither a postorbital bar nor postorbital closure. If you have a friendly pet dog or cat, then you can *very gently* feel the lack of bone around each of their eye sockets. Don't press hard and avoid trying this with a mean dog in your neighbourhood!

Strepsirhines have one infraorder (Lemuriformes) and two superfamilies (**Lemuroidea** and **Lorisoidea**). Extant Lemuroidea (lemurs) exist only on the islands of Madagascar and Comoro, which are located in the Indian Ocean off the southeast coast of Africa. Madagascar contains an incredible diversity of **endemic** plants, insects, and animals. You may recognize lemurs from recent television shows and movies. *Zaboomafoo* is an educational program that features a Coquerel's sifaka (*Propithecus coquereli*). In 2005, Dreamworks Animation released the computer-animated movie

Tapetum lucidum ■ An extra layer of tissue in the eye that reflects light, thereby enhancing night vision.

Postorbital bar ■ A ring of bone around the eye socket.

Lemuroidea ■ Primate superfamily comprising five lemur families (Cheirogalidae, Lemuridae, Indriidae, Lepilemuridae, and Daubentoniidae).

Lorisoidea ■ Primate superfamily comprising Lorisidae, known as lorises and galagos.

Endemic ■ Restricted to a specified locality.

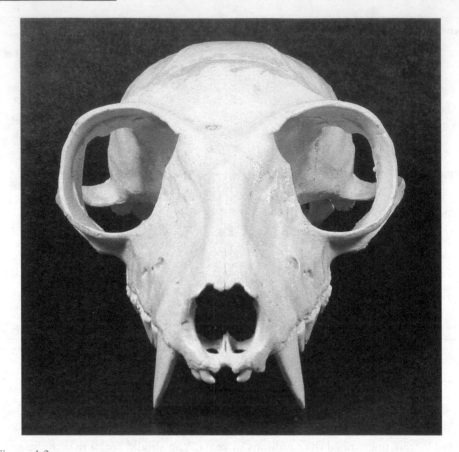

Figure 4.2
Frontal view of a strepsirhine skull.
Note that you can see straight through the eye orbits to the skull, indicating the presence of a postorbital bar rather than full postorbital closure.
© S. M. Lehman

Madagascar, which prominently featured lemurs and one of their main predators, the cat-like fossa (*Cryptoprocta ferox*). Lemurs range in body mass from the world's smallest primate, the aptly named 33 g pygmy mouse lemur (*Microcebus berthae*), to the largest lemur, the 7.5 kg indri (*Indri indri*). The indri is famous for its haunting calls, which sound like whale songs as they echo through the mist-covered jungles. Most lemurs are arboreal **quadrupeds** (meaning they use all four legs to move around), although a few species spend considerable time on the ground. Indriids and lepilemurids have elongated hindlimbs—what we'd normally call back legs—that allow them to use **vertical clinging and leaping** as their primary form of locomotion. This form of locomotion is remarkable to observe when animals jump like ungainly ballerinas across the ground. Most lemurs eat fruits, leaves, flowers, and insects; some have intriguing dietary adaptations. For example, bamboo lemurs (*Hapalemur* sp. and *Prolemur simus*) can detoxify highly toxic cyanide found in giant bamboo, which is their preferred food.

Many of the small-bodied lemurs (under 1 kg) are **nocturnal.** Consequently, nocturnal lemurs have large eyeballs relative to their body size. Nocturnal lemurs tend to forage alone, but they often sleep together during the day in tree holes and small nests

Quadruped ■ Using all four limbs to travel.

Vertical clinging and leaping ■ Clinging to vertical or inclined substrate in upright position and then leaping toward and grasping another vertical or inclined substrate.

Nocturnal ■ Active at night and sleeping during the day.

in dense thickets of tree branches. Nocturnal fat-tailed dwarf lemurs (*Cheirogaleus medius*) store fat in their tails, enabling the animals to **hibernate** for seven months in tree holes. Most of the larger-bodied (over 1 kg) lemurs are **diurnal.** A few lemur species exhibit a **cathemeral** activity pattern, meaning they can be active any time of the day or night. Diurnal lemurs tend to form social groups of varying sizes, from 3 to 35 individuals. Males in these groups leave as they approach sexual maturity. Scientists think this dispersal system evolved to prevent inbreeding.

An intriguing aspect of lemur social life is that females are often dominant to males in ecological and social settings. For example, I observed female Perrier's sifakas (*Propithecus perrieri*) regularly bite a male's neck to displace him from prime feeding spots in fruit trees. The male sifaka would often sit in a nearby tree, hopelessly calling to the wayward females; they rarely responded (Figure 4.3).

The superfamily Lorisoidea contains one primate family, **Lorisidae,** known as the lorises and galagos. Lorises range throughout the forested regions of sub-Saharan Africa and Southeast Asia. With their small ears and large, golden eyes set within a round, fuzzy face, lorises resemble toy teddy bears. They range in body mass from

Hibernate ■ Spend time, typically months, in a state of reduced metabolic activity.

Diurnal ■ Active during the day and sleeping at night.

Cathemeral ■ Varying active cycles from nocturnal to diurnal depending on food availability.

Lorisidae ■ Primate family in the Lorisiformes.

Figure 4.3

An adult male Perrier's sifaka, nicknamed Fred by the author, from northern Madagascar.

Only 500 to 1000 of these extremely rare animals exist in the wild.
© S. M. Lehman

Figure 4.4

A "parked" three-month-old Sumatran slow loris from Aceh, Southeast Asia.
Note the relatively large eyeballs of this animal, indicating its nocturnal lifestyle.
© K. A. I. Nekaris

Allergen ■ A substance that causes an allergic reaction.

100 g to 1.6 kg. Most lorises are arboreal quadrupeds that use slow, deliberate hand-over-hand movements in the trees. Lorises eat a variety of foods, but most of their diet is composed of plant materials (fruit, tree exudates, shoots) and insects. They are nocturnal, solitary foragers. The slow loris (*Nycticebus coucang*) has an intriguing, defensive adaptation unique among most mammals and all primates. Before a female slow loris heads off for a night of feeding, she will bathe her infant in a mixture of saliva and secretions from brachial glands on the inside of her elbows. These glands exude a powerful **allergen**. She will then "park" her infant on a tree branch (Figure 4.4). Any predator attempting to eat the infant will get a rather nasty surprise. Bites inflicted by a slow loris on humans are painful and can cause severe allergic reactions. Primate evolution is truly amazing!

Galagos range into a variety of forest types in sub-Saharan Africa. Because most galagos weigh less than 500 g (range of 69 g to 1.5 kg), they are often referred to as bushbabies. All galagos are nocturnal and arboreal (Figure 4.5). They are solitary foragers, although there is evidence of complex social networks among individuals. Smaller-bodied galagos have a diet composed largely of animal prey (birds, insects) and some fruit. Larger-bodied galagos tend to consume more fruit

Figure 4.5
A nocturnal galago from South Africa.
Note the very large ears of this species, which the primate uses to hunt prey and detect predators.
© *Dreamstime*

and tree exudates than animal prey. Galagos are fascinating to watch because of their rapid quadrupedal running and leaping through the forest. Although galagos have very large eyes and excellent nocturnal vision, they can hunt entirely by smell and sound. Some galagos can capture flying insects out of the air! This hunting technique is remarkable given that galagos hunt in low-light conditions or even in total darkness.

Haplorhini

Most haplorhines have evolved **derived features,** characteristics that differ from those of their ancestors which differentiate them from strepsirhines (Fleagle, 1999). Haplorhines have postorbital closure (Figure 4.6). All haplorhines have a "dry nose" and a greater reliance on their visual senses. Thus, the eyes of haplorhines have a **retinal fovea,** which reduces night vision but improves visual acuity. Haplorhines have a fused mandibular symphysis and frontal bone, except in tarsiers, which retain the primitive conditions seen in strepsirhines. In haplorhines, the upper lip does not directly connect to the nose or gum, enabling a wide range of facial expressions. All haplorhines, except tarsiers, have nails instead of claws. Tarsiers retain a grooming claw on two of their toes. Haplorhines have a single-chambered uterus and one pair of nipples, although tarsiers retain the primitive, strepsirhine condition for both traits (i.e., heart-shaped uterus and multiple pairs of nipples). Haplorhines comprise the following three infraorders: **Tarsiiformes, Platyrrhini,** and **Catarrhini.**

Derived feature ▪ A character state that differs from that of a common ancestor.

Retinal fovea ▪ A characteristic of the eye that reduces night vision but improves visual acuity.

Tarsiiformes ▪ Infraorder comprising tarsiers.

Platyrrhini ▪ Infraorder comprising New World monkeys.

Catarrhini ▪ Infraorder comprising Old World monkeys, apes, and humans.

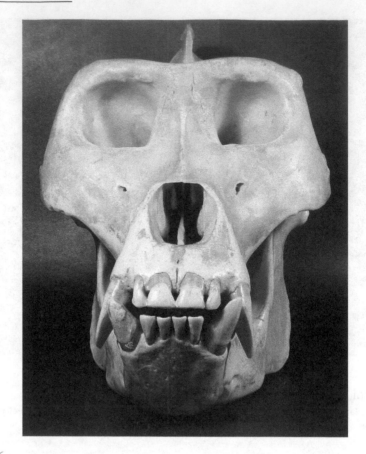

Figure 4.6

Catarrhine skull.

Note that the back of the eye orbits are completely encased in bone except for small holes through which pass the optic nerves and blood supply to the eyes.
© S. M. Lehman

TARSIIFORMES   Tarsiiformes contains only one genus (*Tarsius*; Figure 4.7). Tarsiers exist in tropical forests on the islands of the Philippines, Sulawesi, Borneo, and Sumatra in Southeast Asia. Tarsiers are amongst the smallest-bodied of all living primates, with a body mass of 80 to 130 g. A tarsier's eyeball is larger than its brain! Tarsiers have extremely long legs relative to their body size. In tarsiers, the tibia and fibula (lower leg bones) are fused, presumably to improve leg stability during leaping. Consequently, they are capable of rapid leaps of up to 3 m, which is a remarkable distance given their body length of approximately 11.7 cm. To match this prodigious leap, a 1.8 m tall human would have to jump 46 m! Tarsiers are nocturnal faunivores, with most of the diet made up of small insects, snakes, and lizards. A female tarsier gives birth to a single offspring that equals 30 percent of her weight. Much remains to be learned about the evolutionary ecology of tarsiers. Perhaps you will go on to study these amazing primates.

PLATYRRHINI (NEW WORLD MONKEYS)   Platyrrhines are characterized by having flat noses (hence its name, platyrrhine, which means flat nose) and side-facing nostrils. They are also known as the New World or neotropical monkeys because they are

Figure 4.7

A tarsier from Southeast Asia.

Note the large eyeballs and long legs and digits of this remarkable primate.
© *M. Shekelle*

found only in Central and South America (Figure 4.8). Encompassing three primate families (Cebidae, Atelidae, and Callitrichidae), they range in body mass from the world's smallest monkey, the 110 g pygmy marmoset (*Cebuella pygmaea*), to the 11.4 kg Mexican black howler monkey (*Alouatta pigra*). Neotropical primates are arboreal, although a few species come to the ground for short periods. Although all platyrrhines have tails, only the Atelidae and monkeys in the genus *Cebus* have a **prehensile tail,** which can support their entire body weight, to stabilize themselves during arboreal travel, foraging, and resting. For example, male muriquis (*Brachyteles arachnoides*) will diffuse tension by cuddling while hanging upside down by their tails (Strier, 1999)! Platyrrhines eat a variety of foods, including fruits, flowers, leaves, and insects. Pithecines, a unique subfamily of New World monkeys, can exert up to 50 kg per sq mm of bite force to open heavily armoured fruit and then crush the equally tough seeds. Monkeys in the genus *Aotus* are the only nocturnal catarrhines or platyrrhines. All platyrrhines live in social groups; some have unique modes of communication. Howler monkeys are famous for incredible calls, the loudest made by any terrestrial animal, travelling up to 3 km. The raucous calls of an alarmed troop of howler monkeys can be deafening if they are above your camp! In Suriname, male brown capuchin monkeys (*Cebus apella*) routinely bang tough fruit against hard surfaces to mediate social

Prehensile tail ■ A tail that can support the entire body weight of the animal.

Figure 4.8

A capuchin monkey from South America.

Note the side-facing nostrils of this monkey, which relates to the platyrrhine name (flat nosed).
© S. M. Lehman

Callitrichidae ■
Primate family comprising marmosets, tamarins, and Goeldi's monkeys.

interactions among capuchins elsewhere (Anderson et al., 2007). In other words, the monkeys are "banging a drum" to communicate with conspecifics. There are limitless research questions to explore in studies of the amazing platyrrhines.

Within the platyrrhines is the unique family of the **Callitrichidae,** a primate family that includes tamarins, marmosets, and Goeldi's monkey. Most of these monkeys weigh less than 650 g, females regularly give birth to twins, and they are often brightly coloured. For example, the saddle-back tamarin (*Saguinus fuscicollis*) has a beautiful reddish-black coat and white fur around its mouth that makes it look like a very small, arboreal circus clown (Figure 4.9). Callitrichines seem to be adapted to exploit degraded and secondary habitats. For example, common marmosets (*Callithrix jacchus*) have a remarkable reproductive adaptation. Marmosets live in groups comprising one breeding female, several adult males who mate with this female, and a varying number of non-reproducing females and males. Primatologists found that subordinate (non-reproducing) females in these groups are reproductively suppressed because of their own hormones (Barrett et al., 1990)! When the researchers isolated subordinate females, the monkeys began to ovulate. That's cool evolutionary stuff! Goeldi's monkey (*Callimico goeldii*) is an interesting primate that exhibits transitional features between cebids and callitrichids. Although Goeldi's monkeys have the small body size seen in marmosets and tamarins, they produce single offspring rather than twins.

Figure 4.9

A saddle-back tamarin from Bolivia, South America.

© L. Porter

CATARRHINI (OLD WORLD MONKEYS AND APES)   Catarrhines are characterized by their narrow noses (the name Catarrhini relates to the narrow nose), and comprises three primate families: **Cercopithecidae, Hylobatidae,** and **Hominidae.** Cercopithecidae and Hylobatidae have **ischial callosities,** or what we'd call sitting pads because animals literally use them to sit on! The presence of bilophodont molars and relatively narrow noses distinguish Cercopithecidae from the Hylobatidae and Hominidae, which have **bunodont molars.** Bilophodont molars are associated with the chewing of leafy plant materials, whereas bunodont molars are characteristic of animals that eat different kinds of foods with different physical consistencies (fruits, flowers, grains, meat). Hylobatidae and Hominidae lack a tail and they have larger brains and body size than Cercopithecidae. All extant catarrhines are diurnal.

The family Cercopithecidae has two subfamilies, the **Cercopithecinae** and the **Colobinae.** Cercopithecinae are located predominantly in Africa. One widespread genus known as macaques (*Macaca*) ranges into Gibraltar, northern Africa, Asia, and Southeast Asia. These monkeys range in body mass from the 1 kg talapoin monkey (*Miopithecus talapoin*) to the 32 kg male mandrill (*Mandrillus sphinx*). Male mandrills are also noteworthy for their red and blue snouts and the brilliant colours on their rumps. Many cercopithecines are **sexually dimorphic** in body and canine size, with males larger than females. Cercopithecines prefer ripe fruit, which they often pack into their cheek pouches. I once observed an aged male rhesus macaque (*Macaca mulatta*)

Cercopithecidae ■ Primate family comprising Old World monkeys.

Hylobatidae ■ Primate family comprising gibbons and siamangs.

Hominidae ■ Primate family comprising apes and humans.

Ischial callosities ■ Well-developed sitting pads.

Bunodont molars ■ Teeth possessing four major cusps arranged in a rectangle.

Cercopithecinae ■ Primate subfamily comprising various Old World monkeys.

Colobinae ■ Primate subfamily comprising various Old World leaf-eating monkeys.

Sexually dimorphic ■ Males and females of the same species having different physical features.

Figure 4.10

A baboon from East Africa.

Note the downward-facing nostrils and narrow nose of this monkey, which relates to the catarrhine name (narrow nosed).
Courtesy of sekarb/fotolia

calmly stalking some younger animals in his group. After catching one of the rambunctious youngsters, the aged male gently pried open its mouth and transplanted the food from youngster's cheek pouches into his own! Most cercopithecines are arboreal quadrupeds. However, large-bodied cercopithecines, such as baboons (*Papio*) and geladas (*Theropithecus*), are predominantly terrestrial quadrupeds (Figure 4.10). Cercopithecines live in a variety of social groups, from monogamous groups containing an adult male and female (plus their offspring) to large multi-male, multi-female groups. Field researchers have observed mandrills occasionally forming huge supergroups of 250 animals (Caldecott et al., 1996)!

Colobines exist in the forested regions of Africa and Asia (Figure 4.11). They have high cusps on their molar teeth, long tails and hindlimbs, and short thumbs. Colobines do not have cheek pouches. Colobines range in body mass from 4.2 to 11.2 kg. Although a few colobines come to the ground and some thrive in cities in India, most species are arboreal quadrupeds in tropical forests. Leaf-eating monkeys predominantly eat leaves (called a folivorous diet), with a marked preference for young, palatable leaves. Because leaves are extremely difficult to digest, colobines have evolved a multichambered, **complex stomach.** Colobines live off the volatile fatty

Complex stomach Amazing adaptation to allow bacterial fermentation of leaves.

Figure 4.11

An African colobus (leaf-eating) monkey.

Colobines have unique adaptations associated with their diet of leaves.
Courtesy of Henk Bentlage/fotolia

acids produced by the bacterial colonies. Most primates, including humans, have a single-chambered stomach, meaning we cannot subsist on a diet composed of plant leaves. Colobines live in social troops of 5 to 90 individuals; the groups vary in size and composition depending on the species and habitat.

Hylobatids are the small-bodied apes (4.4–11.1 kg) of Southeast Asia (Figure 4.12). They retain many skeletal features similar to those seen in monkeys. However, they are unique in having the longest forelimbs relative to body size of any extant primate. Gibbons are incredible arboreal aerialists. Their special form of locomotion, swinging from branch to branch using two arms, is known as **brachiation.** Small-bodied gibbons are among the fastest and most agile of all arboreal, non-flying mammals. Gibbons eat plenty of ripe fruit. During times of fruit scarcity, they supplement their diet with young leaves and invertebrates. Gibbons are famous for their haunting and beautiful "song" vocalizations, which can last for up to 30 seconds. These vocalizations serve, in part, to warn conspecifics from trespassing into the callers' territory. Since the 1960s, primatologists thought that male and female gibbons mate for life (monogamy). However, recent field studies reveal that some gibbon species have extra-pair copulations (Reichard, 1995). This intriguing finding calls into question theories on monogamy in animals.

The Hominidae are the large-bodied apes (orangutans, gorillas, and chimpanzees) and humans (*Homo sapiens*). Orangutans (genus *Pongo*) are the only large-bodied apes

Brachiation ▪ Travel involving two-armed swinging from branch to branch.

Figure 4.12

A gibbon in SE Asia.

Note the very long arms of this hylobatid.
Courtesy of Big Face/fotolia

Quadrumanous climbing ■ The use of varying combinations of all four limbs to move through an arboreal habitat.

Knuckle-walking ■ Walking on four limbs by partially supporting body weight on the middle phlanges (bones in finger).

in Asia. Gorillas and chimpanzees range into the equatorial regions of sub-Saharan Africa. Body mass in the Hominidae ranges from an average of 42 kg in chimpanzees (*Pan troglodytes schweinfurthii*) up to 175 kg in the awesome adult male eastern lowland gorilla (*Gorilla gorilla graueri;* Figure 4.13). Orangutans, gorillas, and chimpanzees have long arms, hands, and feet. All the large-bodied apes are sexually dimorphic in body size and dentition, with males being larger than females. Orangutans, gorillas, and chimpanzees are less suspensory than gibbons, meaning that these large-bodied apes are not acrobatic swingers through the forest. Instead, they employ **quadrumanous climbing,** meaning they use three to four limbs to move carefully and methodically through the forest. On the ground, large-bodied apes use quadrupedal walking and running. However, gorillas and chimpanzees employ a unique hand position called **knuckle-walking.** Instead of supporting their body weight on their palms, they support themselves in the dorsal surfaces of their curled-up fingers (Fleagle, 1999). Orangutans, gorillas, and chimpanzees are primarily forest primates.

There is considerable research interest in the diet and feeding ecology of large-bodied apes. Although the initial impetus for these studies was to model hominid evolution, recent studies focus on apes as part of complex tropical environments. Gorillas tend to be highly folivorous in eastern Africa, whereas those in western Africa prefer fruit. Orangutans and chimpanzees prefer to eat fruit, which is termed a

Figure 4.13

Mountain gorillas in Rwanda.

A "silverback" adult male is on the left and an adult female is on the right. Note the overall size disparities between the two individuals.
© P. Sicotte

frugivorous diet. When fruit is unavailable, they supplement their diet with leaves and nuts. Chimpanzees also hunt and eat 35 types of vertebrate animals in eastern Africa, with young red colobus monkeys representing the preferred prey (Stanford, 1998). Groups of adult and adolescent male chimpanzees conduct most hunts. Researchers have documented improved hunting success when the animals hunt socially versus when individuals hunt alone. Adult females rarely join these hunting parties. After a successful hunt, many of the other troop members excitedly beg for pieces of meat. Successful hunters are very particular about who gets these tasty morsels, with the choicest pieces reciprocally offered to maintain social alliances. Sounds like primate politics!

Another remarkable aspect of the feeding ecology of large-bodied apes is that most species make and use tools. For example, chimpanzees in western Africa use stones and hard wood to crack open heavily armoured nuts and then eat the contents. They even use small tools to extract small seed fragments from the hard husk. Nut cracking is a learned behaviour that requires years of observation and practice, which produces plenty of bruised fingers! In eastern Africa, chimpanzees alter local plant materials to create long flexible strips to "fish" for termites or ants (Figure 4.14). An animal inserts the tool into a hole in the insect nest, which causes the soldiers to bite the stem. The "fisherchimp" then carefully pulls out the tool and eats the insects. Chimpanzees fashion tools specific to above-ground and below-ground nests. Researchers recently discovered that chimpanzees also create spear-like tools to skewer and then extract sleeping galagos from tree holes (Pruetz and Bertolani, 2007). Now that is morbidly cool! Scientific studies of hunting and tool use in animals have important implications for our understanding of what it means to be human.

Figure 4.14

An adult female chimpanzee using a tool to probe a tree hole.
Courtesy of Daniel Bellhouse/Dreamstime

There have been numerous, fascinating studies of the social life of orangutans, chimpanzees, and gorillas. Orangutans lead a largely solitary life, although males and females will spend considerable amounts of time together when a female is sexually receptive. Conversely, all gorillas and chimpanzees are highly social and live in groups ranging from 9 to 12 individuals in gorillas and up to 50 animals in chimpanzees. Dr. Jane Goodall and other researchers conducted ground-breaking studies of chimpanzee social life at Gombe Stream in Tanzania (Goodall, 1986). This research was the first to discover infanticide, courtship rituals between males and females, hunting and meat consumption, and even a primitive form of "warfare" in non-human primates. For example, Dr. Goodall and her local assistants documented chimpanzees in one group systematically annihilating members of a nearby splinter group. Despite the length and breadth of this seminal work, much remains to be learned about the social life of large-bodied apes.

Body Size

Body size is a fundamental aspect of the evolutionary anthropology of primates. Large primates are not simply scaled-up versions of small primates (Fleagle, 1999). The reason for this scaling difference is that area and volume change at different rates as the linear dimensions of an animal increase. The area of an animal increases as a function of the square of its linear dimensions (length × width). Volume increases as a function of the cube of the linear dimensions (length × width × height). If an animal doubles in size (i.e., double in length, breadth, and width), then the area would be four times larger and the volume would be eight times greater. Consequently, large animals are proportioned differently than small animals. For example, let's compare the thigh bone, or femur, of a small-bodied marmoset, weighing 500 g, to that of a gorilla, weighing 175 kg. If we were to expand the length of the marmoset femur to equal the length of the gorilla femur, then the bones would not be of the same thickness. In fact, the gorilla femur would be thicker than the marmoset femur. Why? Because the gorilla femur must support a much greater volume and weight than the marmoset femur (Fleagle, 1999).

These scaling patterns also mean that a small animal loses more energy, in the form of heat loss, to the environment than a large animal. You can conduct a simple experiment with two ice cubes to understand some of the consequences of size and heat loss. Place one large ice cube and one small ice cube in a sink full of warm water. As you will see and may have already deduced, the small ice cube melts first. The reasons for this are more complex than they appear: specifically, the small ice cube has a greater proportion of its internal volume exposed to the ambient temperature than the large ice cube. In other words, the difference in melting time results from size-related differences in scaling.

Effects of Body Size on Primate Life

Size-related scaling applies to almost every ecological aspect of an organism, including diet, locomotion, and life history. Large primates, such as gorillas, eat more food and require more overall energy than small primates, such as galagos. However, a small-bodied primate requires more energy per unit of weight than a large-bodied primate. Because of these differences in relative energy requirements, two 20 kg primates require more energy than one 40 kg primate in the same habitat (Fleagle, 1999). These size-related differences in energy requirements also mean that large primates can subsist on large amounts of low-quality (low energy) foods whereas small primates must eat small amounts of high-quality (high energy) foods. For example, a small-bodied (under 500 g) primate is more likely to be insectivorous than folivorous because an insect represents a compact, energy rich package. A small-bodied primate cannot survive on a diet of bulky, low-energy leaves because it would expend more energy in heat loss than it could gain from the slow digestion of leafy foods. Conversely, a primate weighing more than 500 g cannot acquire enough energy from a diet composed entirely of insects, which are energetically expensive to catch in large numbers. Body size also influences fallback foods exploited by frugivores during periods of fruit scarcity. Small frugivores supplement their diet with insects, whereas large frugivores often supplement their diet with leaves. Small-bodied primates tend to leap more than the more suspensory, large-bodied primates. This pattern likely reflects both the energetic costs of leaping and the limitations imposed by branch size on an arboreal lifestyle.

The effects of body size on primate life history are a little more complex. In general, gestation period and lifespan scale positively to body size. In other words, larger animals tend to have longer gestation periods, have smaller litters, and live longer than small animals. You should note that this is not a perfect one-to-one relationship, in that a doubling of body size does not result in a doubling of lifespan. If this were the case, then an adult male gorilla, which weighs 2.5 times that of an adult human, would live approximately 150 to 175 years. The natural life span of a gorilla is around 25 to 35 years.

Ecology and Behaviour

Primate Habitats

Habitat ▪ A place
that provides adequate
nutrients, water,
and living space.

Tropical rainforests ▪
Forest habitats typi-
cally near the equator
that are characterized
by high annual tem-
peratures and rainfall.

Primates are adapted for life in forest **habitats,** particularly **tropical rainforests** (Figure 4.15). Tropical rainforests can receive up to 3 m of rainfall per year. Consequently, tropical rainforests tend to be hot, humid places teeming with life and energy. Scientists estimate that tropical rainforests contain two-thirds of all the living plant and animal species on Earth, with literally millions more yet to be discovered. One hectare (10 000 sq m) of tropical rainforest can contain up to 750 tree species. To put this diversity in perspective, there are only 180 tree species in all of Canada (area of 998 467 000 ha). Walking through tropical rainforest is like walking through nature's cathedral, with awe-inspiring trees reaching up to 80 m in height. These forests represent one of the ultimate ecosystems for exploring the evolution of species diversity on our planet. For example, the Amazon basin encompasses 8 235 430 sq km of tropical forests drained by the Amazon River and its tributaries in South America. In this ecosystem, pink river dolphins squeak and chirp like birds as they glide through the water, hunting for fish in flooded forests. Male cocks-of-the-rock are fiery orange birds that dance on the forest floor to attract the rather drab females as potential mates. Hummingbirds with feathers like jewels duel like miniature fighter planes for

Figure 4.15

The author, who is 1.93 m tall, stands beside a giant tree in the tropical rainforest in South America. This tree is approximately 40 m tall!

© S. M. Lehman

access to flower-laden trees. Unique and fascinating species also exist in the tropical rainforests of Africa, Asia, and Southeast Asia.

Some primates exploit habitat types other than those found in tropical forests, ranging from deserts to mountainous pine forests. Furthermore, primates often range into habitats that have been subject to disturbance. Primary forest is an intact natural forest characterized by an abundance of mature trees that have not been disturbed or modified by human activities, such as logging or natural disturbances (e.g., hurricanes, volcanic eruptions, etc.) in several hundred years. Secondary forest is what re-grows after a disturbance, and tends to contain denser, shorter vegetation than that seen in primary forest. The canopy of secondary forests is discontinuous and lets in more light, which can result in a greater abundance of leaves and fruit. Each habitat and its disturbance regime present resident primate populations with different decisions to make about locating food, finding places to raise young, and avoiding predators. Consequently, different forest habitats exert differing selection pressures upon resident primates. We need to understand not just what primates do in the forest, but also where they do it.

Each primate species tends to occupy a specific and largely non-overlapping **ecological niche** in a forest habitat; that is, a primate makes a living in its particular habitat. A primate's niche can be best understood by looking at the vertical aspects of its habitat. The **understorey,** the area beneath the system of horizontal branches, called the **canopy,** is a remarkably dark and humid place dominated by the vertical trunks of large, mature trees. Plants near the forest floor provide vertical supports because each one is striving to reach the light above the canopy. Although most temperate trees produce fruit high up in the leafy part of the tree, some tropical fruiting trees produce fruit over the entire length of the tree trunk. Some primates eat the exudate (sap) that flows from holes they gouge in tree trunks. Many insectivorous primates hunt in the understorey. However, few food resources tend to be available for frugivorous and folivorous primates in the understorey. Higher in the forest, the canopy provides more horizontal branches that are ideally suited to primates seeking plants foods. Many primate species prefer the canopy layer, particularly the upper parts of the canopy. Although primates will forage in the **emergent layer,** the top of the tree that is exposed to sunlight, few do so for any great length of time. Recent studies have revealed that fruit quantity varies vertically within the tree canopy in eastern Africa (Houle et al., 2007). Specifically, fruit production is higher in the upper-most part of the canopy and lower in the bottom canopy. Thus, there are subtle but important selective pressures faced by primates within each forest habitat.

Primates in Tropical Ecosystems

The evolutionary ecology of primates is a result of complex **bottom-up** (resource-driven) and **top-down** (consumer-driven) processes. The energy and important food resources for most primates derive from plants. Thus, any changes in the ecosystem that alter plant production and growth will have a cascading effect on primates. For example, if a severe drought strikes a forest area, then the plants grow fewer leaves, fruit, and flowers. These changes in plant growth may inhibit primate consumers. If the drought is extreme, then the local primates may die out or be forced to leave the area to search for other food resources. Clearly, the growth and reproduction of plants in tropical rainforests represent one of the most important bottom-up processes to the evolutionary ecology of primates. Each tree species represents a continuum of millions of years of natural selection. Plants did not evolve juicy and sweet-tasting fruits just to provide food and nutrients to primates. Rather, plants evolved **seed dispersal,** characteristics that make the fruit attractive to eat, because of increased germination rates compared to seeds that do not pass through the gut tract of frugivores. Although

Ecological niche ■ Sum of all the interactions between an organism and its ecosystem.

Understorey ■ Area between the ground and the lowest horizontal branches.

Canopy ■ System of horizontal branches and foliage formed by tree crowns (i.e., the leafy parts).

Emergent layer ■ Topmost level of the tree, which is usually exposed to sunlight.

Bottom-up processes ■ Interactions between organisms involving physical or chemical factors such as temperature or nutrient availability

Top-down processes ■ Influence of consumers, such as predators, on prey.

Seed dispersal ■ Specific fruit characteristics to entice animals to eat the juicy parts and then disperse the seeds in feces dropped away from the parent plant.

Pollinator ▪ Agent that transports small amounts of nectar and pollen, e.g., on fur or by mouth, between flowers.

many primates consume flowers, some species serve as **pollinators:** animals transport small amounts of nectar and pollen between plants, thereby aiding in the plant's reproduction.

Predators can have a top-down influence on primates. Even if primate food resources are available and abundant, intense predation can wipe out primates in a given area. For example, the creation of the Guri Dam in Venezuela resulted in the flooding of an enormous area of tropical forest, except for some hilltops that became islands that were inhabited by some howler monkeys. For a time, the monkeys thrived because food was plentiful on the islands within the lake behind the dam. However, an enterprising jaguar swam from the mainland out to one island and eventually ate all but one of the monkeys on that island (Peetz et al., 1992). Thus, each primate population must deal with issues of acquiring food resources from plants (bottom-up processes) and avoiding predation (top-down processes).

Natural selection has favoured plants that evolved physical defences (spines, tough shells) and chemical protection of seeds from consumers. You may be familiar with some of these plant chemicals, such as the caffeine in coffee beans and chocolate made from cocoa beans. Although we exploit these plant products as stimulants and treats, the chemicals can be toxic for non-human primates and other mammals. For example, animals that eat caffeine or cocoa products can become very sick, and even die, because they lack adaptations to detoxify the plant chemicals. Plants have also evolved a variety of physical and chemical defences to protect leaves, flowers, and other structures from consumers. Some plants have evolved stinging hairs (trichomes) on their stems and leaves. These hairs can inject a variety of potent chemicals. Primates have consequently evolved adaptations for dealing with plant defences. Some of these adaptations can be as simple as avoiding mature leaves, which tend to contain a greater quantity of toxic chemicals than immature leaves. Primates and their predators also fit within this evolutionary arms race. All but the largest-bodied primates are subject to predation (Sussman, 1999). As primates evolve adaptations to avoid predation—such as cryptic coloration and living in groups—predators are changing to overcome these evolutionary strategies.

Ranging Patterns

Daily path length ▪ Refers to the one-dimensional distance travelled by a primate during its daily active period.

Day range ▪ Two-dimensional area used by a primate throughout a 24-hour period.

Home range ▪ Two-dimensional area used by a primate throughout months or years.

Core area ▪ Most frequently used part of the home range.

Territory: An area actively defended by an individual or group.

Primatologists study the horizontal movements of primates within and between habitats. Because primates lack road maps and weather reports, they restrict their movements to known areas to improve their chances of locating food resources and sleeping sites. This "mental map" is particularly valuable during periods of food scarcity, when primates need to know the location of critical food resources. There is a common misconception that a jungle is always bursting with readily accessible food; it's not. Forest habitats are constantly changing throughout days, weeks, seasons, and years. Fruit trees, in particular, tend to be patchily distributed, and the timing of fruit production is often unpredictable and irregular. Despite leaves being ubiquitous in the forest, recent studies reveal that the best, tastiest leaves are available only at certain times of the year. Thus natural selection has favoured the use of restricted areas within a habitat.

Primatologists use the following standardized terms when referring to primate ranging patterns: **daily path length, day range, home range, core area,** and **territory.** Although many primates have home ranges that slightly overlap those of conspecifics, few primate species are exclusively territorial. The size and location of each home range is not necessarily static for a species. Primate ranging patterns can be influenced by the distribution and abundance of food resources, the size and shape of the habitat, altitude, and the type and abundance of predators. Furthermore, in many species, individuals reaching sexual maturity leave voluntarily, presumably because of a lack of mating opportunities, or because older resident members force them to leave. These young primates must disperse to set up a new range elsewhere. In a few primate species, adults cut out a part of their home range to set up their offspring, which is something like a starter home range! Much remains to be learned about spatial and temporal patterns of primate land use.

Sociality

Human and non-human primates love to watch each other! If you go to a shopping mall or restaurant, you will often observe people. You may find yourself observing social dynamics between people. In a general sense, this activity relates to a special type of research within the field of primatology: the study of primate social life (Strier, 2006). A primatologist seeks to **habituate** primates to observe their natural behaviour, meaning the scientist carefully and quietly follows the group until it becomes used to the human observer. This process can take considerable time and energy depending on the primate species and its previous experiences with humans. Nonetheless, it's a joy to live the rugged life of a field primatologist: spending time in nature, living in tents or sleeping in hammocks, and eating food cooked over an open fire (Figure 4.16)!

Habituate ▪ To allow a primate group to become used to the presence of human observers by quietly and carefully following the group.

One of the main behavioural characteristics of primates is that they have complex and fascinating social lives. In fact, the social life of some primate species is remarkably similar to that portrayed by actors in television soap operas! Primatologists have discovered evidence of deception, female mate choice, homosexuality, kin recognition, spite, warfare, friendship, and even sex for pleasure in primates. For example, bonobos (*Pan paniscus*), which are a close phylogenetic relative of chimpanzees, engage in a variety of sexual activities, including face-to-face genital sex (particularly among females) and oral sex (de Waal, 1995).

Social Grooming

Social grooming is one of the best-studied and most interesting aspects of primate sociality. A common misconception is that primates groom each other only because they are dirty. In fact, primates groom each other to establish and maintain alliances, to reconcile conflict, and to exchange for other resources such as food and sex. A recent report, provocatively titled *Payment for Sex in a Macaque Mating Market,* describes sexual behaviour in long-tailed macaques (*Macaca fascicularis*). The author discovered that male-to-female grooming led to an increase in female rates for sexual activity (Gumert, 2007). Conversely, female-to-male grooming resulted in decreased rates of mating in the groomed males. The amount of grooming a male performed on a female during grooming–mating interchanges was a function of the number of females around the interaction (i.e., a mating market).

Dominance Hierarchies

Some primate species have **dominance hierarchies,** which are roughly analogous to a pecking order, with some individuals more dominant than others in a social group. A common misconception is that all dominance systems are maintained by aggressive behaviours, such as fighting and biting. Although some primate species do maintain their hierarchies in this way, other species use affiliative behaviours, such as grooming, vertical position in the group, and even sex as tools for climbing the primate social ladder (Figure 4.17)! A classic description of primate dominance hierarchies is in Frans de Waal's book *Chimpanzee Politics: Power and Sex among Apes* (de Waal, 2000). Dr. de Waal provides an engrossing description of sexual rivalries and coalitions in a colony of captive chimpanzees. However, only a few primate species—such as chimpanzees and ring-tailed lemurs—have been studied with sufficient time and focus to begin to understand how biological evolution and natural selection have shaped their social lives (Strier, 2006).

Dominance hierarchy ▪ A social order sustained by aggression, affiliation, or other behaviour patterns.

Figure 4.16

Primatologists seek to habituate primates, although researchers never know for sure whether the animals ever get completely used to their presence.

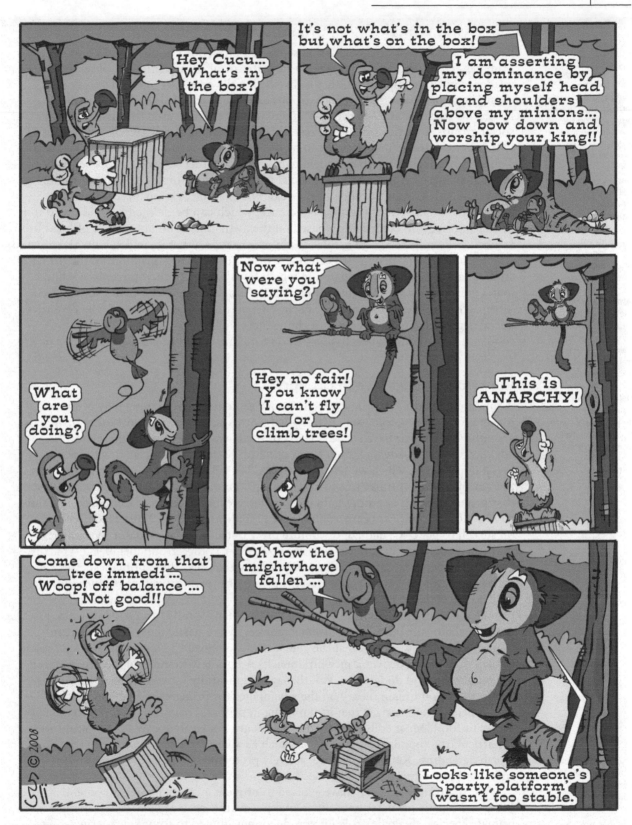

Figure 4.17

In many primate species, an individual's dominance rank is not necessarily a function of its aggressive tendencies, as vertical placement can be an indicator of status.

Classifying Primate Social Organizations

Primatologists use four classification schemes to describe social organization in primates. First, primatologists classify primate social organization by observing **residence group composition,** that is, by sorting the group by age and sex. For example, multi-male–multi-female groups are composed of several adult males, numerous females, and offspring. **Mating systems** are also used to classify primate social groups. In other words, the researcher defines a group based on who mates with whom. **Foraging coherence** can be used to classify primate social organization. This system focuses on which individuals forage together in time and space. Although individuals may be part of a larger social network, each animal may forage alone or in fluid sub-groups throughout the year. For example, chimpanzees exhibit a fission–fusion pattern of foraging coherence, which can be defined as fluid social units of varying size and composition based on the availability and abundance of local food resources. Finally, researchers look at philopatry type—that is, which animals stay and which leave a social group—to categorize primate social organization. In the primates studied to date, **female philopatry,** in which females stay in their birthplace while males emigrate, is more common than **male philopatry,** in which males stay in their birthplace while females emigrate. Each scheme is not necessarily mutually exclusive. Social organization in the common chimpanzee includes multi-male, multi-female residence and mating types; fission–fusion foraging coherence; and male philopatry.

Why Do Primates Live in Groups?

A fundamental issue in primate evolutionary ecology is determining why primates live in groups. Primatologists are intrigued by this issue because most other mammals are either solitary or have reduced levels of sociality. Consequently, there must be advantages and disadvantages in terms of natural selection associated with group living in primates, which we will now review. We will discuss three main theories on the advantages for primates of living in groups. First, researchers have hypothesized that primates living in groups gain increased protection from predators. Larger groups have additional eyes and ears available for predator detection. Most predators rely on stealth to get close enough to capture prey. Detection of a predator by an alert individual can then lead to warning vocalizations to other group members. Typically, predator detection results in a flight response by the prey. Some primate species also mob a predator. In Guyana, I observed a group of brown capuchins (*Cebus apella*) mob a jaguar that they discovered had been stalking them. An adult male and several juvenile monkeys hung upside down by their prehensile tails from tree branches, just out of reach of the jaguar. The juvenile monkeys were particularly enthusiastic in taunting and throwing sticks at the jaguar, which seemed to be waiting for one broken branch that would deliver a nice little snack! After a few minutes of intently watching the monkeys—and dodging sticks—the jaguar gracefully moved off into the forest.

In the second main theory on the advantages for primates of living in groups, researchers have theorized that group living in primates may have evolved to improve access to food. Most edible fruits and flowers are not easily located in tropical forests. A particularly abundant food resource, such as a large tree laden with ripe fruit, is worth defending. **Resource defence,** actively protecting a source of food, is most successful by animals in large groups.

Third, group living may have evolved to provide increased access to potential mates. Male and female primates have different reproductive costs (Strier, 2006). In most primate species, the male's role in reproduction is limited to some short-term aspects of infant development and, in extreme cases, only to insemination. A male primate can potentially mate with multiple females and father numerous offspring. Reproductive

---

Residence group composition ■ Primate social groupings based on the number of individuals in differing age-sex classes.

Mating system ■ Mating patterns exhibited by individuals.

Foraging coherence ■ Which individuals forage together in time and space.

Female philopatry ■ A female spends her entire life in her natal (birth) group, and males typically emigrate upon reaching sexual maturity.

Male philopatry ■ A male spends his entire life in his natal (birth) group, and females typically emigrate upon reaching sexual maturity.

Resource defence ■ Active defence of a food resource by an individual or group.

rates are much lower for females because they incur relatively greater time and energy costs due to gestation, birth, and infant rearing. Depending on the species, gestation length ranges from 60 to 250 days and weaning ranges from 50 to 1500 days (Fleagle, 1999). A female must acquire sufficient resources to ensure her survival as well as that of her offspring. Consequently, primatologists have suggested that male reproductive strategies are limited by their access to females, whereas female strategies reflect limitations imposed by access to food resources (Wrangham, 1980). Mothers also benefit from having group members assist with infant rearing (i.e., babysitters).

Disadvantages to group living are based on counter-arguments to some of the ideas outlined above. Although larger groups may enjoy improved predator detection, these groups may also attract greater predator attention. In other words, larger groups make more noise and travel farther, increasing chance encounters with local predators. Individuals in larger groups benefit from the defence of scarce food resources, but they must also deal with having too many mouths to feed. Thus, members of larger groups suffer from more intragroup competition for food then animals in smaller groups.

Animals in larger groups typically travel farther to find sufficient food resources, which likely places an upper limit on group size. Until recently, many researchers thought that there was no within-group competition for food among folivores. After all, leaves are everywhere in the tropical forest, so there is no need to defend them. Thus, we would expect folivores to live in very large groups in order to protect themselves from predators. However, some folivorous primates live in small groups, which has been termed the folivore paradox (Steenbeek and van Schaik, 2001). This paradox may have been solved by studies that revealed that those folivores living in small groups prefer to feed on high-quality leaves from trees that are irregularly and unevenly distributed (Snaith and Chapman, 2005). Smaller group size occurs because the costs of within-group competition outweigh the benefits of improved predator detection.

Finally, recent studies have revealed the devastating effects of infectious diseases on group-living primates. Entire populations of gorillas have succumbed to outbreaks of highly infectious Ebola hemorrhagic fever in Africa (Walsh et al., 2003). Solitary species should have reduced transmission rates. Despite these potential costs, most primates do live in groups. Thus, the benefits must have outweighed the costs for group living in primate evolution.

Conservation

Primates are increasingly threatened by human activities, particularly habitat disturbance and hunting pressures (Cowlishaw and Dunbar, 2000). Habitat disturbance results primarily from logging and agriculture. Huge swaths of tropical forests have been lost due to logging of large, commercially valuable trees. For example, the government of Guyana handed out 8.8 million hectares of state forests as logging concessions to foreign companies from the early 1970s to the late 1990s (Richardson and Funk, 1999). Many of the trees removed by loggers also serve as important food resources for primates. Roads built to improve access for heavy machinery involved in large-scale, intensive logging result in considerable collateral damage to forests. Logging roads also cause siltation of nearby rivers and erosion of thin tropical soils. Many primate species are sensitive to small-scale selective logging operations, in which loggers remove only a few tree species. Thus, both the extent and intensity of logging are important factors influencing primate survival in disturbed habitats.

Effects of Agriculture on Primates

Agriculture has deleterious effects on primates by altering tropical forests. Humans have been using **slash and burn** or swidden agriculture for millennia in the tropics

Slash and burn ■ Involves the burning and clearing of forests for planting of agriculture.

Figure 4.18

Deforestation in Madagascar.

Light areas in the background are caused by slash and burn agriculture on hill slopes. A lemur snare trap used by local people is in the foreground.
© S. M. Lehman

(Figure 4.18). The ash produced by burning the forest provides some fertilization for the soil, which tends to be nutrient poor in the tropics. After several years of cultivation, fertility declines and farmers move to pristine areas, allowing for plant regeneration. Although agriculture displaces forest-dwelling primates, some species prefer the secondary habitats adjacent to active and abandoned fields. However, the cumulative effects of explosive human growth and reduced forest coverage over the past 100 years place increasing pressure on resident primate populations. Sedentary farming combined with slash and burn methods can eliminate forest regeneration, eventually resulting in an impoverished landscape that cannot support either crops or forest. Farmers remove considerable volumes of hard wood for use as firewood. Furthermore, slash and burn farmers often supplement their low-protein diets by hunting local primates. Large-scale tree plantations are perhaps the most devastating form of agriculture affecting primates. Commercial interests have converted huge areas of formerly diverse tropical forests into monocultures of palm oil trees, particularly in Southeast Asia. Few primates can survive in plantations that lack connections to nearby undisturbed forests.

Effects of Forest Fragmentation on Primates

Habitat disturbance can also result in large, continuous blocks of forest shrinking into small, isolated forest fragments of varying sizes and shapes (Marsh, 2003). For example, huge tracts of forest have become highly fragmented in eastern Madagascar. Generally, larger forest fragments contain more primate species. As fragments shrink in size, species begin to disappear because local habitats can no longer provide the necessary resources to support the animals. Displaced primates must move between or permanently disperse to other fragments, which makes the animals susceptible to increased predation. Furthermore, there are no guarantees that dispersing primates can successfully colonize nearby forest fragments. These fragments may be smaller than the ones the primates just left, or they may maintain conspecifics that prevent the dispersing primates from securing suitable habitats. Some primate species choose not to disperse in fragmented landscapes, resulting in the extirpation of populations within shrinking fragments.

The shape of a forest fragment is another essential factor influencing the survival probability of resident primate populations. Long, thin fragments do not contain sufficient interior forest to support primate species in such habitats. Primatologists need to determine the critical thresholds in terms of size and shape of forest fragments that will maintain each primate species.

Effects of Hunting on Primates

Hunting pressures on primates vary throughout the tropics. As with agricultural practices, humans have hunted primates for millennia. For example, Figure 4.18 shows a simple snare trap used by people to capture lemurs in Madagascar. When human populations were small and mobile, primates had an opportunity to recover from hunting pressures after hunters moved on to new areas. Increasing human populations near shrinking forests has typically resulted in the extirpation of primates favoured as prey. However, some local people do not hunt primates due to cultural beliefs. For example, people from the Antakaran tribe of northern Madagascar do not hunt the rare Perrier's sifaka because of their beliefs that these lemurs were once human. Immigration of people from tribes lacking taboos on hunting lemurs into these regions has increased hunting pressures on Perrier's sifakas. In many primate-source countries, which are countries that have naturally occurring primate populations, hunting practices are also changing due to the introduction of firearms. Compared to indigenous hunting tools (blowguns, bows and arrows), modern firearms require less skill to use and they intensify hunting pressures on large-bodied primate species. Larger species have relatively slower reproduction rates than small species, resulting in reduced population recovery. Although many primate-source countries have outlawed primate hunting, enforcement is lax or non-existent due, in part, to insufficient funds for patrols by enforcement authorities.

In recent years in parts of Africa, the hunting of mammals, including primates, has become a purely economic activity, known as the bushmeat trade. Hunters now sell massive numbers of prey to loggers employed by European and Malaysian companies. Bushmeat is available in ethnic restaurants in Africa, Europe, and North America. Although large-bodied primates comprise less than 1 percent of the bushmeat trade, their high value to hunters and their low numbers place an inordinately high pressure on surviving populations. Entire populations of gorillas and chimpanzees have been lost to the bushmeat trade. Efforts to solve the bushmeat crisis are ongoing, but even with a complete hunting ban there will be a considerable lag in population recovery for chimpanzees and gorillas.

Conservation Status of Primates

Field research conducted by primatologists contributes to the International Union for the Conservation of Nature and Natural Resources (IUCN) **Red List** of Threatened

Red List ■ A comprehensive listing of the conservation status of plant and animal taxa on a global scale.

Species, which lists the global conservation status of plants and animals. The IUCN is the world's largest conservation network and is the main authority on the conservation status of species. To produce this list, authorities from the IUCN evaluate data on each taxon using 12 conservation criteria, such as population size and area of occupancy. They then use thresholds for the criteria data to place each taxon into a specific conservation category. Of the 426 primate taxa in the 2014 Red List, 58 are considered **critically endangered,** meaning they are at extremely high risk of extinction in the wild, and 115 are listed as **endangered,** meaning they are at very high risk. Remarkably, there are 18 primate species on the IUCN Red List for which we have inadequate information on their distribution and/or population status to make a direct, or indirect, assessment of their extinction risk. Authorities from the IUCN desperately need current information on the conservation status of wild primates, indicating enormous research possibilities for primatologists in primate source countries.

Summary

1. Primates are cool! Primates are mammals because they have hair or fur, a four-chambered heart, spinal cord, and sweat glands, and are homeothermic. Primates are distinguished from other orders of mammals by a suite of characters associated with locomotion, neural and sensory systems, and life history traits.
2. The Primate order contains two suborders, the Strepsirhini and the Haplorhini. Strepsirhines include lemurs, lorises, and galagos. These primates retain primitive features similar to those seen in Eocene primates. Haplorhines include tarsiers, monkeys, apes, and humans. These taxa have more derived features.
3. Body size is a fundamental aspect of the evolutionary anthropology of primates. Many ecological, morphological, and life history traits of primates relate to differences in body size and therefore energy requirement between species.
4. Most primates exploit forest habitats. Although primates fill a variety of ecological niches, many species prefer life in the canopy. Primates are part of ecosystems that represent millions of years of biological evolution and co-evolution. Natural selection has resulted in primates being among the most social of all mammals. Group living in primates may have evolved as a means to reduce predation, improve access to food, and find mates.
5. Human disturbances and hunting pressures are the main conservation issues for primates. Intensive logging and agriculture can destroy or alter forests to the point where remaining habitats cannot support primate populations or species. Economic exploitation of African primates for the bushmeat trade has decimated populations of large-bodied species, which cannot rapidly recover due to their slow reproductive rates.

INTERNET RESOURCES

1. Interested in becoming a primatologist?

   Primate Info Net
   http://pin.primate.wisc.edu/edu/careers/employment.html

   What is a Primatologist?
   http://pin.primate.wisc.edu/edu/careers/whatis.html

2. Visit the websites of some Canadian primatologists to learn more about their research:

   Dr. Drew Rendall
   http://people.uleth.ca/~d.rendall/Drew_Rendall/Home.html
   Learn about Dr. Rendall's research into primate communication.

   Dr. Linda M. Fedigan
   www.ucalgary.ca/~fedigan/fedigan.htm
   Read about Dr. Fedigan's research into primate socioecology.

Dr. Colin Chapman
http://chapmanresearch.mcgill.ca/
Here you will find information about Dr. Chapman's research into primate behavioural ecology.

Dr. Steig E. Johnson
http://homepages.ucalgary.ca/~stjohnso/Home_Page/Home.html
Read about Dr. Johnson's research into lemur conservation.

3. Visit the following website to listen to primates:

Primate Information Network
http://pin.primate.wisc.edu/av/vocals/
Listen to amazing primate vocalizations!

4. Visit the following websites to see images of primates:

Primates.com
www.primates.com
A wonderful primate photo gallery!

Primate Gallery
https://primategallery.wordpress.com/
Another primate photo gallery, this time by Tim Knight.

5. Watch some cool movie clips about primates:

Life of Mammals
http://www.bbc.co.uk/programmes/p00dzdsk
Lemur footage taken from David Attenborough's *Life of Mammals*.

JungleWalk
www.junglewalk.com/video/Primate-movie.htm
Excellent source for primate videos and pictures.

BBC Motion Gallery
http://www.gettyimages.ca/bbcmotiongallery
Amazing BBC site full of images and movies about primates.

6. Visit some primate conservation sites:

IUCN Primate Specialist Group
www.primate-sg.org
Network of scientists and conservationists working to save primates from extinction.

IUCN Red List
www.iucnredlist.org
Science-based network of volunteers who assess the conservation status of biodiversity.

Primate Conservation, Inc.
www.primate.org
An all-volunteer not-for-profit foundation dedicated to studying, preserving, and maintaining the habitats of the least known and most endangered primates in the world.

Bushmeat Crisis Task Force
http://www.bushmeat.org/
International organization seeking to eliminate the illegal commercial bushmeat trade.

LITERATURE CITED

Anderson, J. D., Owren, M. J., and Boinski, S. (2007). Impact-amplitude of controlled percussive strikes provides evidence of site-selection for enhancement of acoustic display behavior in brown capuchins (*Cebus apella*) in Suriname. *American Journal of Physical Anthropology*, Suppl 44, 64.

Barrett, J., Abbott, D. H., and George, L. M. (1990) Extension of reproductive suppression by pheromonal cues in subordinate female marmoset monkeys, *Callithrix jacchus*. *Journal of Reproduction and Fertility*, 90(2), 411–418.

Bligh, J. (1973), *Temperature Regulation in Mammals and Other Vertebrates*. Amsterdam: North-Holland.

Caldecott, J. O., Feistner, A. T. C., and Gadsby, E. L. (1996). A comparison of ecological strategies of pig-tailed macaques, mandrills and drills. *Evolution and Ecology of Macaque Societies* (ed. by J. E. Fa and D. G. Lindburg), pp. 73–94. Cambridge, MA: Cambridge University Press.

Cowlishaw, G., and Dunbar, R. (2000). *Primate Conservation Biology*. Chicago: University of Chicago Press.

de Waal, F. (1995). Bonobo sex and society. *Scientific American*, 272(3), 82–88.

de Waal, F. (2000). *Chimpanzee Politics: Power and Sex among Apes*. Baltimore: Johns Hopkins University Press.

Fleagle, J. G. (1999). *Primate Adaptation and Evolution*. San Diego: Academic Press.

Goodall, J. (1986). *The Chimpanzees of Gombe: Patterns of Behavior*. Cambridge, MA: Harvard University Press.

Gumert, M. D. (2007). Payment for sex in a macaque mating market. *Animal Behaviour*, 74(6), 1655–1667.

Houle, A., Chapman, C. A., and Vickery, W. L. (2007). Intratree variation in fruit production and implications for primate foraging. *International Journal of Primatology*, 28(6), 1197–1217.

Marsh, L. K., Ed. (2003). *Primates in Fragments: Ecology and Conservation*. New York: Kluwer Academic/Plenum Publishers.

Peetz, A., Norconk, M. A., and Kinzey, W. G. (1992). Predation by jaguar on howler monkeys (*Alouatta seniculus*) in Venezuela. *American Journal of Primatology*, 28, 223–228.

Pruetz, J., and Bertolani, P. (2007). Savanna chimpanzees, *Pan troglodytes verus*, hunt with tools. *Current Biology*, 17(5), 412–417.

Reichard, U. (1995). Extra-pair copulations in a monogamous gibbon (*Hylobates lar*). *Ethology*, 100(2), 99–112.

Richardson, K. S., and Funk, V. (1999). An approach to designing a systematic protected area system in Guyana. *Parks*, 9, 7–16.

Snaith, T. V., and Chapman, C. A. (2005). Towards an ecological solution to the folivore paradox: Patch depletion as an indicator of within-group scramble competition in red colobus monkeys (*Piliocolobus tephrosceles*). *Behavioral Ecology and Sociobiology*, 59(2), 185–190.

Stanford, C. (1998). *Chimpanzee and Red Colobus: The Ecology of Predator and Prey*. Boston: Harvard University Press.

Steenbeek, R., and van Schaik, C. (2001). Competition and group size in Thomas's langurs (*Presbytis thomasi*): The folivore paradox revisited. *Behavioral Ecology and Sociobiology*, 49(2), 100–110.

Strier, K. B. (1999). *Faces in the Forest: The Endangered Muriqui Monkeys of Brazil*. Cambridge, MA: Harvard University Press.

Strier, K. B. (2006). *Primate Behavioral Ecology*. Boston: Pearson Allyn and Bacon.

Sussman, R. W. (1999). *Primate Ecology and Social Structure: Lorises, Lemurs, Tarsiers*. Needham Heights, NJ: Pearson Custom Publishing.

Walsh, P. D., Abernethy, K., Bermejo, M., Beyers, R., De, W. P., Akou, M., Huijbregts, B., Mambounga, D., Toham, A., Kilbourn, A., Lahm, S., Latour, S., Maisels, F., Mbina, C., Mihindou, Y., Obiang, S., Effa, E., Starkey, M., Telfer, P., Thibault, M., Tutin, C., White, L., and Wilkie, D. (2003). Catastrophic ape decline in western equatorial Africa. *Nature*, 422(6932), 611–614.

Wrangham, R. W. (1980). An ecological model of female-bonded primate groups. *Behaviour*, 75(3–4), 262–300.

CHAPTER 5

Primate Origins

GOALS

By the end of this chapter you should understand:

1. Basic morphological features used to describe and classify fossil primates.
2. How morphological features are used to infer diet and locomotion in fossil primates.
3. Theories on primate origins.
4. General patterns of morphology and phylogenetics for fossil primates from 65 to 1.8 million years ago.

CHAPTER OUTLINE

Introduction

As an undergraduate, I was fortunate to have the opportunity to attend the annual meeting of the American Association of Physical Anthropologists. Many of the world authorities on primate origins happened to attend these meetings. As I trailed behind my academic advisor from one fascinating presentation to another, I was amazed by the enthusiasm for science exhibited by senior professors whose texts I considered to be required reading: They loved their jobs! One night I joined a throng of boisterous professors and students in the hotel lounge. Amidst the crush of bodies, I was introduced to a famous paleoanthropologist, who was carrying a mysterious large case. My advisor, who knew the old paleoanthropologist well, suggested I be shown the "new toy" from Africa. With a sparkle of humour in his eye, the old paleoanthropologist reached into his cavernous case and gently placed this "toy" in the palm of my hand. It was no toy! There, nestled ever so precariously, was the fossilized skull from a primate that was almost 33 million years old! Not only was the fossil incredibly old, it also represented a newly discovered species! Despite my nervousness at holding such a rare thing, I was fascinated by thoughts of what the creature was like when alive: what did it think about, how did it behave, did it have a mate and offspring, was it intelligent, and why did it die? I suddenly realized the sheer joy and wonder that comes from discovering a fossil primate.

In this chapter, we discuss the evolutionary anthropology of non-human primates in the fossil record. In the sections below, we undertake a broad review of primate origins from the time of the dinosaurs up until the emergence of the first hominins. Each section starts with a review of the major global patterns of geography and climate. This information is needed to understand how environmental factors influenced primate macroevolution. We then undertake only a brief review of the major morphological characteristics and ecological interpretations of the primates associated with that epoch. Finally, we piece together the phylogenetic relationships of early primates.

Introduction to Fossil Primates

Fossil primates represent a factual record of evolutionary patterns and processes over the last 65 million years. Despite the incomplete nature of these fossils, fascinating things have been learned from studies of their dental and skeletal features. We have gained invaluable insights into the diet and behaviour of fossil primates by comparing their dentition and skeletal features with those of extant primates. Therefore, we first need to cover basics of primate dentition and skeletal morphology. Macroevolutionary studies of the primate fossil record reveal intriguing evidence of intermediate forms that link extinct and extant taxa. Put differently, we find evidence for so-called missing links between some primate taxa. Thus, the fossil record provides us with information on ebbs and flows of primate diversity over tens of millions of years. Based on this information, researchers have formulated theories on how and why the first primates evolved. Finally, we review the hypothesized phylogenetic relationships of fossil primates within specific time periods. So let's learn about teeth!

Basics of Primate Dentition

Understanding basic primate dentition is important for two reasons. First, because of their extreme hardness, teeth are the most common fossilized remains found by paleo-anthropologists. Second, dental morphology provides information on the diet of fossil primates. Our review focuses on dental development, tooth structure, and the kind and number of teeth found in primates. All primates have **diphyodonty,** meaning they have two sets of teeth. The first set of teeth, often termed "baby" or deciduous teeth, appear early in infant development and then are replaced by a full set of adult teeth. Teeth are found in the **maxilla,** the part of the upper jaw from which the teeth grow, and the

Diphyodonty ■ Having two successive sets of teeth.

Maxilla ■ Part of the upper jaw from which the teeth grow.

mandible, the lower jaw. Each tooth can be divided into the following three parts: **crown, neck,** and **root** (Figure 5.1). The tooth crown is covered by a hard substance called **enamel** and has varying numbers and kinds of **cusps**—the pointed or rounded biting surface of the tooth. The crown is supported by dentin, which is softer than enamel. The pulp cavity underlies dentin and forms the central chamber of the tooth. Pulp comprises soft tissue, blood vessels, and nerves that provide sensitivity to heat and cold.

All primates are characterized by **heterodonty,** meaning they have different kinds of teeth (Figure 5.2). Specifically, most primates have the following four kinds of teeth (from front to back): **incisors, canines, premolars,** and **molars.** These teeth can be categorized into two parts: anterior dentition (incisors and canines) and posterior dentition (premolars and molars). Paleoanthropologists use the dental formula to describe the number of each kind of tooth in one half of the maxilla and mandible of a species.

Mandible ▪ Lower jaw.

Crown ▪ The part of the tooth that is visible above the gum.

Neck ▪ Part of the tooth that is at the gum line.

Root ▪ Part of the tooth that is below the gum line.

Enamel ▪ Outer surface of a tooth, the hardest biological substance in the body.

Cusp ▪ Pointed or rounded part of the biting surface of a tooth.

Heterodonty ▪ Different kinds of teeth.

Incisors ▪ Front teeth between the canines.

Canines ▪ Front teeth between the incisors and premolars.

Premolars ▪ Cheek teeth found between canines and molars.

Molars ▪ Teeth behind the premolars.

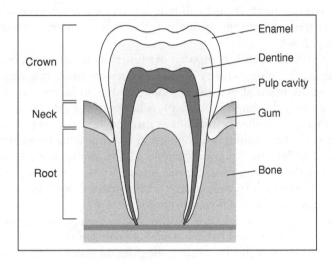

Figure 5.1

Basic tooth anatomy of an adult molar tooth in a modern human.

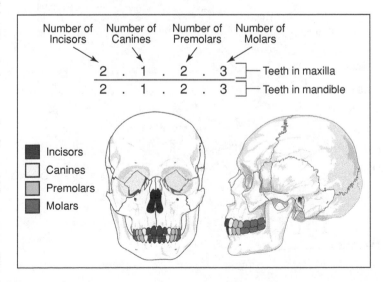

Figure 5.2

The dental formula and the different kinds of teeth in an adult human.
© S. M. Lehman

Why only one half? Because primate morphology is the same on the left and right sides. For example, the dental formula for modern humans in 2.1.2.3./2.1.2.3., which means that you should have a total of four incisors, two canines, four premolars, and six molars on the left or right side of your mouth. In primates, such as humans, which also have symmetrical upper and low dentition, it is common to see the dental formula listed only as 2.1.2.3.

Basics of the Primate Skeleton

Cranial skeleton ■
Bones of the head.

Postcranial skeleton ■
Bones below the head.

We now look at the basic anatomy of the **cranial** and **postcranial skeletons** of primates. This introduction to the bones of the head and below the head is also necessary as a foundation for understanding the diet and locomotion of fossil primates. We'll do a broad overview because it is extremely rare for a complete primate skeleton to be fossilized and recovered. In most cases, all that is found are a few cranial fragments, and in even rarer cases, parts of the postcranial skeleton. We start at the top (skull) and work our way down.

In primates, the adult skull is composed of numerous bones of varying shapes and sizes that encase the brain, sensory organs, and mastication (chewing) system (Figure 5.3). As we discussed above, the mandible and maxilla are part of the cranial skeleton. However, only the mandible and a few bones of the middle ear are unfused and capable of movement. The other cranial bones fuse together to form the cranium or brain case. The top of the cranium is composed of the following three bones: frontal (forehead), parietal (side), and temporal (temple). The occipital bone forms the back and bottom parts of the cranium. The foramen magnum is an opening in the occipital bone through which passes the spinal cord. The zygomatic bone (cheekbone) is another important anatomical feature in paleoanthropology.

POSTCRANIAL SKELETON AND LOCOMOTION   Although the postcranial skeleton serves numerous functions, we focus our basic introduction on skeletal features associated with locomotion (Figure 5.4). In this regard, the primate skeleton can be divided into

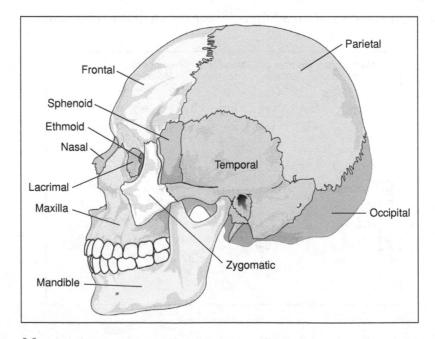

Figure 5.3

Basic skeletal anatomy of a skull in an adult, modern human.

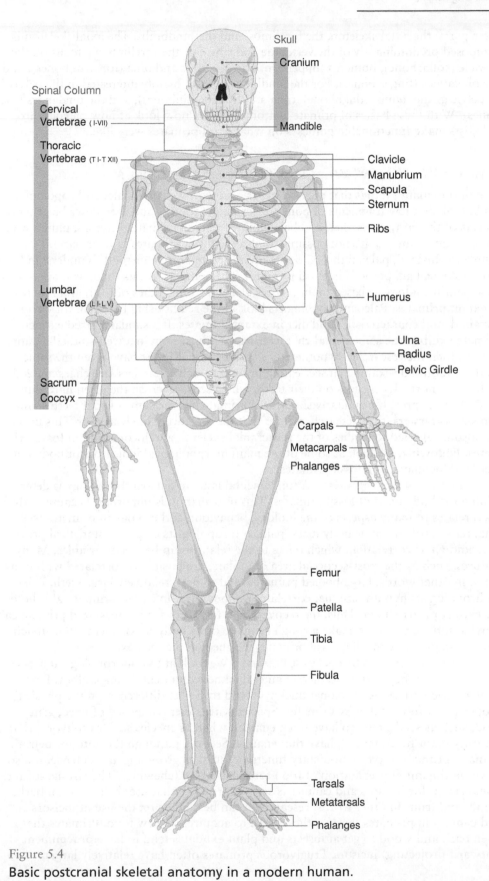

Skull
Cranium

Spinal Column
Cervical Vertebrae (I-VII)

Thoracic Vertebrae (T I-T XII)

Mandible

Clavicle
Manubrium
Scapula
Sternum

Ribs

Lumbar Vertebrae (L I-L V)

Humerus

Ulna
Radius
Pelvic Girdle

Sacrum
Coccyx

Carpals
Metacarpals
Phalanges

Femur

Patella

Tibia

Fibula

Tarsals
Metatarsals
Phalanges

Figure 5.4

Basic postcranial skeletal anatomy in a modern human.

three parts: the axial skeleton, the forelimbs, and the hindlimbs. The axial skeleton is composed predominantly of the vertebrae and ribs. For the forelimb, we focus on the clavicle (collarbone), humerus (upper arm bone), radius and ulna (forearm bones), and the phalanges (finger bones). For the hindlimbs, we are mainly interested in the pelvis or pelvic girdle, femur (thighbone), tibia and fibula (shinbones), and the phalanges (toe bones). With these basics of primate anatomy, we can now look at how paleoanthropologists make functional hypotheses on what fossil primates were like.

How Do We "Know" What Fossil Primates Were Like?

One of the (many) things that puzzled me as a student was how paleoanthropologists could look at a few fragments of bone—or even one tooth—and then describe general aspects of the body mass, diet, and behaviour of a fossil primate. After all, unlike studies of extant primates, it's not possible to observe fossil primates in their natural environments. Instead, paleoanthropologists use the comparative method to understand morphological adaptations in fossil primates. The comparative method, as it applies to palaeoanthropology, is based on inferences gleaned from studies of form and function in extant primates. Paleoanthropologists look at the relationship between, for example, certain dental characteristics and diet in extant primates. If a similarly sized extinct primate exhibits the same dental characteristics as those seen in a well-studied extant species, then the researcher hypothesizes that the animals must have eaten the same kinds of food. For example, insect-eating primates, such as tarsiers, are characterized by having short, sharp cusps on their teeth, which serve to crush the often hard outer shell of insect prey. If a similarly sized fossil primate has the same overall teeth shape and size as tarsiers, then researchers infer that the diets were likely similar. This process can also be applied to studies of the postcranial skeleton and locomotion in fossil primates. Following, we look at some of the main morphological indicators of body mass, diet, and locomotion in fossil primates.

BODY MASS IN FOSSIL PRIMATES   A fundamental issue in paleoanthropology is determining the body mass of fossil primates. This information is important because body mass relates to many aspects of the biology, behaviour, and ecology in primates (see Chapter 4). To determine body mass, paleoanthropologists employ a statistical procedure known as **correlation**, which refers to the relationship between variables. Many features, such as the cross-sectional area of molars, are positively correlated with body mass. In other words, large-bodied primates tend to have relatively large teeth. Paleoanthropologists hypothesize that correlates to body mass in extant primates also hold for extinct primate taxa. Thus, the recovery of a few teeth from a fossilized primate can provide sufficient data to make a rough estimate of its body mass. Teeth tell us much more than just how much a fossil primates weighed, as we see next.

DENTAL CORRELATES TO DIET IN FOSSIL PRIMATES   We look at two morphological aspects of dentition as they pertain to diet: enamel thickness and dental morphology. First, interspecific variations in enamel thickness tend to reflect differences in the physical properties of foods eaten by primates. Species with a diet composed of hard, gritty food, such as seeds, tend to have thick enamel, whereas species such as folivores that eat leafy plant foods tend to have thin enamel. Second, although the anterior dentition of many primates serves non-dietary functions, such as grooming and defence, it also serves in the initial preparation of food for **mastication** (chewing). The strongest functional signal for incisors and canines is seen in primates that use their teeth on bark, wood, and fruit. In other words, researchers can best interpret the use of incisors and canines in primates that use these teeth to acquire or chew food. Primates that open bark and wood to get at insects and plant exudates tend to have **procumbent** (forward-projecting) incisors. Frugivorous primates often have relatively larger,

Correlation ■ A statistical relationship between two variables such that high values on one factor tend to go with high values on the other factor.

Mastication ■ Chewing of food.

Procumbent ■ Teeth that project forward.

broader incisors than those seen in folivores. This pattern exists because a frugivore first bites into its food using the anterior dentition, just like most people do when eating an apple or even peeling the rind off an orange. However, anterior dentition also serves social and defensive roles, including threatening open-mouth displays and biting. As a result, it can be difficult to separate dietary and socioecological roles for anterior dentition in fossil primates. Conversely, posterior dentition has a stronger dietary component than anterior dentition. A primate that eats leafy materials passes the food directly to its premolars and molars. In other words, it's easier to chew up salad using your posterior dentition than your incisors and canines. For folivores, the combination of thin enamel and long, sharp crests enables them to efficiently slice leaves, just like a pair of scissors. Insectivorous primates also have sharp cusps on their teeth, but not necessarily thin enamel, because they must cut through the hard outer body parts of insects to get to the soft, yummy insides. The molars of frugivores tend to have low, rounded cusps (called bunodont), which serve as a broad basin for masticating fruit pulp. Other clues to the diet of extinct primates can be found on their cranial skeleton.

CRANIAL CORRELATES TO DIET AND LOCOMOTION IN FOSSIL PRIMATES   The cranial skeleton is unique because it provides information on both diet and locomotion in fossil primates. The most important dietary aspect of cranial morphology involves features associated with chewing. Chewing is achieved predominantly by the actions of the following four muscles: masseter, temporalis, medial pterygoid, and lateral pterygoid. Each of these muscles connects the mandible to various parts of the skull. To find one of these muscles, place your fingers on your temple the next time you are chewing. You will feel the temporalis muscle twitching under your skin. As you chew, slowly move your fingers up to the top of your skull. At a certain point, you will notice that you no longer feel the twitching muscle. This point marks the origin of the muscle on your skull, which then terminates or inserts on the top of your mandible. Paleoanthropologists can look at the size and location of the muscle attachments on the skull and mandible to gain information on the relative bite force involved in mastication. Primates that feed on hard objects, such as tough seeds or fibrous plant parts, tend to have larger muscles and muscle attachments on their skull and mandible.

Cranial anatomy and morphology also provide information on the activity patterns and locomotion of extinct primates. Information on activity patterns can be determined by looking at the relative size of the eye orbits compared to the overall size of the skull. Nocturnal primates tend to have relatively larger eye orbits compared to their skulls, whereas diurnal primates usually have relatively smaller eye orbits compared to the crania. Paleoanthropologists also look at the location of the foramen magnum to approximate body posture and locomotion (Figure 5.5). In quadrupedal primates, the foramen magnum tends to be placed more at the back of the head, indicating a prone body posture. In upright primates, such as bipedal humans, the foramen magnum is located directly under the skull.

POSTCRANIAL CORRELATES TO LOCOMOTION IN FOSSIL PRIMATES   The postcranial skeleton can be examined to deduce the locomotor behaviour of extinct primates. We focus on basic postcranial features associated with the following four common locomotor patterns utilized by primates: arboreal quadrupedalism, terrestrial quadrupedalism, leaping, and suspension. We discuss bipedalism in Chapter 6. Arboreal quadrupeds tend to have a narrow axial skeleton, long tails, moderately long digits, and short forelimbs and hindlimbs of equal length. These primates tend to be in a constantly flexed position (i.e., bent knees and elbows). Consequently, the elbows and knees of arboreal quadrupeds exhibit specific adaptations to support the animal in a flexed posture. These adaptations and body posture lower the centre of gravity of an arboreal quadruped, which enhances stability and balance on an inherently unstable **substrate**,

Substrate ■ Surface on which an organism moves.

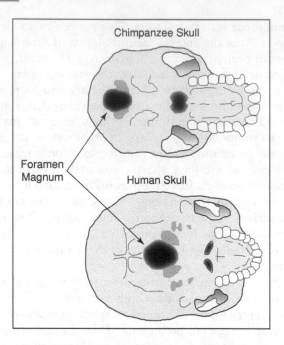

Figure 5.5

Graphical representation of the base of the skull in a modern chimpanzee and human.

In the human, the foramen magnum is located in a more anterior (frontal) position than in the chimpanzee. Note that the skulls are not drawn to scale.

or surface (i.e., tree branches). For example, perhaps you recall playing as a child on a playground tightrope or walking along a fence or wall. Your first reaction to any destabilization of the substrate was to crouch down, thereby lowering your centre of gravity and, hopefully, regaining stability. Otherwise, you were likely to fall to the ground.

The limbs of terrestrial quadrupeds are built more for speed than for stability. The forelimbs and hindlimbs are long and tend to be held in an extended position. Terrestrial quadrupeds also tend to have a short tail and digits. In leaping primates, numerous postcranial features are associated with strong propulsive forces needed by the animals to jump. We focus on one main feature, which is their long hindlimbs. In fact, leapers tend to have much longer hindlimbs than forelimbs. Interestingly, they also have a narrow tibia, which likely reflects the simple hinge-like flexion and extension used by the animals during a leap. Conversely, suspensory primates have longer forelimbs than hindlimbs. Their hips and shoulders are very mobile, ensuring they can grasp a wide array of constantly changing support structures. They also tend to have very long, curved fingers, which are used to hook onto a branch. Most suspensory apes lack a tail.

You should note that the above morphological descriptions represent only a small proportion of the information used by paleoanthropologists to reconstruct the behaviour and ecology of fossil primates. Nonetheless, we can now turn to theories on how and why primates evolved.

Hypotheses on Primate Origins

Just as we're intrigued by the question of human origins, paleoanthropologists are fascinated by questions about when and why the first primates evolved. In fact, these questions are interrelated because humans are descendants of the first primates. However, there is considerable controversy regarding primate origins. Put differently, we don't yet know the evolutionary relationships among the first primates, their descendants, and other broadly contemporaneous mammals. Despite this question, researchers have formulated numerous theories on why primates evolved in the first place. Of these, the most widely accepted encompass three slightly different views on primate origins: arboreality, predation, and ecology.

Fred Szalay and Marion Dagasto (1988) developed the grasping-leaping hypothesis of primate origins. In this theory, primate origins represent a primitive condition for grasping branches and leaping in trees seen in earlier euarchontans. Euarchontans include the Dermoptera or colugos (an amazing gliding mammal), the Scandentia or treeshrews, the extinct Plesiadapiformes (who we will meet in the pages ahead), and the Primates. More evolved grasping hands and feet came about in the early primates to facilitate moving about in the complex web of flexible tree branches (Szalay, 1972). Similarly, these early primates undertook a more acrobatic leaping form of locomotion, not seen in earlier euarchontans, such as Plesiadapiformes. Although this theory accounts for changes in limb morphology, it fails to explain certain aspects of primate dental morphology and visual systems. Specifically, why do other arboreal mammals lack the orbital convergence and stereoscopic vision exhibited by primates and visual predators, such as owls and hawks?

Thus, Mart Cartmill (1992) came up with an alternative idea on primate origins, the visual predation hypothesis. In this hypothesis, primate origins can be traced back to visual adaptations for hunting prey in arboreal habitats. Cartmill also suggested that arboreal hunting resulted in the evolution of grasping hands and nails, rather than claws, to capture and hold prey in small, terminal branches. Despite explaining a broader suite of primate characters, Cartmill's hypothesis has not been supported by detailed ecological studies of insectivorous primates. Specifically, nocturnal insectivores are more likely to hunt using smell and sound rather than sight (Wright et al., 2003). Furthermore, field studies revealed that tamarins, which have claw-like nails, are adept at both hunting for insects in terminal branches and clinging to tree trunks to feed on exudates (Garber, 1980).

These observations led, in part, to Robert Sussman's (1991) more ecologically based idea on primate origins, called the angiosperm co-evolution hypothesis. Sussman suggested that the major impetus for primate origins and adaptations was the roughly contemporaneous diversification of angiosperm plants, which produced tasty and nutritious fruit in their terminal branches. However, field studies of extant mammals similar to those that led to the first primates failed to provide conclusive evidence in support of either Sussman's or Cartmill's hypotheses (Rasmussen, 1990). In fact, field studies provide support for aspects of both hypotheses. Therefore, the incomplete fossil record, particularly during the earliest stages of primate evolution, makes it impossible to determine which of the above hypotheses is correct. These issues reveal exciting research and career opportunities for students just like you.

Ecosystem and Temporal Aspects of Primate Origins

Dinosaurs were the dominant vertebrates from about 230 to 65.5 million years ago (MYA), at which point the fossil record indicates a mass extinction of non-avian dinosaurs, reptiles, and plants in both terrestrial and aquatic environments. Although the causes of this mass extinction are hotly debated, the prevailing theory is that a massive asteroid impact threw up a long-lasting, worldwide layer of debris, thereby blotting out sunlight and disrupting plant growth. The loss of plant species caused an extinction cascade of herbivores and their predators in many parts of the planet. For reasons that are poorly understood, some mammal and bird lineages survived this mass extinction event. This information dispels the common misconception that mammals evolved after the extinction of dinosaurs. In fact, mammals evolved from cynodonts (mammal-like dinosaurs) about 220 MYA. Thus, mammals were already an ancient lineage by the time the

Era ■ One of approximately 11 units of geological time that cover the ca. 4.6-billion-year age of Earth (e.g., Cenozoic Era from 65.5 million years ago to present).

Epoch ■ A unit of geological time that is a subdivision of an era.

dinosaurs went extinct. The Cenozoic Era, which began about 65.5 million years ago and continues through today, marks the end of the "Age of the Dinosaurs" and the beginning of the "Age of the Mammals." An **era** is one of 11 geologically determined and clearly defined periods of time. This geological period is, therefore, particularly relevant to primate origins and evolution. There were considerable geological and climatic changes during the Cenozoic (Figure 5.6). The Cenozoic is subdivided into the following epochs: Paleocene, Eocene, Oligocene, Miocene, Pliocene, Pleistocene, and Holocene (Table 5.1). An **epoch** is a span of time smaller than an era. We start with the Paleocene, and then work our way forward in time to the Pliocene. We'll cover the Pleistocene and Holocene in the next chapter on hominin origins.

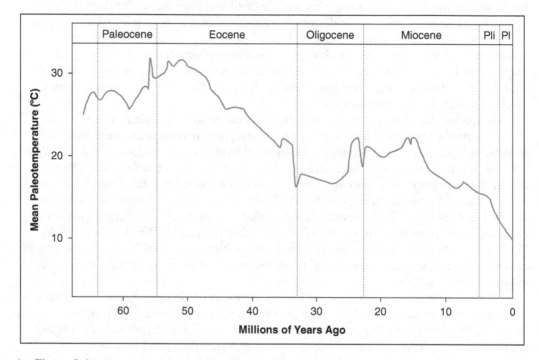

Figure 5.6

Changes in temperature during the Cenozoic Era.

Table 5.1		
EPOCHS OF THE CENOZOIC ERA		
Epoch	**Start (MYA)**	**End (MYA)**
Holocene	0.01	On-going
Pleistocene	2.59	0.01
Pliocene	5.33	2.59
Miocene	23.03	5.33
Oligocene	33.90	23.03
Eocene	55.80	33.90
Paleocene	65.50	55.80

Paleocene "Primates"

The Paleocene epoch lasted from 65.5 to 55.8 MYA. Compared to the present-day world, global geography was very different during the Paleocene. North America, South America, Africa, and India were island continents; much of Europe and western Asia were inundated with water; and Australia had only just separated from Antarctica. The global climate also differed markedly from present-day conditions, in that the world was a considerably warmer and wetter place. Much of the northern hemisphere and parts of the southern hemisphere had a warm, temperate climate. Greenland and Antarctica had cool, temperate climates, which is very different from their current frigid conditions. Central Africa and parts of southern Asia had hot, tropical climates, just as they do today. Tropical forests covered much of central Africa and southern Asia, whereas temperate forests covered much of North America, Europe, and eastern Asia. Regions formerly covered in temperate forests now contain some of the best sites for locating Paleocene mammals. In fact, each year there are opportunities for students, just like you, to join paleoanthropologists in looking for Paleocene mammals in places such as Utah and Wyoming. What did Paleocene mammals look like and do?

Paleocene Mammals: Any Primates Here?

Palaeontologists have found fossilized remains of Paleocene mammals, including rodents, in various parts of the world. Of these mammal fossils, some remarkably primate-like taxa, best represented by a group known as Plesiadapiformes (Figure 5.7), have been found in North America, Europe, and Asia. Plesiadapiformes ranged in body mass from 7 to 3000 g. They had a primitive dental formula of 3.1.3.3. Although researchers have recovered considerable cranial remains of Plesiadapiformes, the unique morphology seen in these specimens precludes determination of their activity pattern. Put differently, we don't know if Plesiadapiformes were diurnal or nocturnal. Based on studies of their dentition, paleoanthropologists are confident that most Plesiadapiformes were omnivorous, but there is indication in some taxa of dietary specializations for seeds, fruit, and insects. Analysis of the many postcranial remains suggests an arboreal, scampering mode of locomotion similar to that seen in squirrels.

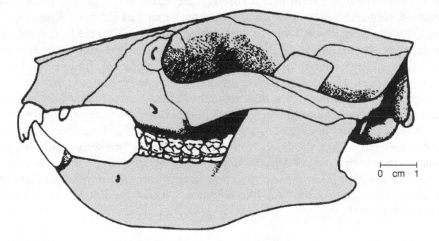

0   cm   1

Figure 5.7

Plesiadapis skull.

Note the rodent-like incisors and lack of postorbitol closure in this Paleocene mammal.

Phylogenetic Relationships among Paleocene "Primates"

As a student, I always wondered why scientists got excited each time some new fossil was found. After all, it's just one fossil, right? The reason for this excitement is that due to the paucity of quality fossils of Paleocene mammals, particularly those with primate-like features, the addition of even one new specimen can alter the interpretation of primate origins. If paleoanthropologists have only the anterior dentition of a fossil primate, then their interpretations of its life ways can be changed by the discovery of posterior dental remains. It should come as no surprise to you that our idea of primate phylogeny during the Paleocene has changed over the years. Up until about 40 years ago, Plesiadapiformes were classified as primates because of certain aspects of their teeth and because their limbs were adapted for an arboreal lifestyle. More recent investigations indicate that plesiadapids are unlikely to be members of the Primate Order because they retain the following primitive mammalian traits: no postorbital bar, claws instead of nails on their digits, eyes placed on the side of the head, and greatly enlarged incisors. However, genetic research places the timing of primate origins at about 85 MYA (Springer et al., 2003), well before the start of the Paleocene epoch. Thus, we either haven't found any primate remains from the Paleocene epoch or interpretations of a few cranial characters in Plesiadapids are flawed. A possible answer to this long-standing issue can be found in a recent study on primate origins (Bloch et al., 2007). Specifically, a cladistic analysis of newly discovered and beautifully preserved Paleocene mammals indicates that plesiadapids, and a few other contemporaneous mammals, are sister taxa to primates of modern aspect, known as the Euprimates. Put differently, if this cladistic analysis holds up to scientific scrutiny, then Plesiadapiformes are, in fact, in the Primate Order. In the following section, we look at Euprimates of the Eocene epoch.

Eocene Primates: Are We There Yet?

Plate tectonics ■ Geological theory that the plates of the Earth's crust move, resulting in changes in the position, size, and shape of continents and oceans.

During the Eocene epoch (55.8–33.9 MYA), the continents continued to move, albeit incredibly slowly because of **plate tectonics**: the plates of the Earth's crust move, resulting in changes to the position, size, and shape of continents and oceans. South America and Africa were still island continents, as was North America during the early parts of the Eocene. The main differences in paleogeography involved land bridges between the major continents. For example, early in the Eocene there was a connection between North America and Europe, as well as between Asia and Europe. Over the next few millions of years, these connections were lost, resulting in divergence of the various mammals on each continent. These global patterns of continental geography contributed to some of the most extreme climatic conditions of the Cenozoic Era. The global climate was extremely warm and wet during the early parts of the Eocene, followed by a slow reduction in temperature and humidity for the remainder of the epoch. Consequently, warm, temperate forests expanded into polar regions. Although many lineages of modern mammals, such as **ungulates** (hoofed mammals), evolved during the Eocene, most were typically smaller in body size and mass than extant forms. Fossil deposits dated to this epoch also provide the first evidence of primates similar in form to extant strepsirhines. Moreover, we have the first tantalizing evidence of monkey-like primates. Clearly, the Eocene was an ideal time to be a mammal.

Ungulates ■ Mammals with hooves (e.g., horses, deer, sheep).

Finally, the First "Modern" Primates!

Some fossil mammals recovered from Eocene deposits exhibit morphological features similar to those seen in extant strepsirhines and even one special group of haplorhines. Specifically, these mammals have a postorbital bar and nails instead of claws. Because of this abrupt morphological transition from the more primitive features of Plesiadapiformes of the Paleocene, the primates of the Eocene are often categorized as **Euprimates,** meaning that they look very much like some modern primates. Most Eocene primates are typically divided into four taxonomic groups based on suites of unique characters: the Adapoidea (adapoids), Omomyoidea (omomyoids), Eosimiidae (eosimiids), and Oligopithecidae (oligopithecids).

Euprimates ▪ Primates of modern aspect.

ADAPOIDEA: ANCESTRAL LEMURS? Adapoids were common to the Eocene animal communities in North America and Europe, but relatively rare in Asia and Africa. Paleoanthropologists have described approximately 116 species of adapoids, with more being dug up each year. Body mass estimates for adapoids range from 100 g up to 6900 g, which makes this taxon similar in size to extant strepsirhines. Most adapoids had small eye orbits indicative of a diurnal lifestyle, a long snout, and a primate-like dental formula of 2.1.4.3. They also had small incisors and large canines. The dental morphology of these early primates indicates that their diet was remarkably similar to that seen in earlier Plesiadapiformes, with most species being categorized as omnivores. Put differently, the molar morphology of adapoids is almost identical to that seen in Plesiadapiformes. Adapoids had long legs as well as a long body and tail. Although some adapoids exhibit peculiarities in their postcranial morphology, most taxa had movement patterns that likely ranged from quadrupedal running and leaping in small-bodied forms to leaping in larger-bodied taxa. Thus, adapoids exhibit a lemur-like suite of morphological features.

OMOMYOIDEA: ANCESTRAL TARSIERS? Eocene omomyoids first appeared in North America, Europe, and Asia. Like the adapoids, there were numerous species of omomyoids, particularly in North America. These primates ranged in body size from 45 to 2500 g, although most weighed less than 1000 g. Thus, omomyoids were somewhat smaller in body mass than adapoids. Omomyoids were characterized by having large eyes, indicating a nocturnal activity pattern, and short snouts (Figure 5.8). They had large incisors and small canines. Taxa in the early Eocene had a dental formula of 2.1.4.3., whereas latter taxa lost one of their premolars, resulting in a dental formula of 2.1.3.3. Their dental morphology indicates interspecific variations in diet, ranging from insectivory in small-bodied forms to frugivory and even folivory in larger-bodied taxa. Omomyoids were predominantly arboreal leapers and quadrupeds. A few species exhibit a partially fused tibia-fibula, like that seen in extant tarsiers. Therefore, omomyoids exhibit a tarsier-like suite of morphological features.

EOSIMIIDAE AND OLIGOPITHECIDAE: ANCESTRAL HAPLORHINES? Paleoanthropologists have recovered some fragmented jaws, loose teeth, and a few postcranial bones of Eocene primates from China and Egypt. Those from China are placed in the Eosimiidae family and those from Egypt are in the Oligopithecidae family. Eosimiids were rather small creatures, weighing about 100 g. They have a platyrrhine-like dental formula of 2.1.3.3., with small incisors and broad premolars and molars. The postcranial material hints at monkey-like properties. The oligopithecids weighed about 900 to 1500 g. Surprisingly, oligopithecids have a 2.1.2.3. dental formula, just like in modern catarrhines (Old World monkeys and apes). Moreover, their cranial morphology, such as the shape of the auditory bulla, bears some remarkable similarities to extant Catarrhines. The diet of oligopithecids was probably composed of insects and leafy materials. Hopefully, future expeditions will recover additional eosimiids and oligopithecids because little functional or phylogenetic information can be obtained from the current assemblage of fossils.

Phylogenetic Relationships among Eocene Primates

A fundamental issue in primate evolution is resolving phylogenetic relationships in Eocene primates. Why? Because these mammals are the first to be definitively identified as members of the Primate Order (Figure 5.9). Thus, they represent, at this

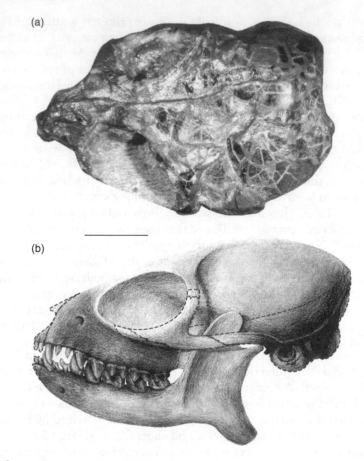

Figure 5.8

Top view of fossilized skull (a), and artist's reconstruction of the skull (b), from an Omomyoid primate, *Teilhardina*.

Note the post-orbitol bar in this specimen. Scale bar equals 5 mm.

Adapted by permission from Macmillan Publishers Ltd: NATURE (427, 65–68), © 2004.

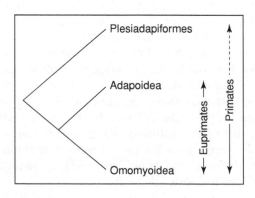

Figure 5.9

Phylogenetic relationships of Eocene primates.

Inclusion of Plesiadapiformes in Primates indicated by dotted line, follows recent work by Bloch et al., 2007.

time, the most likely common ancestor for all extant primates. Moreover, paleoan-thropologists are seeking answers to the following fascinating questions: Are adapoids the first strepsirhines, and are omomyoids the first tarsiers? Part of the issue with resolving issues of primate origins in the Eocene is that some taxonomists use only a few, obvious morphological features to define each taxonomic group (e.g., size of eye orbits). Recall from the previous chapter that this kind of scientific debate fails to resolve phylogenetic relationships between taxa. On the other hand, cladistic studies of primates from the Paleocene and Eocene led to the formulation of three hypotheses on primate origins. First, this research supports adapoids and omomyoids as separate primate lineages. Second, adapoids and strepsirhines form a distinct group, as do omomyoids and haplorhines. Finally, there is support for haplorhines to have evolved from omomyoids. However, the recent discoveries of unique adapoids and omomyoids in Asia and Africa mean that the above three points should be viewed only as hypotheses, which paleoanthropologists will test and revise in the future.

One of the most hotly debated issues in primate evolution involves the phyloge-netic relationship of eosimiids and oligopithecids to other primates. The highly frag-mented remains of the eosimiids make it difficult to conduct phylogenetic analyses because doing so can result in erroneous conclusions that are eventually refuted by the discovery and analysis of more complete fossil specimens. For example, some dental features of the Eosimiidae point to a broad haplorhine relationship, whereas others indicate a close phylogenetic relationship to tarsiers. Although most specimens of oligo-pithecids tend to be better preserved, their unique combination of primitive and derived features has made it difficult to resolve the phylogenetic relationships of this taxon to other Eocene primates as well as those found in Oligocene deposits. More eosimiids and oligopithecids must be found and analyzed before any definitive phylogenetic assessments can be made. At present, all that can be said is that the discovery of the eosimiids and oligopithecids may push haplorhine origins as far back as the Eocene.

Oligocene Primates: Hey, Is It the Monkeys?

The transition from the Eocene to the Oligocene (33.9–23.0 MYA) marked continued changes in global geography, climate, and primate habitats. The continents were located close to where they are today, except that there was no land connection between North and South America. Perhaps the most important geological change was the separation of South America and Australia from Antarctica, which resulted in major changes in ocean currents around the newly frozen South Pole. Consequently, there was a major drop in global temperatures and sea levels, which greatly reduced the extent of forest cover, particularly in the northern hemisphere.

Morphological Features of Oligocene Primates

Although many Euprimates disappeared from North America and Europe, new primate taxa evolved in Asia, Africa, and South America. Most importantly, these new taxa exhibit some morphological features similar to those seen in extant monkeys rather than strepsirhines. Most Oligocene primates can be divided into the following three taxonomic groups within the Haplorhini suborder: Parapithecidae, Propliopithecidae, and Platyrrhini. Fragmentary remains of quite a few fossil taxa have, so far, defied attempts to be taxonomically classified. What is it about these fossil primates that indicates they were monkeys rather than lemurs or, for that matter, apes? No single feature can unite Oligocene primates with extant monkeys. Rather, many of these fossil taxa have most but not necessarily all of the main diagnostic features of monkeys. These features include full postorbital closure, a 2.1.3.3. or 2.1.2.3. dental formula, and derived aspects of the molar and skeletal morphology, which we don't cover in this text. However, other morphological aspects of Oligocene primates are unique and differ from those seen in extant monkeys. Below, we take a closer look at these three groups of Oligocene primates.

PARAPITHECIDAE   Much our information on Oligocene primates comes from long-term excavations at the Fayum Depression in Egypt. The Fayum is a remarkable geological outcrop of Eocene-Oligocene deposits surrounded by desert. Although present conditions are uniformly hot and dry, 34 MYA this area was covered in tropical swamps that contained a remarkable array of plants and animals, including ancestral manatees, rhinos, and primates. The Parapithecidae have been found in late Eocene to early Oligocene deposits. This fascinating primate family contains 8 to 10 species, which ranged in body mass from 300 to 3000 g. Although their dental formula of 2.1.3.3. is just like that seen in extant Platyrrhines, other dental features indicate affinities with both lemurs and monkeys. In parapithecids, the mandible symphasis is fused, as in modern monkeys. Of the few cranial remains recovered to date, all exhibit relatively small eye orbits and full postorbital closure. Other cranial and postcranial skeletal features are like those seen in modern platyrrhines. Parapithecids were likely to have been diurnal frugivores and excellent leapers.

PROPLIOPITHECIDAE   Propliopithecids have been found in early Oligocene deposits at the Fayum. Although propliopithecids share certain haplorhine features with contemporaneous parapithecids, such as a fused mandibular symphysis and postorbital closure, there are some important morphological differences between the two families. Propliopithecids were larger in size, with species-specific estimates of body mass ranging from 900 to 6700 g. They had a dental formula of 2.1.2.3., like that seen in modern Old World monkeys and apes (Figure 5.10). Propliopithecids have an ape-like arrangement of five molar cusps, rather than the bilophodont molars common in modern catarrhine monkeys. The recent discovery of a complete cranium from *Aegyptopithecus,* the best known propliopithecid, reveals two rather startling things about its brain size and intersexual size differences (Simons et al., 2007). First, the brain-to-body size ratio was similar to that found in extant lemurs, indicating that the evolution of large brain size had not yet occurred in Oligocene catarrhines. Second, there was considerable sexual dimorphism in this taxon. Postcranial remains of *Aegyptopithecus* are more primitive than modern catarrhines but more advanced than extant strepsirhines. Studies of the cranial and postcranial morphologies of *Aegyptopithecus* indicate that it had a diurnal activity pattern, ate a frugivorous and folivorous diet, and was an arboreal quadruped.

FOSSIL PLATYRRHINES   Researchers have unearthed Oligocene primates in South America, which at that time was an island continent. These discoveries are remarkable because no primates have been recovered from earlier epochs in the Neotropics, indicating that the origin of these early platyrrhines lies outside South America. So how did these early platyrrhines get to South America? Despite years of scientific speculation, the prevailing theory is that some unknown Oligocene primate rafted over from Africa. Models of continental geography indicate that Africa and South America were closer together during the Oligocene epoch and that ocean currents flowed quite strongly in a westerly direction between these continents. Thus, some small-bodied primates are thought to have survived a few weeks eating insects and fruit on a large tree that

Figure 5.10

Skull from a *Aegyptopithecus zeuxis*.

Count the number of teeth and you'll see that this early primate shares our dental formula (2.1.2.3.).
© S. M. Lehman

floated across the Atlantic Ocean from Africa to South America. Yes, that's the best we can come up with!

What do we know about these monkeys? The earliest platyrrhines were small monkeys weighing about 500 to 1000 g. Although they have the characteristic platyrrhine dental formula of 2.1.3.3., the low, rounded cusps on their teeth are similar to those seen in some primate fossils from the late Eocene in the Fayum region of Egypt. Paleoanthropologists conclude that these early fossil platyrrhines were frugivores. Few cranial and no postcranial remains have been recovered, which limits any theories on the activity and locomotor patterns of fossil platyrrhines from the Oligocene.

Phylogenetic Relationships among Oligocene Primates

Phylogenetic analysis of Oligocene primates has resulted in more debate than consensus on their evolutionary relationships. Because the remains are fragmentary and the vast majority of Oligocene fossils come from only a few sites in Africa and South America, a conservative approach is needed to summarize their phylogenetic relationships. What we can say here is that there is general support for the parapithecids being ancestral to a clade forming the propliopithecids and the fossil platyrrhines (Figure 5.11). Put differently, propliopithecids share a more recent common ancestor with each other than either does with the parapithecids. As with earlier epochs, we desperately need students

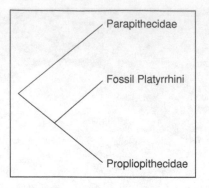

Figure 5.11

Phylogenetic relationships of Oligocene primates.

like you to unearth Oligocene primates from new sites. Only with these additional specimens will paleoanthropologists be able to start sifting through the bewildering array of hypotheses on evolutionary relationships among fossil lemurs, Old World monkeys, and New World monkeys.

Miocene Primates: Planet of the Apes

The Miocene epoch, which lasted almost 18 million years (23.0–5.3 MYA), marks the evolution of primitive apes. The main paleogeographic feature relevant to primate origins involved cycles of expansion and reduction in the size of primate habitats in the Mediterranean and Eurasia. Land bridges formed and disappeared between Africa, Europe, and Eurasia. During the early stages of the Miocene, the climate was similar to today's conditions, but warmer. About 15 MYA, the climate became considerably cooler and drier as glaciers formed in Antarctica. Consequently, tropical forests transitioned to a mosaic of woodland savannah (trees and grass) and savannahs (grass). This cooling also resulted in the expansion of savannah-woodland environments in Africa and Eurasia. During this time, Old World monkeys and apes diverged, and these apes then underwent an adaptive radiation into 80 to 100 species. To put this number in context, there are only approximately 20 to 25 species of extant apes.

Morphological Features of Miocene Primates

How do we distinguish Miocene apes from contemporaneous monkeys? Although many morphological features are associated with apes, we focus on just a few key ones (Table 5.2). As you can see, most of the diagnostic features represent relative rather than absolute differences between the taxa. The overall set of character traits represents a more derived suite of features compared to monkeys. However, paleoanthropologists have failed to reach any consensus on a taxonomic classification for Miocene apes; each researcher favours sometimes radically different ideas. Because of this issue and because of the diversity of fossil apes during this time period, we'll split our review into three sequential sub-epochs: early, late, and middle Miocene.

EARLY MIOCENE APES   The early Miocene lasted from about 23 to 16 MYA. During this time, ape-like primates evolved in eastern Africa. Of the many species that have

Table 5.2

MAIN MORPHOLOGICAL DIFFERENCES BETWEEN MIOCENE AND EXTANT APES

Feature	Miocene Apes	Extant Apes
Placement of scapula	Side	Back
Ribcage depth (front to back)	Deep	Shallow
Extension of elbow joint	Partial	Full
Shoulder joint	Restricted	Mobile
Spine	Long, flexible	Short, rigid
Hip joint	Restricted	Mobile
Arm to leg length	Equal	Arms longer
Hands	Variable	Large

From Begun, 2003.

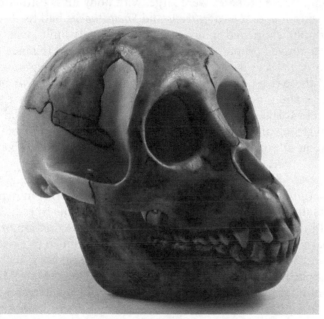

Figure 5.12

Reconstructed skull from *Proconsul africanus*.

© S. M. Lehman

been found, the best, most abundant specimens are in the family Proconsulidae and genus *Proconsul*. These diurnal apes weighed from 17 to 50 kg, marking a major increase in body size within the primate clade. Estimates of Proconsulidae brain size are approximately 167 cc, which is much larger than estimates of cranial capacity in Miocene monkeys.

Proconsul had sexually dimorphic canines and a largely frugivorous diet (Figure 5.12). Most Proconsulidae were quadrupeds, although some species were more arboreal than others. Overall, *Proconsul* exhibits a mixture of both ape-like and monkey-like traits. For example, these Miocene primates have the following ape-like features: relatively large body size, thick molar enamel, and no tail. However, *Proconsul* species retain some monkey-like features, such as certain morphological aspects of their backbone and pelvis. Other ape-like fossils, such as *Afropithecus* and *Kenyapithecus,* from the early Miocene also exhibit a variety of ape-like, monkey-like, and unique features. Thus, these early Miocene apes were probably better suited to travelling on top of tree branches rather than hanging or swinging below tree limbs, as seen in extant apes. Nonetheless, these cranial and postcranial features in early Miocene apes provide strong evidence for transitional changes in primate evolution.

MIDDLE MIOCENE APES   During the middle Miocene (16.0–11.6 MYA), African apes moved across land bridges to colonize Eurasia and eventually parts of eastern Europe and Asia. Furthermore, David Begun (2003) hypothesizes that in the early stages of the middle Miocene epoch some European apes migrated back to Africa. However, these African immigrants did not last long, as most species appear to have gone extinct by about 13 MYA. Some of the best known and most interesting apes from middle Miocene are *Dryopithecus* from Europe and *Sivapithecus* from modern-day India and Pakistan. These primates were large, with body mass estimates of 20 to 90 kg. Just as in extant apes, *Dryopithecus* and *Sivapithecus* had teeth suited for masticating fruit pulp, shortened snouts, and long, strongly built jaws. A reduced snout represents a derived primate feature reflecting a reduced reliance on olfaction. The cranium of *Sivapithecus* is very similar to that of extant orangutans, although the postcrania of these two taxa have little in common. *Dryopithecus* brains were similar in size and proportions to those seen in extant chimpanzees, which are remarkably clever! Morphological interpretations of *Dryopithecus* and *Sivapithecus* postcrania reveal strong affinities to the suspensory locomotion utilized by extant apes. In sum, *Dryopithecus* and *Sivapithecus* were more ape-like than monkey-like.

LATE MIOCENE APES   The late Miocene epoch lasted from 11.6 to 5.3 MYA, and experienced a continuous, gradual decline in global temperatures. In many regions of the world, temperate and tropical forests contracted in size due to reduced rainfall and temperatures. Although these changes likely resulted in the extinction of many ape taxa in Europe and parts of Asia, other taxa travelled to or continued to exist in the tropical zones of Africa and Southeast Asia. Consequently, some fossil apes, such as *Dryopithecus* and *Sivapithecus,* from the middle Miocene survived into the late Miocene. In addition, paleoanthropologists have recovered remains of some latecomers to the ape lineage, such as *Oreopithecus, Ouranopithecus, Lufengpithecus,* and *Ankarapithecus*. *Oreopithecus* is perhaps the best known of all the Miocene apes due to the abundant fossils discovered in Italy. This ape had the classic catarrhine dental formula of 2.1.2.3., and its dental morphology indicates a folivorous diet, which is a rather remarkable adaptation in the ape lineage. Most extant apes, except for some species of gorilla, are more frugivorous than folivorous. The body mass for *Oreopithecus* is estimated to be approximately 30 kg, which is rather large. Examination of the numerous postcranial remains for *Oreopithecus* indicates suspensory locomotion, just like in modern apes. *Ouranopithe- cus* was a large-bodied ape (70–110 kg) from what is modern-day Greece. This ape likely had a diet of hard, gritty foods. No postcranial materials have been recovered. *Lufengpithecus* was another large ape (50 kg), but from parts of southern China. These apes had extreme sexual dimorphism in their dentition and cranial feautures, which are similar to those seen in *Dryopithecus* specimens. You're probably just about ready to scream if you read about even one more -*pithecus*; but hold on, we have to consider only one more fascinating ape from the late Miocene. *Ankarapithecus* was a large-bodied (82 kg) ape from what is modern-day Turkey, and had teeth with very thick enamel and large jaws with which it likely masticated hard or gritty foods. *Ankarapithecus* retained the primitive trait of a **prognathic** face, which differs markedly from the flatter, more derived face of *Sivapithecus*. Now we can turn to the few monkeys known from the Miocene.

Prognathic ■ A forward or projecting aspect of anatomy, typically referring to the face.

MIOCENE MONKEYS   Although there were plenty of apes running around during the Miocene, this epoch seems to have supported few monkeys. Of the fossil monkeys that have been found, most have been recovered from the early to middle Miocene deposits in Africa and some isolated sites in Eurasia. Very few fossil monkeys have been found from the late Miocene. The reasons for this temporal variation in the fossil monkey assemblage are unknown at this time. What we do know is that the earliest Old World monkeys belong to a unique primate family called the Victoriapithecidae. Victoriapithecids ranged in body mass from 7 to 25 kg. They exhibit an interesting mixture of dental features, being more primitive than those seen in extant Old World monkeys yet more derived than those observed in Oligocene monkeys. For example, victoriapithecids had bilophodont molars with low molar cusps, as in cercopithecines. However, their mandibular morphology differs from that seen in earlier fossil monkeys and extant cercopithecines. Their postcranial morphology provides tantalizing evidence for partial terrestriality, which is not typically associated with the primitive arboreal lifestyle of fossil monkeys. The consensus of many paleoanthropologists is that victoriapithecids represent a mosaic of primitive and derived features indicative of a clade that eventually evolved into colobines and cercopithecines.

Phylogenetic Relationships among Miocene Primates

Each paleoanthropologist has his or her own slightly differing view on phylogenetic relationships within Miocene apes. Moreover, each researcher has formulated different hypotheses on which Miocene ape(s) evolved into living apes, like gorillas and chimpanzees. In most cases, these issues result from researcher speciality in one biogeographic region (e.g., Africa vs. Europe). We're only going to cover the "within" aspect of phylogenetics in fossil apes—in other words, we're not going to look at phylogenetic relationships between fossil and modern apes—as there is only tenuous evidence for relationships between fossil apes and extant apes. Many researchers group the small-bodied forms into the catarrhine monkey clade and the large-bodied taxa into the hominoid clade. You should note, again, that this over-reliance on one phenetic feature, body size, is not a particularly strong scientific method. Using a strict cladistic analysis of the total evidence, David Begun (2002) provides an interesting theory on the evolutionary history of Miocene apes (Figure 5.13). This theory holds that over the course of millions of years there were waves of migrations by Miocene apes out of and then back into Africa. In the early Miocene, fossil apes originated with *Proconsul* and then *Afropithecus* in Africa and the Arabian Peninsula. More derived forms then evolved during the middle to late Miocene in Africa (*Kenyapithecus*) and Europe (*Oreopithecus*). During the middle to late Miocene, two clades of Miocene apes existed in Europe (*Ouranopithecus* and *Dryopithecus*) and across a wide area of Eurasia (*Ankarapithecus*) and Asia (*Sivapithecus, Lufengpithecus*). Finally, the victoriapithecids tend to be positioned as basal to all extant Old World monkeys.

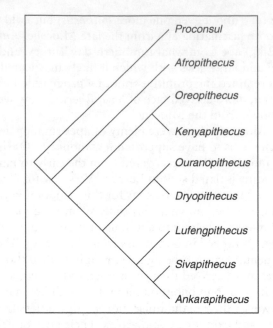

Figure 5.13
Phylogenetic relationships of Miocene primates.

Pliocene Primates: Return of the Monkeys!

The Pliocene epoch lasted from 5.3 MYA to approximately 1.8 MYA. During this epoch, a land connection formed between North and South America via the Panama isthmus. The Tethys Sea became isolated and eventually formed part of what is now the Mediterranean Sea. Due in part to the formation of continental land bridges and isolated seas, the climate continued to be cool and dry over the course of the Pliocene, further reducing the size and expanse of tropical forests. Temperate regions continued to transition from forests to grasslands.

Morphological Features of Pliocene Primates

The above geographic and climate changes spelled the end of the "Age of the Apes" and heralded a broad radiation of monkeys and the earliest hominins, which we meet in Chapter 6. Pliocene monkeys have been unearthed in Africa, Europe, and Asia. In fact, some specimens have been recovered from southeastern Britain and the island of Sicily, representing places you might not think of as former monkey habitats. These Pliocene primates are similar in many ways to extant cercopithecines and colobines, which are part of the Cercopithecidae family. Let's meet the cool Pliocene monkeys!

FOSSIL CERCOPITHECINAE   Fossil cercopithecines represent a diverse assemblage of primates from Africa and Asia. Of the 10 genera of Pliocene cercopithecines described to date, 5 still exist (*Macaca, Papio, Cercocebus, Theropithecus,* and *Cercopithecus*), indicating the success of this radiation to last for millions of years. Body mass estimates for these monkeys range from 9.5 kg in the relatively small-bodied *Macaca* up to the so-called giant geladas, which weighed about 96 kg (Figure 5.14)! Modern geladas weigh only 11 to 19 kg. Given the diversity of fossil cercopithecines, it is beyond the scope of this book to summarize all their interesting dental and postcranial morphologies. What we can say here about these fossil primates is that they share a suite of dental, cranial, and postcranial features similar to those seen in extant macaques, in mangabeys, baboons, and geladas, and in guenons. Consequently, their diet and locomotor behaviour are likely similar to those seen in extant congenera.

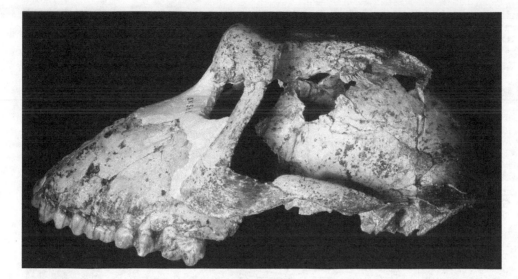

Figure 5.14
Side view of skull from *Theropithecus oswaldi*.
This was a giant, extinct cercopithecine that lived during the Pliocene.
© K. Folinsbee

FOSSIL COLOBINAE   Fossil colobines have been unearthed in many of the same
regions as those that produced fossil cercopithecines (i.e., Europe, Asia, and Africa).
Paleoanthropologists have described approximately 12 genera of fossil colobines
from the Pliocene. These Pliocene monkeys ranged in body mass from 4 to 35 kg.
Although some fossil and extant colobines share morphological similarities, many fossil
colobines look remarkably different from extant members of this subfamily. Specifically,
many of the fossil colobines retain primitive Cercopithecidae characteristics of low
molars cusps, compared to high molar cusps used for shearing leafy materials in extant
colobines, and postcranial evidence for terrestriality. Extant colobines are almost
exclusively arboreal. Moreover, some fossil colobines were much larger in body size
than extant taxa in this subfamily. The largest living colobine weighs about 11 kg.

Phylogenetic Relationships among Pliocene Monkeys

The phylogenetic relationships among Pliocene monkeys are, for lack of a more scientific word, a mess, particularly for the colobines. Part of this phylogenetic issue results
from the fact that we define extant cercopithecines and colobines by certain aspects
of soft tissues, such as cheek pouches and stomach anatomy. It is extremely rare for
any soft tissue to fossilize, and that which does is usually skin and hair rather than
any internal structures. The incomplete fossil record for many Pliocene monkeys also
contributes to heated debates about their phylogenetic relationships. There are as
many morphological similarities between fossil and extant cercopithecines as there
are morphological differences between fossil and living colobines. Therefore, given
that we cannot resolve evolutionary relationships between these basal monkeys, a
complete review of the phylogenetic relationships to extant monkeys is best left for
more advanced work and study. Despite these issues, there is no valid scientific reason
to invoke either intelligent design or creationism as alternatives to evolution when
reviewing Pliocene monkeys (Figure 5.15). As more fossil primates are recovered and
new phylogenetic techniques are employed, researchers will be better prepared to
resolve phylogenetic relationships in Pliocene monkeys.

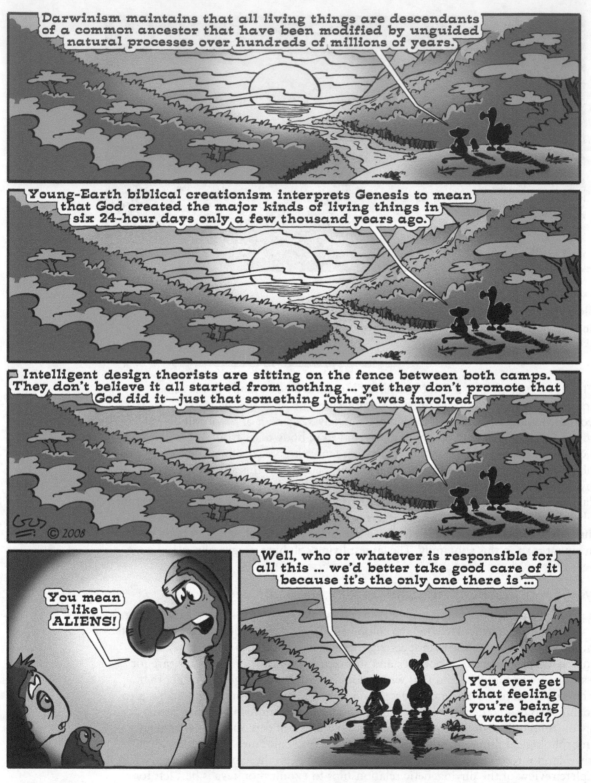

Figure 5.15
Just because evolutionary anthropologists are unable to answer every question on primate and human origins does not mean that there is any support for creationism or intelligent design.

Summary

1. Fossil primates are represented largely by dental remains; cranial and postcranial materials are rarely found. Thus, most research on primate origins involves detailed analysis of teeth.
2. General patterns of diet, locomotion, activity patterns, and even social organization can be learned from careful studies of fossil primates. Specifically, paleoanthropologists use the comparative method to understand morphological adaptations in fossil primates.
3. There are three main hypotheses on primate origins: the arboreal theory, the visual predation theory, and the angiosperm co-evolution theory.
4. The earliest mammals somehow survived a massive global extinction event about 65 million years ago. It is possible that the first primates evolved before or during the Paleocene, although the first definitive primates show up in the Eocene. Oligocene primates exhibit broad morphological similarities to some modern monkeys. The Miocene witnessed an explosive radiation of ape-like primates, which slowly disappeared during the Pliocene.

INTERNET RESOURCES

PALEOMAP Project
www.scotese.com
See some cool geological maps and climatic models for the Cenozoic.

Dental Microwear
http://comp.uark.edu/~pungar
Learn about reconstructing the diet of fossil primate and hominins.

eSkeletons Project
www.eskeletons.org
See and compare primate dental, cranial, and postcranial morphologies.

Duke University Lemur Center
www.fossils.duke.edu/learn/BAA246/BAA246.html
See photos and learn about fossil primates.

LITERATURE CITED

Begun, D. R. (2003). Planet of the apes. *Scientific American*, 289(2), 74–83.

Bloch, J. I., Silcox, M. T., Boyer, D. M., and Sargis, E. J. (2007). New Paleocene skeletons and the relationship of plesiadapiforms to crown-clade primates. *Proceedings of the National Academy of Sciences, USA*, 104(4), 1159–1164.

Cartmill, M. (1992). New views on primate origins. *Evolutionary Anthropology*, 1(3), 105–111.

Garber, P. (1980). Locomotor behavior and feeding ecology of the Panamanian tamarin (*Saguinus oedipus geoffroyi*, Callitrichidae, Primates). *International Journal of Primatology*, 1(2), 185–201.

Rasmussen, D. (1990) Primate origins: lessons from a neotropical marsupial. *American Journal of Primatology*, 22(4), 263–277.

Simons, E. L., Seiffert, E. R., Ryan, T. M., and Attia, Y. (2007). A remarkable female cranium of the early Oligocene anthropoid *Aegyptopithecus zeuxis* (Catarrhini, Propliopithecidae). *Proceedings of the National Academy of Sciences, USA*, 104(21), 8731–8736.

Springer, M. S., Murphy, W. J., Eizirik, E., and O'Brien, S. J. (2003). Placental mammal diversification and the Cretaceous-Tertiary boundary. *Proceedings of the National Academy of Sciences, USA,* 100(3), 1056–1061.

Sussman, R. W. (1991). Primate origins and the evolution of angiosperms. *American Journal of Primatology,* 23(4), 209–223.

Szalay, F. (1972). Paleobiology of the earliest primates. *The Functional and Evolutionary Biology of Primates* (ed. by R. Tuttle), pp. 3–35. Chicago: Aldine-Atherton.

Szalay, F. and Dagasto, M. (1988). Evolution of hallucial grasping in the Primates. *Journal of Human Evolution* 17:1-33.

Wright, P. C., Simons, E. L., and Gursky, S. L., Eds. (2003). *Tarsiers: Past, Present, and Future.* New Brunswick, NJ: Rutgers University Press.

CHAPTER 6

The First Hominins

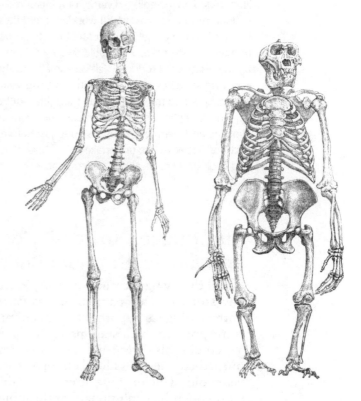

GOALS

By the end of this chapter you should understand:

1. Morphological trends in hominin evolution.
2. How to find and age fossil hominins.
3. Morphological features of transitional hominins and australopithecines.

CHAPTER OUTLINE

Introduction to Fossil Hominins: From Small Brains and Big Teeth to Big Brains and Small Teeth

Finding and Estimating the Age of Fossil Hominins

Transitional Forms: Advanced Apes or Primitive Hominins?

Australopithecines: The First "Real" Hominins

Introduction

I recall my first brush with the immense time scale of life on earth. My family took a camping trip to the famous Dinosaur Valley in Drumheller, Alberta. This valley contains some of the richest fossil beds in North America. As a precocious youth, I excitedly explored dried-out gullies that long ago were the swampy realm of the dinosaurs! I was drawn to a rock wall with exposed layers of sediments, which contained tiny fossils. As I stepped away from the wall, the blazing sun momentarily illuminated an incredible diversity of mineralized creatures that had evolved, lived, and become extinct millions of years ago. I wondered, did these creatures live when my earliest human ancestors walked the planet? And, for that matter, how old are human beings? What were my oldest human ancestors like, and would they have been as excited about my trip? Despite being thrilled by my discovery, I suddenly felt very small and short-lived in the face of such incredible biodiversity and long stretches of time. Like any growing youth on a camping trip, my mother's call for lunch pulled me—and my evolutionary thoughts—out of the gully!

In the sections below, we discuss the evolutionary anthropology of human origins during the Pliocene and Pleistocene epochs up to just before the first representatives of our genus (*Homo*). For each fossil species, we undertake only a brief review of their major morphological characteristics and ecology. Let's meet our earliest relatives!

Introduction to Fossil Hominins: From Small Brains and Big Teeth to Big Brains and Small Teeth

Of all the living creatures on the planet, humans share our closest common ancestor with chimpanzees (genus *Pan*). Put differently, evolutionary anthropologists hypothesize that chimpanzees and humans are sister taxa. At some point in the distant past, chimpanzees diverged from the human lineage. When did this divergence happen? Although paleoanthropologists have unearthed a few fossilized chimpanzee teeth, the specimens are only 500 000 years old, which is long after the establishment of the human lineage. Consequently, evolutionary anthropologists have turned to other sources of data on the timing of human evolution. Using advanced molecular techniques, researchers have estimated the divergence time between chimpanzees and humans. Although the process itself is complicated, the basic principle is that there exists a so-called "evolutionary clock" wherein the genetic building blocks of proteins (i.e. amino acids) change at a known or inferred rate over time between different branches of a cladogram. By comparing the number of changes through time between two lineages and assuming a certain rate of change, researchers can estimate the date of divergence between the branches. The catch is that the rate of change can vary through time in each branch, such as when there are fluctuating selection pressures or changes in population size. Moreover, the clock itself has to be calibrated by the largely incomplete fossil record. Because of these complexities, the estimated divergent times change as we learn more about the rates of change in the amino acid sequence of proteins and new fossils are found. For example, Kumar and colleagues (2005) estimated that chimpanzees and humans diverged 4.9 to 7.0 MYA (millions of years ago). Langergraber and colleagues (2012) used a different "evolutionary clock" that did not need fossil calibration, dating the human–chimpanzee split to at least 7.0–8.0 MYA. Shortly thereafter, another team of researchers explored the question of the human–chimpanzee split using different genetic sequences, arriving at a divergence date of 3.7-6.6 MYA (Sun et al., 2012). Many of these researchers concluded that we need more chimpanzee and human fossils as well as accurate dating estimates for these fossils to better calibrate "evolutionary clocks." It is likely that the invention of new genetics techniques and models will further refine these estimates and phylogenetic relationships between chimpanzees and humans. Therefore, in the sections below, we review the earliest purported representatives of the hominin lineage in the Pliocene (5.2–2.59 MYA) epoch. First, we need to answer the question, what's a hominin?

What's a Hominin?

For much of the 20th century, paleoanthropologists tended to rather loosely describe new fossil taxa and their placement within the human lineage. This phenetic approach, which involves the use of only a few physical features to define a taxonomic group, resulted in considerable confusion as experts argued over the validity of their personal taxonomic assessments. To a layperson, it seemed as if each team of scientists was motivated principally to be the first to find and name the earliest human ancestor! In time, many paleoanthropologists embraced the phylogenetic species concept (see Chapter 3), which alleviated some taxonomic and phylogenetic issues. A phylogenetic species is one encompassing the smallest set of organisms that share a common ancestor and that can be distinguished from other such sets of organisms. By applying this concept to fossils, the researchers dropped issues associated with focusing on only a few physical features. Consequently, these new approaches to human evolution revealed that fossil and extant primates, including humans, are more divergent than originally thought. In fact, gibbons (genus *Hylobates*) and humans represent distinct taxonomic families, Hylobatidae and Hominidae (Figure 6.1). Orangutans (genus *Pongo*) are in the subfamily Ponginae, and gorillas belong in the tribe Gorillini. Finally, there is the **hominini** tribe. In this chapter, we focus on five of the extinct genera within this tribe. Now we can review some of the morphological trends in hominin evolution.

Hominini ▪ Tribe within the Homininae comprising humans (*Homo*), chimpanzees (*Pan*), and our most recent common ancestors.

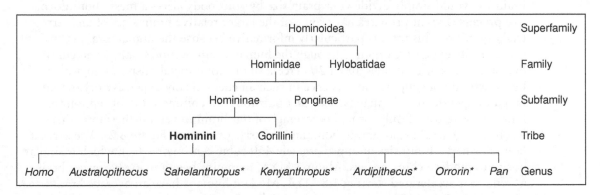

Figure 6.1

Hominoid taxonomy.

This shows how various genera of living and extinct primates are categorized from general, high-level categories, such as superfamily, down to more specific categories, such as tribe. This figure is *not* a phylogeny. Taxa marked with an asterisk may not be hominins.

Morphological Trends in Hominin Evolution

Reviewing morphological trends in hominin evolution is important for two reasons. First, we need to understand what features contributed to an adaptive radiation of hominins at a time when contemporaneous fossil apes were disappearing. Second, we need to understand that there is no singular feature that resulted in the biological evolution of human beings. Rather, modern humans are the result of millions of years of **mosaic evolution**. This evolution is ongoing, meaning that our species continues to be subject to natural selection. We will change and eventually go extinct. With that unsettling thought in mind, what are the main morphological trends in hominin evolution? Simply put, there are many! We focus on only the following key features: changes in cranial and dental morphologies, increased brain size, and **bipedalism**.

CRANIAL AND DENTAL MORPHOLOGIES   Some specimens of early hominins have faces that are more ape-like than human-like, with a longer snout and shallow face. Others have large bony crests on their skulls, which served to anchor strong chewing muscles. Concomitantly, these heavy chewers also had **robust** mandibles. The earliest hominins have small molars with thin enamel. They also tend to have large canines, which in some species are sexually dimorphic. Later hominins evolved smaller canines and transitioned to larger molars covered in thick enamel. Finally, the earliest species in our genus (*Homo*) evolved a large, globular cranium, a more **gracile** jaw, and smaller teeth. These changes in jaw and dental morphology reflect selection pressures for a diet composed of less gritty and softer food items.

INCREASED BRAIN SIZE   What do you think of when you hear the word *brain*? Typically, we associate the brain with some measure of intelligence. For example, we might say that a smart person is "big-brained" or a "brainiac." However, there is only a general relationship between the **absolute** size of the brain and supposed intelligence in mammals. Otherwise, we would expect blue whales, which have the absolute largest body and brain sizes of any organism, to be more intelligent than humans. There are obvious issues with using human-based tests to determine intelligence in animals. Nonetheless, there is clearly something else going on here because modern humans are the most technologically and culturally advanced animals on the planet. A better measure of intelligence may lie in the number of **neurons** and the speed at which they communicate in the brain. Because we can't measure neuron abundance in fossil hominins, we stick with brain size.

Furthermore, perhaps it's not necessarily the absolute but rather the relative size of the brain that's most important. For example, to compute the relative volume of your brain we would simply divide your brain size by your body size—a messy but informative process! Extant primates have some of the larger relative brain sizes of any terrestrial organism. This ratio is particularly informative because the human brain is an energetically expensive organ. Although the human brain occupies only 2 percent of our body mass, it consumes about 20 percent of our total metabolism. Biological evolution would not support the existence of such an energetically expensive organ that failed to operate at full capacity. This fact puts to rest a common misconception that humans make use of only a small percentage of our brainpower. Furthermore, there has been a general expansion in hominin brain size over time (Figure 6.2). The earliest hominins had a brain size of approximately 450 cubic centimetres (cc), which is similar in size to modern chimpanzees. About 3 MYA, hominins began to evolve larger brains, a trend that accelerated starting 1.8 MYA. Modern humans have an average brain size of approximately 1450 cc, representing a tripling in brain volume from our earliest hominin ancestors.

So, why did hominins evolve bigger brains? The hypotheses formulated by evolutionary anthropologists to understand this pattern fall into three main categories: ecological, epiphenomenal, and socialization (Dunbar, 1998). First, the ecological hypothesis holds that early hominins evolved larger brains to improve their ability to hunt or forage for unpredictable food resources. A hominin would presumably need to

Mosaic evolution ▪ The evolution at different rates of various related or unrelated features within a lineage or clade.

Bipedalism ▪ Habitual upright locomotion on two feet.

Robust ▪ Physically strong, durable.

Gracile ▪ Slight, slender.

Absolute ▪ A complete measure without restriction or qualification.

Neuron ▪ A specialized cell that delivers information within the body.

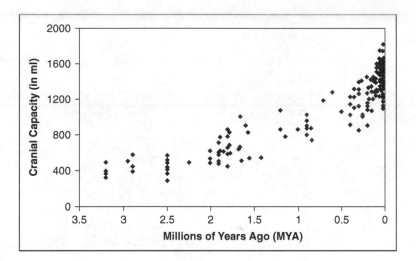

Figure 6.2

Changes in hominin brain size over the last 3.2 million years.

The general pattern is one of progressive expansion of brain size over time.

Chart by Nick Matzke of NCSE ww.ncseweb.org.

improve its mental map of a large area in order to assure access to food, particularly during periods of resource scarcity. Second, the epiphenomenal hypothesis states that an increase in hominin body size resulted in a concomitant increase in brain size. (The term *epiphenomenal* refers to a secondary by-product of some process. For example, pain is an epiphenomenal result of damage to nerves in some part of your body.) Most internal organs scale positively to body size, such that larger-bodied humans tend to have larger livers and brains. Finally, the social brain hypothesis suggests that hominins evolved larger brains to deal with the increasing complexity of their social organization. In other words, natural selection favoured individuals with an increased ability to network and scheme in large, complex societies! The answer to the question of why hominins evolved larger brains will be answered only when we understand how our brains differ from non-hominins and when we identify the genes responsible for neuron growth and conductivity (Bradbury, 2005). Therefore, there are exciting research opportunities for you to study the evolutionary anthropology of hominin brains!

BIPEDALISM   Perhaps no other morphological feature is of more interest and importance to paleoanthropologists than bipedalism. Before we get into the specifics of this feature, we need to clear up a common misconception about hominin bipedalism. If you have a cat or a dog, then you may be familiar with its ability to stand and even move about using only its hindlimbs, particularly if a favourite toy or treat is dangled above its head. This stance or movement is a form of temporary bipedalism; it is not habitual bipedalism. Why? Because cats and dogs lack specific morphological features associated with the type of bipedalism used by many hominins. The same holds for some extant apes, such as chimpanzees, which can stand or move bipedally. In other words, although a gorilla can walk bipedally like a human being, this ape lacks adaptations specific to being a habitual biped (Figure 6.3). Hominin bipedalism represents unique adaptations of both hard and soft tissue systems. These systems serve principally to preserve balance in what is essentially controlled falling! After all, bipedalism involves all of the body weight being held on one hindlimb while the other swings through to make contact with the ground in front of the biped.

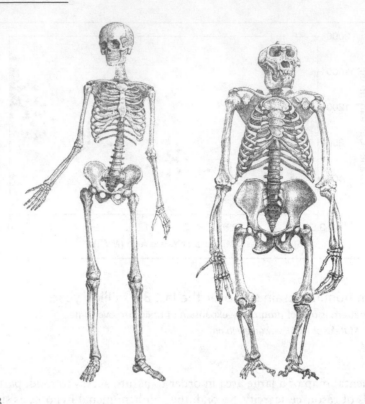

Figure 6.3

Comparison of extant human and gorilla skeletons in a bipedal posture.
Note the differences in the size and shape of the rib cage, arms, and legs. In particular, notice the differences in the shape and size of the pelves.

Table 6.1		
MORPHOLOGICAL DIFFERENCES BETWEEN BIPEDAL HOMININS AND QUADRUPEDAL APES*		
Feature	**Bipedal Hominins**	**Quadrupedal Apes**
Foramen magnum	Located anteriorly	Located posteriorly
Spinal curvature	Dual	Singular
Pelvis shape	Shorter, broader	Longer, narrower
Femur length	Longer	Shorter
Knee orientation	Valgus (adducted)	Straight
Foot shape	Narrower	Broader
Hallux ("big toe") placement	Non-opposable	Opposable

*Note: some bipedal hominins have postcranial features similar to quadrupedal apes.

We focus on the location, shape, and size of certain bony structures associated with hominin bipedalism, by starting at the head and working our way down to the feet (Table 6.1). For example, an **adducted** or valgus knee characterizes bipedal hominins. This means that the top of the femur is naturally farther away from the middle of the body than the bottom of the femur. Paleoanthropologists are particularly interested in examining hominin specimens that include the hip or knee joints.

Adducted ■ Toward the midline of the body.

The question arises as to why early hominins became bipedal. After all, many quadrupeds, including large predators such as lions, can outrun even the fastest Olympian. There are at least 10 theories on the origins of hominin bipedalism, the majority of which are either not falsifiable or just inexplicable. We review the three most plausible theories: feeding posture, behaviour, and thermoregulation. First, the feeding posture hypothesis holds that early hominins were pre-adapted to an upright posture due to their evolving from an ape-like primate that maintained an upright body posture in the trees (Hunt, 1996). In extant apes, such as chimpanzees, arboreal foraging is typically accomplished by the animal hanging from its forelimbs below a branch, which is typically referred to as using a below-branch, arm-hanging posture. As early hominins transitioned from an arboreal to a more terrestrial lifestyle they maintained their upright feeding patterns, which led eventually to habitual bipedalism.

Second, the behavioural theory states that bipedalism evolved to improve the ability of males to carry food resources to their mates and offspring. In this theory, male provisioning was a necessary outcome of the monogamous mating system in early hominins (Lovejoy, 1981). At this same time, monogamous, bipedal hominins enjoyed increased fitness because they could invest more care and protection into a few offspring. This theory implies a sexual division of roles in infant caregiving, with a female looking after the immediate physical needs of the offspring and a male undertaking much of the foraging needed to feed the female, offspring, and himself.

Finally, the thermoregulatory theory posits that bipedalism evolved to improve the heat-dissipating abilities of early hominins (Wheeler, 1991). As we'll soon see, the earliest hominins evolved in equatorial Africa, which has intense solar radiation and heat, particularly in open environments. A vertical body posture increases convective heat loss and evaporative cooling. In other words, early hominins became bipedal to cool off in a breeze, thereby reducing the need to locate and drink water. Due to the highly speculative nature of each of these theories, it is unlikely that an answer will be presented anytime soon to the question of the origin of hominin bipedalism.

Now that we've covered morphological trends in hominin evolution, we can look at how paleoanthropologists locate and estimate the age of fossil hominins.

Finding and Estimating the Age of Fossil Hominins

How do you picture paleoanthropologists conducting fieldwork? Perhaps you see teams of labourers working in large excavations, similar to scenes in some of the *Indiana Jones* movies. Do you see them using complex computer models, lasers, and other advanced technologies to locate fossils? Although paleoanthropologists do make periodic use of these technologies, the best tools for locating fossil hominins remains detailed geological maps, a broom, and a shovel. Maps are indispensable because they identify geological deposits in which fossils may occur. These geologic maps assist paleoanthropologists by enabling them to look for fossil hominins in the deposits associated with the correct time periods. Within these deposits, researchers look specifically for areas where the geological processes of uplifting and erosion have exposed sedimentary rock. Then it's simply a matter of using a broom to brush aside surface soil or digging a pit to locate fossils. Both excavation processes require plenty of field assistants and take considerable time and patience, either walking aimlessly with your head down as you scan the surface or bent over in a hole as you carefully remove small layers of soil. Some people have a natural and highly coveted ability to locate fossils amidst rubble. After all, fossils are made of rock, and it can be extremely difficult to tell them apart from plain old rocks.

Despite the importance of these techniques, luck has played and will likely continue to play a role in finding fossil hominins (Figure 6.4). Some people just have a

Figure 6.4
Even if a dead creature becomes fossilized, there's no guarantee that researchers can locate it in the ground.

knack for looking in the right place at the right time. For example, workers found the first fossil hominin after dynamiting in a South African rock quarry and then offered their discovery to a nearby professor (Dart, 1925). In another example, Dr. Martin Pickford's good luck resulted in the discovery of a new Miocene hominoid (*Otavipithecus namibiensis*) within one of the hundreds of **breccia** boulders he and his team members collected randomly from an abandoned mine in Namibia, Africa (Conroy et al., 1993)! Thus, finding hominin fossils requires detailed geological information, plenty of assistants, and lots of hard work; and a little luck never hurts.

Breccia ■ A coarse-grained rock composed of angular fragments of pre-existing rocks.

After a hominin fossil is found, and the excitement has died down, one of the most important things is to find some means of dating it. Accurate dating of fossil hominins is important for two reasons. First, dating is critical to determining a chronological framework for the hominins. Put differently, dating methods provide an answer to the question of which species predates or comes after another species. Second, there is a strong interest in determining the oldest evidence for hominins and their material remains. Thus, paleoanthropologists, and many non-paleoanthropologists, are fascinated by the oldest evidence for humans, first evidence for controlled use of fire, and the first evidence for cultural remains (Gibbons, 2006). There are two categories of dating methods: relative and absolute.

RELATIVE DATING   Relative dating techniques involve determining whether a fossil or the sediment it is buried in is younger or older than another fossil or sediment. Because there are many relative dating techniques, we focus on the following three methods used most often in studies of fossil hominins: stratigraphy, palynology, and biostratigraphy. Stratigraphy, the study of vertical sequences of rock layers, is perhaps the oldest yet still one of the best relative dating methods. Stratigraphy holds that deeper sedimentary layers were deposited earlier and are therefore older than shallower layers. Put differently, sedimentary layers represent sequential intervals of time. A layer may not be continuous because it can be interrupted by erosion or by another intervening sedimentation. The same layer can be exposed in different places. If a hominin fossil is found in one layer atop another, then the researcher presumes that the fossil comes from a later (more recent) time (Figure 6.5). Furthermore, if the overlaying layer has been dated, then the fossil can be said to be older than that date.

Relative dating can also be done using **palynology**, the study of fossilized pollen, and **biostratigraphy**, the study of fossilized animals in vertical sequences of rock layers. Both methods require the use of fossilized plants and animals that are located in only certain sedimentary layers and geographic regions. Moreover, the approximate dates for these fossils must be known. If each of the symbols in Figure 6.5 represents different fossil animals, then knowing the approximate time span in which they lived can be used to derive a relative date for the fossil hominin. However, due to a desire to obtain more precise dates, paleoanthropologists collaborate with geologists and geochemists to use absolute dating methods.

Palynology ■ The study of fossilized pollen.

Biostratigraphy ■ The study of fossilized animals in vertical sequences of rock layers.

ABSOLUTE DATING   Absolute or chronometric dating methods provide a direct age listed in years before present (BP), with *present* referring to the year 1950. For example, an absolute date would be listed 125 000 ± 2500 years BP. The first number refers to the average age derived from multiple samples. The ± symbol stands for "plus or minus," the meaning of which will be clear in just a moment. The second number represents the **standard deviation**, which is a measure of variation, usually calculated by measuring the spread of values within a data set. Standard deviation is important because it indicates how much of the data varies around the average value. For example, a standard deviation of 2500 indicates a relatively greater degree of variability than a standard deviation of 100. Large standard deviations imply less **precision**.

Standard deviation ■ Measure of dispersion, typically 67% of data from the average.

Precision ■ The closeness of repeated measurements to the same value.

Figure 6.5

Example of stratigraphic dating of a fossil hominin.
The skull is located in the star layer, which is presumed to be more recent than the polygon layer but older than the spiral layer.

A researcher questions the validity of any average value that is smaller than its standard deviation. For example, if the average and standard deviation of a dataset is 100 ± 1000, then there is likely too much variation in the dataset for the researcher to be comfortable that a distinct pattern exists. Thus, in our example, the absolute date indicates that the researcher can be confident that 67 percent of the sample data falls within the range from 127 500 years (125 000 + 2500) to 122 500 years (125 000 − 2500).

Radioactive decay ■
The process of a material giving off particles to reach a stable state.

Absolute dating methods are based on the phenomenon of **radioactive decay**, which is the breakdown of an atom by the emission of various subatomic particles. Approximately 10 chronometric methods are used, each of which is relevant to different kinds of samples and timeframes. You should note that most of these methods do not find the age of the fossil, but rather the geological deposits in which the fossil is embedded. For example, the potassium-argon (K/Ar) method is applied to substrates of volcanic origin. The K/Ar method is based on the decay of potassium-40 (K-40) to the gas argon-40 (Ar-40). The geochemist dates each sample by first comparing the proportion of K-40 to Ar-40 in a sample of volcanic rock, and then applying the known decay rate of K-40. The K/Ar method can date samples from 100 000 to 5 million years BP, although this method is best applied to samples greater than 1 million years of age. Moreover, researchers use supplementary chronometric tests to calibrate and confirm their dating estimates. The idea is to ensure that all the tests are as similar as possible, thereby reducing error estimates. So, after all these potentially confusing statistics and geochemistry, where exactly did hominins evolve and what did they look like?

Transitional Forms: Advanced Apes or Primitive Hominins?

Evolutionary anthropologists have found tantalizing evidence that the first hominins existed almost 7 million years ago in Africa (Figure 6.6)! The unique combination of ape-like and human-like traits in these early hominins makes them something of a phylogenetic enigma. In other words, researchers are seeking an answer to the following question: Were the earliest human-like primates advanced apes or transitional hominins? Some paleoanthropologists still employ the outdated phenetic approach to hominin evolution and systematics (see species designations in Chapter 3), meaning they define hominins based on only a few physical features. Consequently, the reliance on a few fixed properties from fragmented fossils has resulted in a bewildering array of genera and species. For example, it is not uncommon for paleoanthropologists to describe a new species within an existing genus, and then a short time later elevate this species to an entirely new genus based on little to no phylogenetic data! Unfortunately, rivalries and professional disputes between research teams have further complicated hominin taxonomy and phylogenetic relationships (Gibbons, 2006). In order to put some order to this taxonomic mess, we employ a chronological approach to our review of transitional hominins.

Sahelanthropus tchadensis

Sahelanthropus tchadensis was discovered near Bahr el Ghazal, Chad (Brunet et al., 2002) (Figure 6.6). This species is the oldest known transitional hominin, having existed about 7 million years ago. At that time, the site where it was unearthed was on the margins of a large lake, which likely supported a variety of plant and animal life. This creature is known from a reconstructed cranium, fragmented mandible, and a few teeth. *S. tchadensis* has an ape-like brain size of 320 to 380 cc (Figure 6.7). It has been suggested that the anterior position of the foramen magnum is indicative of bipedalism. The size and shape of the supraorbital torus (brow ridge) and canine teeth are similar to those seen in later hominins. Because of this combination of ape-like and hominin-like cranial features, the discoverers hypothesized that *S. tchadensis* represents a possible common ancestor of hominins and African apes. There is considerable debate on the validity of this hypothesis.

Orrorin tugenensis

Orrorin tugenensis (6.0–5.7 MYA) was unearthed at the Kapsomin site in Kenya (Senut et al., 2001) (Figure 6.6). Paleoanthropologists discovered fragments of a mandible, teeth, a finger, and, most remarkably, parts of the femur and humerus. When researchers analyzed the dental remains, they found an interesting mixture of ape-like and hominin-like traits. The femur attributed to *O. tugenensis* provides evidence of bipedalism. Morphological correlates to bipedalism in *O. tugenensis* indicate a locomotor pattern different from that used by modern humans and more like that employed by other Pleistocene hominins. Conversely, the upper arm bones from *O. tugenensis* reveal that it was an adept climber, which is an ape-like trait. The researchers who discovered *O. tugenensis* suggest that it displaces other hominins as the direct ancestor of *Homo* (Senut et al., 2001). In other words, they theorized that *O. tugenensis* represents a direct ancestor to human beings, which is a rather remarkable statement given the paucity of specimens and lack of skull material. A more recent and conservative analysis

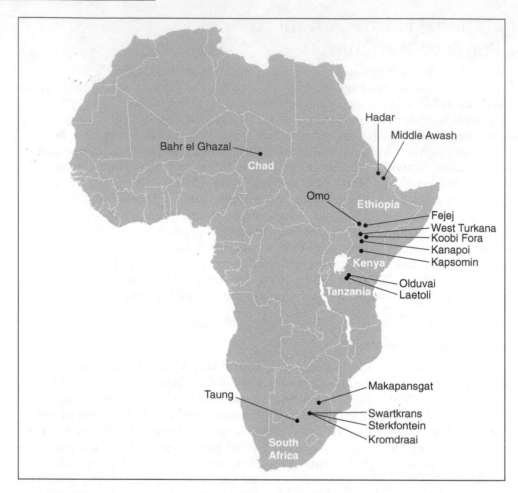

Figure 6.6
Locations of sites in Africa containing hominins.

Figure 6.7
Front and side views of skull from *Sahelanthropus tchadensis*.
Adapted with permission from Macmillan Publishers Ltd., NATURE (418, 145–151), © 2002.

of the postcranial materials indicates that *O. tugenensis* represents a basal member of the hominin lineage (Richmond and Jungers, 2008). Therefore, *O. tugenensis* is important because it may represent the earliest and first bipedal hominin.

Ardipithecus ramidus and *Ardipithecus kadabba*

In the span of a few years, Dr. Tim White and his team described a new genus, *Ardipithecus*, and two new species of transitional hominins, *A. ramidus* and *A. kadabba* (White et al., 1994). *A. ramidus* (4.4 MYA), or Ardi as the first specimen has been nicknamed, is represented by fossil fragments found near the Middle Awash, Ethiopia. Ardi was an adult female when she died, standing only 120 cm tall and weighing around 50 kg. The teeth and part of a humerus reveal transitional features, with both ape-like and hominin-like traits. For example, the teeth have thin enamel (ape-like trait) but the canines have reduced sexual dimorphism (hominin-like trait). *A. ramidus* has an anteriorly placed foramen magnum. This feature as well as recent analysis of the fossil foot bones indicates some form of bipedalism in *A. ramidus*, linking this species to the hominin lineage. However, Ardi also had a divergent hallux (big toe), which is a trait seen in quadrupedal apes. Other ape-like features have been noted in the pelvis, indicating that *A. ramidus* was also capable of arboreal quadrupedalism. Studies of the microscopic wear patterns on the teeth of *A. ramidus* led researchers to hypothesize that it had a largely omnivorous diet (i.e. chewing and swallowing a variety of plant and animal foods), but that Ardi avoided foods that were fibrous or hard. Moreover, studies of other fossil animals and plants found with *A. ramidus* indicate that this remarkable creature likely foraged for food in woodland habitats and small patches of forest, rather than in open savannas. The combination of Ardi's transitional features with an existence just after the date for the human–chimpanzee split has led some paleoanthropologists to conclude that the last common ancestor of chimpanzees and humans was neither a chimpanzee nor a human! Shortly after the discovery of *A. ramidus*, Dr. White and his team described a new fossil species, *A. kadabba* (5.8–5.6 MYA), based on some fossilized teeth and a foot bone recovered in Ethiopia. The dental remains reveal transitional features, such as canines that seem to partly sharpen against one of the lower teeth (ape-like trait). However, the canine shape is more hominin-like than ape-like. The foot bone purportedly shows some morphological features associated with bipedalism. After reviewing the fossil animals found at the excavation site, the researchers suggested that *A. kadabba* lived in closed, densely wooded habitat that provided ready access to lakes and other sources of fresh water. If these hypotheses hold for exploitation of woodland habitats by both *A. ramidus* and *A. kadabba*, then we must rethink some of our theories that hold that bipedalism evolved in early hominins living in open grassland environments. Not surprisingly, there is considerable debate on the phylogenetic relationships of *A. ramidus* and *A. kadabba to* other hominoids.

Kenyanthropus platyops

Kenyanthropus platyops (3.5–3.2 MYA) was discovered at West Turkana, Kenya (Leakey et al., 2001). *K. platyops* is represented by a highly fragmented cranium (the upper portion of the skull), a few mandibles, and some fragments of skull bones

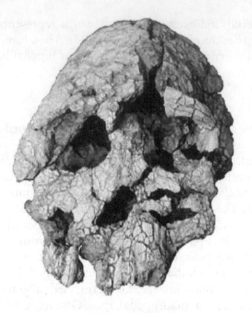

Figure 6.8
Front view of skull from *Kenyanthropus platyops*.
Note how fragmented the specimen was before reconstruction.
Adapted by permission from Macmillan Publishers Ltd., NATURE (410, 433–440), © 2001.

(Figure 6.8). The overall size and shape of the reconstructed cranium and teeth are similar to those seen in contemporaneous australopithecines, which we cover in just a moment. For example, both taxa exhibit thick enamel on their molars. However, the discoverers note a suite of features that differ from those seen in contemporaneous hominins, such as a highly distinctive flat face. Due to the highly fragmented nature of the cranium, it has been argued that *K. platyops* and other similarly distorted specimens represent regional variants of australopithecines (White, 2003). So, who were the australopithecines?

Australopithecines: The First "Real" Hominins

There is general consensus among paleoanthropologists that species in the genus *Australopithecus* represent the first definitive hominins. *Australopithecus* is a widespread genus of early hominins, having been found at sites in central, eastern, and southern Africa. Compared to extant apes, *Australopithecus* have relatively small canines and incisors, and they lack a **sectorial premolar**, a tooth that is reduced in size to allow the large upper canine to pass by it without obstruction. Without this sectorial premolar, animals with large canines would be unable to close their mouths completely. These early hominins exhibit ape-like traits, such as sexual dimorphism in canine size and body size, with males being larger than females. The upper limb morphology indicates that *Australopithecus* were adept tree climbers. *Australopithecus* retain ape-like features, such as small brains, large faces, large teeth, and small body size. *Australopithecus* have large molars, which have bulbous cusps and are covered in thick enamel. So, what exactly is it about australopithecines that make them hominins? Although rare in the fossil record, lower limbs of *Australopithecus* reveal morphological adaptations for bipedalism. Furthermore, the incredible discovery and analysis of footprints made

Sectorial premolar ▤
First lower premolar with a shearing edge for the upper canine.

3.5 MYA in volcanic ash, presumably by an australopithecine, demonstrate that Pliocene hominins walked in a way similar to what you would use during a stroll along a beach (Leakey and Hay, 1979; Charteris et al., 1981). Therefore, the morphological suite of characters exhibited by *Australopithecus* is intermediate in form between extant apes and modern humans. Take that, creationists!

Australopithecus anamensis

Australopithecus anamensis (4.2–3.9 MYA) was discovered near Kanapoi, Kenya (Figure 6.6). The dental remains reveal considerable sexual dimorphism and a tooth row that is parallel, as in apes, rather than parabolic, as in modern humans (Leakey et al., 1995; Leakey et al., 1998). The mandible is similar to those seen in earlier fossil apes. Paleoanthropologists suggest that the partial tibia provides strong evidence for bipedality in *A. anamensis,* which would make this the earliest evidence for bipedalism in definitive hominins. Thus, *A. anamensis* exhibits a primitive (ape-like) cranial morphology and a derived (human-like) postcranial morphology.

Australopithecus afarensis

Australopithecus afarensis (4.2–3.0 MYA) has been found at sites in Ethiopia (Hadar, Omo, and Fejej) and Tanzania (Laetoli) (Figure 6.6). In fact, paleoanthropologists have recovered more *A. afarensis* remains than any other australopithecine. Consequently, much is known about *A. afarensis* morphology. The estimated body size is 30.2 kg for females and 44.6 kg for males (Fleagle, 1999). *A. afarensis* brain size is approximately 410 cc, which is similar to extant chimpanzees. This fossil hominin retains the ape-like traits of having a long snout, shallow face, and **sagittal** and **nuchal crests** (Figure 6.9). A sagittal crest is a ridge of bone that runs lengthwise from the front to the back along the top of the skull, where strong chewing muscles attach. A nuchal crest is a ridge of bone that runs horizontally at the back of the skull where large neck muscles attach. *A. afarensis* have canines and incisors larger and more sexually dimorphic than modern humans but smaller and less sexually dimorphic than extant apes. The upper body retains ape-like traits of a funnel-shaped chest area and long, curved finger bones. These traits are associated with suspensory locomotion. Although some features of the hindlimbs strongly suggest bipedalism, others are similar to those observed in arboreal apes. For example, *A. afarensis* has the valgus knee of a habitual biped and long, curved feet like those seen in arboreal apes. This suite of divergent characters is particularly evident between the larger, more human-like specimens and the smaller, more ape-like specimens. There is a vigorous debate about whether this variability indicates either a single, sexually dimorphic species or two ecologically divergent (i.e., larger, more terrestrial or smaller, more arboreal) species. Moreover, a phylogenetic rather than typological interpretation of the australopithecines indicates that *A. afarensis* should be placed in a unique genus, resulting in *Praeanthropus afarensis* (Strait and Grine, 2004). For simplicity's sake, we use *A. afarensis* throughout this chapter. Despite the relative abundance of *A. afarensis* material, there is considerable work to be done on studying this fascinating hominin. Perhaps you will make the next great discovery of *A. afarensis* remains in Africa!

Sagital crest ■ A lengthwise (front to back) ridge of bone along the top of the skull where strong chewing muscles attach to the top of the skull.

Nuchal crest ■ A horizontal ridge of bone where large neck muscles attach to the back of the skull.

Australopithecus bahrelghazali

The discovery of *Australopithecus bahrelghazali* (3.5–3.0 MYA) shocked paleoanthropologists because this early hominin was found in Bahr el Ghazal, Chad (Figure 6.6)— approximately 2500 km further west than any other australopithecine discovered to date

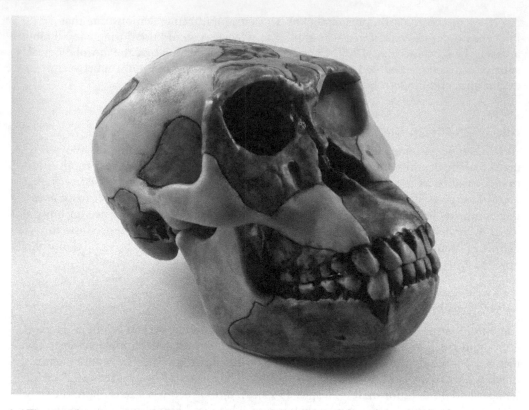

Figure 6.9

Reconstructed *A. afarensis* skull.

Note the long snout and large canines of this species, which are ape-like traits.
© S. M. Lehman

(Brunet et al., 1995). Although analysis of the mandible and teeth reveals some unique features not seen in other australopithecines, the overall size and shape of the specimens fall within the range exhibited by contemporaneous *A. afarensis*. Lack of access to the original fossils has limited an independent assessment of species designation for this early hominin. Some paleoanthropologists consider *A. bahrelghazali* to be a regional variant of *A. afarensis* and, therefore, not a unique species (Kimbel et al., 2004).

Australopithecus africanus

Australopithecus africanus (3.0–2.3 MYA) was both the first australopithecine to be described and the first to be found in South Africa (Dart, 1925). The original fossil was found in a quarry in Taung, and other specimens followed from Sterkfontain and Makapansgat (Figures 6.6 and 6.10). The estimated body size is 30.2 kg for females and 40.8 kg for males (Fleagle, 1999). The average brain size of *A. africanus* is 458 cc, which is only slightly larger than *A. afarensis*. Compared to *A. afarensis*, *A. africanus* has a shallower snout and face, smaller canines, broader incisors, and smaller premolars and molars. *A. africanus* lacks nuchal and sagittal crests. *A. africanus* shares many postcranial features with *A. afarensis,* indicating a combination of bipedal and arboreal locomotion. Therefore, paleoanthropologists suggest that *A. africanus* was ecologically similar to *A. afarensis*.

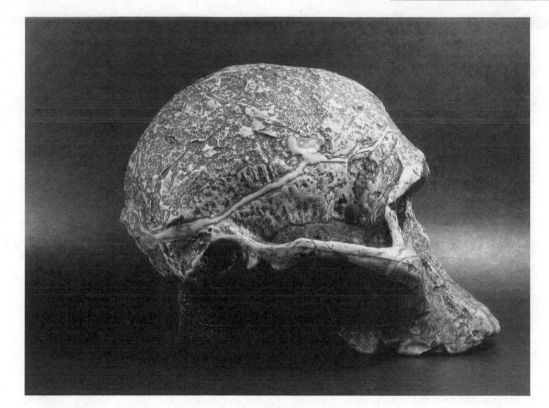

Figure 6.10
Side view of *A. africanus* skull.
© S. M. Lehman

Australopithecus garhi

Australopithecus garhi (2.5 MYA) is an early hominin discovered near Middle Awash, Ethiopia (Figure 6.6). This species is represented by some cranial fragments and part of the maxilla (Asfaw et al., 1999). Compared to its face, *A. garhi* has relative large molars. This interesting fossil also has a prognathic lower face and procumbent incisors. This combination of traits makes it difficult to fit this specimen within a pre-existing taxon of australopithecines. This discovery fills an important temporal gap in the fossil hominin record in Africa, although the small size and number of specimens limits testing of phylogenetic hypotheses. In other words, we need you to look for more fossil hominins in East Africa!

Australopithecus aethiopicus

Australopithecus aethiopicus (2.7–2.3 MYA) is a "hyper-robust" hominin discovered at West Turkana, Kenya (Walker et al., 1986) (Figure 6.6). This hominin has a large face, huge cheek bones (zygomatics), very large sagittal and nuchal crests, and enormous teeth (Figure 6.11). In fact, an *A. aethiopicus* skull looks like the biological equivalent of a helmet worn by 16th-century Portuguese soldiers! The discovery of a primitive hominin at such a late date dispels notions of constant progression in hominin evolution. In other words, we have further evidence that biological evolution is not goal-oriented.

Figure 6.11

Skull of the hyper-robust *A. aethiopicus*.

Note the extremely prominent sagittal crest and large, flat face of this species. Dark areas are unrecovered parts of the skull.

© S. M. Lehman

Australopithecus boisei

Australopithecus boisei (2.2–1.2 MYA) is a "hyper-robust" hominin discovered by Mary Leakey at Olduvai, Tanzania (Leakey, 1959)(Figure 6.6). Its morphology is broadly similar to that seen in *A. aethiopicus* and, as we'll see in a moment, other robust specimens from South Africa. The estimated average brain size is 498 cc. *A. boisei* has small anterior teeth and enormous posterior teeth, which are covered in thick enamel. This hominin also has a very robust mandible. Larger specimens, which may represent males, have sagittal and nuchal crests. This hominin was contemporaneous with members of the genus *Homo*.

Australopithecus sediba

Australopithecus sediba (2.0 MYA) is a recently described species that was discovered at the Malapa Nature Reserve in South Africa (Berger et al., 2010). The first specimen of this new species was discovered by Matthew Berger, the nine-year-old son of the researcher in charge of the excavations at the site. Matthew just happened to turn over a large bolder while following his pet dog through the bush, immediately noting the remains of a hominin collarbone. This original find turned out to be part of an amazingly well preserved juvenile male, and further excavations unearthed an adult female, adult male, and three infants. It is thought that these hominins fell down and then died in a deep cave at the site, resulting in a remarkable level of skeletal and dental preservation. Morphological analyses of these specimens indicate that *A. sediba* exhibits a mosaic of features that are transitional between earlier australopithecines and later members of the genus *Homo*. In *A. sediba*, estimates of brain size (420–450 cm³) and body size (30-37 kg) are at the high range of those in earlier *A. africanus*. The

upper arm bones are long, which is a an ape-like trait similar to that seen in
A. afarensis (Figure 6.12). Conversely, the overall size of the jaw bone and teeth are very
similar to those found in later specimens of *Homo*. The lower limb bones of *A. sediba*
indicate a more human-like pattern of bipedalism than that seen in earlier transitional
forms. The phylogenetic relationship of *A. sediba* to earlier australopithecines and later
Homo is complex, particularly as the type specimen is a juvenile. In fact, some
researchers have suggested that *A. sediba* is either a regional variant of *A. africanus* or
that the recovered specimens belong in *Homo*. Further analysis of the recovered fossils
as well as the recovery of new specimens will help resolve these scientific issues.

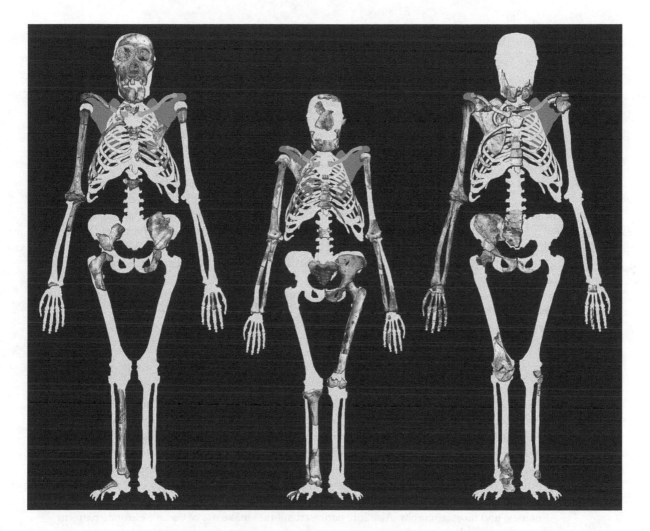

Figure 6.12

An adult female *A. sediba* left, *A. afarensis* center, and adult male *A. sediba*
right.

Note the similarities in the shape of the rib cage and long arms compared to differences in body
size and lower limb morphology between *A. sediba and A. afarensis.* •
© Image compiled by Peter Schmid courtesy of Lee R. Berger, University of the Witwatersrand

Table 6.2

MORPHOLOGICAL DIFFERENCES BETWEEN GRACILE AND ROBUST AUSTRALOPITHECINES.

Feature	Gracile	Robust
Sagittal and nuchal crests	Absent	Present (males)
Temporal fossa	Smaller	Larger
Forehead	Steeper	Flatter
Mandible	Less robust	More robust
Incisors and canines	Relatively larger	Relatively smaller
Premolars and molars	Relatively smaller	Relatively larger

Gracile and *Robust Australopthecines*

Some authorities divide *Australopithecus* into two morphological groups, the gracile and robust australopithecines (Table 6.2), based on phenetic differences in the skull and teeth among some early hominins. Gracile autralopithecines typically include *Australopithecus afarensis* and *Australopithecus africanus*. These early hominins are characterized by thinner bones, particularly the bones of the skull, and smaller teeth. Robust australopithecines include *Australopithecus aethiopicus*, *Australopithecus boisei,* and *Australopithecus robustus*. These early hominins typically have thicker skull bones and larger teeth. For example, robust australopithecines are characterized by a larger **temporal fossa**, that is, a larger space between the eyes and the cheek bone, which is a feature indicative of powerful chewing. Others place the robust taxa in its own genus, *Paranthropus*. To avoid confusion, we do not make this genera-level distinction, using *Australopithecus* instead.

In the next chapter, we meet the earliest members of our genus (*Homo*) and discuss their overall phylogenetic relationships to transitional hominins and australopithecines.

Temporal fossa ■ A large space between the eye orbit and the cheek bone (zygomatic).

Summary

1. We focused on three main morphological trends in the mosaic evolution of hominins: general reduction in the size and robustness of teeth and the skull, increasing brain size, and the transition to habitual bipedalism. Paleoanthropologists tend to see bipedalism and concomitant morphological changes as hallmarks of the hominin lineage.
2. Finding hominin fossils requires use of good geological maps, plenty of assistants, and even a little bit of luck! Age estimates for fossil hominins are typically done using a combination of relative and absolute dating techniques. Relative dating techniques include stratigraphy, palynology, and biostratigraphy. Absolute dating techniques make use of complex atomic patterns of radioactive decay, resulting in a direct age of a sedimentary layer encasing a hominin fossil, or even the fossil itself.
3. Early hominins in the genus *Australopithecus* have been recovered from central, eastern, and southern Africa. These early hominins exhibit ape-like traits, such as sexual dimorphism in canine size and body size, with males being larger than females; large faces and small brains; and the ability to adeptly climb trees. Although rare in the fossil record, lower limbs of *Australopithecus* reveal morphological adaptations for bipedalism.

INTERNET RESOURCES

The Smithsonian Institution Human Origins Program
http://anthropology.si.edu/humanorigins
See fossil hominins and learn about research being conducted by paleoanthropologists as part of this program.

Human Evolution: The Fossil Evidence in 3D
www.anth.ucsb.edu/projects/human
Cool site with 3D images of skulls of fossil hominins, plus lots of other interesting stuff!

PBS: Evolution
www.pbs.org/wgbh/evolution/humans
This is a great website on human origins.

Phylogeny and Reconstructing Phylogenetic Trees
http://aleph0.clarku.edu/%7Edjoyce/java/Phyltree/cover.html
Check out this very informative site on reconstructing phylogenetic trees, which also contains a cool JAVA applet that enables you to manipulate a phylogenetic tree.

LITERATURE CITED

Asfaw, B., White, T., Lovejoy, O., Latimer, B., Simpson, S., and Suwa, G. (1999). *Australopithecus garhi*: A new species of early hominid from Ethiopia. *Science,* 284(5414), 629.

Berger, L. R., de Ruiter, D. J., Churchill, S. E., Schmid, P., Carlson, K. J., Dirks, P. H. G. M., Kibii, J. M. (2010). *Australopithecus sediba*: a new species of *Homo*-like australopith from South Africa. *Science* 328 (5975): 195–204.

Bradbury, J. (2005). Molecular insights into human brain evolution. *PLoS Biology,* 3(3), e50.

Brunet, M., Beauvilain, A., Coppens, Y., Heintz, E., Moutaye, A., and Pilbeam, D. (1995). The first australopithecine 2,500 kilometres west of the Rift Valley (Chad). *Nature,* 378(6554), 273–275.

Brunet, M., Guy, F., Pilbeam, D., Mackaye, H. T., Likius, A., Ahounta, D., Beauvilain, A., Blondel, C., Bocherens, H., Boisserie, J.-R., and others. (2002). A new hominid from the Upper Miocene of Chad, Central Africa. *Nature,* 418(6894), 145–151.

Charteris, J., Wall, J. C., and Nottrodt, J. W. (1981). Functional reconstruction of gait from the Pliocene hominid footprints at Laetoli, northern Tanzania. *Nature,* 290, 496–498.

Conroy, G. C., Pickford, M., Senut, B., and Mein, P. (1993). Diamonds in the desert: The discovery of *Otavipithecus namibiensis*. *Evolutionary Anthropology: Issues, News, and Reviews,* 2(2), 46–52.

Dart, R. A. (1925). Australopithecus africanus: The man-ape of South Africa. *Nature,* 115, 195–199.

Dunbar, R. I. M. (1998). The social brain hypothesis. *Evolutionary Anthropology: Issues, News, and Reviews,* 6(5), 178–190.

Fleagle, J. G. (1999). *Primate Adaptation and Evolution.* San Diego: Academic Press.

Gibbons, A. (2006). *The First Human: The Race to Discover Our Earliest Ancestors.* New York: Doubleday.

Hunt, K. D. (1996). The postural feeding hypothesis: An ecological model for the evolution of bipedalism. *South African Journal of Science,* 92, 77–90.

Kimbel, W., Rak, Y., and Johanson, D. (2004). *The Skull of Australopithecus Afarensis.* Oxford: Oxford University Press.

Kumar, S., Filipski, A., Swarna, V., Walker, A., and Hedges, S. B. (2005). Placing confidence limits on the molecular age of the human-chimpanzee divergence. *Proceedings of the National Academy of Sciences, USA,* 102, 18842–18847.

Langergraber, K. E., Prüfer, K., Rowney, C., Boesch, C., Crockford, C., Fawcett, C., Inoue, E., Inoue-Muruyama, M., Mitani. J.C., and Muller, M.N. (2012) Generation times in wild chimpanzees and gorillas suggest earlier divergence times in great ape and human evolution. *Proceedings of the National Academy of Sciences* 109(39): 15716–15721.

Leakey, L. (1959). A new fossil skull from Olduvai. *Nature, 184*(4685), 491–493.

Leakey, M., Feibel, C., McDougall, I., Ward, C., and Walker, A. (1998). New specimens and confirmation of an early age for *Australopithecus anamensis. Nature, 393*(May 7), 62–66.

Leakey, M., and Hay, R. (1979). Pliocene footprints in the Laetolil Beds at Laetoli, northern Tanzania. *Nature, 278*(5702), 317–323.

Leakey, M. G., Feibel, C. S., McDougall, I., and Walker, A. (1995). New four-million-year-old hominid species from Kanapoi and Allia Bay, Kenya. *Nature, 376*(August 17), 565–571.

Leakey, M. G., Spoor, F., Brown, F. H., Gathogo, P. N., Kiarie, C., Leakey, L. N., and McDougall, I. (2001). New hominin genus from eastern Africa shows diverse middle Pliocene lineages. *Nature, 410*(6827), 433–440.

Lovejoy, C. O. (1981). The origins of man. *Science, 211,* 341–348.

Marzke, M. W. (1997). Precision grips, hand morphology, and tools. *American Journal of Physical Anthropology, 102*(1), 91–110.

Richmond, B. G., and Jungers, W. L. (2008). *Orrorin tugenensis* femoral morphology and the evolution of hominin bipedalism. *Science, 319*(5870), 1662–1665.

Senut, B., Pickford, M., Gommery, D., Mein, P., Cheboi, K., and Coppens, Y. (2001). First hominid from the Miocene (Lukeino Formation, Kenya). *Comptes Rendus de l'Academie des Sciences Series IIA Earth and Planetary Science, 332*(2), 137–144.

Strait, D., and Grine, F. (2004). Inferring hominoid and early hominid phylogeny using cranio-dental characters: The role of fossil taxa. *Journal of Human Evolution, 47*(6), 399–452.

Sun, J. X., Helgason, A., Masson, G., Ebenesersdóttir, S.S., Li, H., Mallick, S., Gnerre, S., Patterson, N., Kong, A., and Reich, D. (2012). A direct characterization of human mutation based on microsatellites. *Nature Genetics* 44(10): 1161–1165.

Susman, R. (1994). Fossil evidence for early hominid tool use. *Science, 265*(5178), 1570–1573.

Walker, A. C., Leakey, R. E., Harris, J. M., and Brown, F. H. (1986). 2.5-Myr *Australopithecus boisei* from West of Lake Turkana, Kenya. *Nature, 322,* 517–522.

Wheeler, P. E. (1991). The thermoregulatory advantages of hominid bipedalism in open equatorial environments: The contribution of increased convective heat loss and cutaneous evaporative cooling. *Journal of Human Evolution, 21,* 107–115.

White, T. (2003). Paleoanthropology: Early hominids—diversity or distortion? *Science, 299*(5615), 1994–1997.

White, T., Suwa, G. and Asfaw, B. (1994). *Australopithecus ramidus,* a new species of early hominid from Aramis, Ethiopia. *Nature, 371*(6495), 306–312.

Human Origins: Rise of the Genus *Homo*

GOALS

By the end of this chapter you should understand:

1. Morphological features of *Homo* species.
2. General aspects of the stone tools manufactured by early hominins.
3. Phylogenetic relationships among hominins.

CHAPTER OUTLINE

Homo: Bigger Brains, Smaller Teeth

Early Hominin Tools: From Pebbles to Works of Art

Hominin Phylogenetic Relationships

Introduction

I remember my first attempt at making a simple stone tool. I was fortunate to be able to observe an archaeologist with expertise in reconstructing stone tools made by early hominins. He slowly and carefully chipped away unwanted pieces of rock from a large piece of volcanic glass to form a simple tool suited for scraping organic materials. Most of his efforts seemed devoted to spinning the core around, looking for the ideal striking platform with his bone "hammer." After observing the process, I asked for and was granted an opportunity to make my own tool. Grasping a small nodule of black volcanic glass in my hand, I marvelled at its beauty as each dark facet reflected the light. With considerable guidance from the archaeologist, I located the ideal striking platform and practised my strike with the "hammer." My very gentle tap resulted in a completely shattered nodule, forming dozens of small and rather useless pieces. At best, I'd just made some lithic letter openers! The friendly archaeologist chuckled, as he told me that his decades spent making tools equated with the abilities of an inattentive 12-year-old Neanderthal!

Paleoanthropologists pursue answers to the intriguing question of what it is to be human. The incomplete fossil record and serendipitous discovery of fossil hominins complicate answering this question. However, with each passing year, paleoanthropologists recover additional specimens of existing species and sometimes are fortunate to discover new species. In fact, it's not uncommon for undergraduate students acting as field assistants to discover, with one swing of a hammer or one sweep of a broom, a new fossil species! It is for these reasons that paleoanthropology is such an exciting and rewarding academic pursuit: Anyone can make the next, big scientific discovery. In the sections below, we discuss the evolutionary anthropology of human origins starting with the emergence of the first species in our genus (*Homo*). For each species, we undertake only a brief review of its major morphological characteristics and ecology. We also look at the origins of and changes in tool use over the course of millions of years. Finally, we try to piece together the phylogenetic relationships of our ancestors. Let's meet our relatives!

Homo: Bigger Brains, Smaller Teeth

Congratulations are in order: you're African! In fact, all modern humans (*Homo sapiens*) are descended from early members of our genus that evolved about 2 million years ago (MYA) in Africa. I often wonder what life was like for the first members of our genus. As you may know, modern Africa is a remarkably diverse and beautiful place. Pleistocene Africa was even more wild and diverse. The forests and savannahs were teeming with life, including some rather large, dangerous predators. As we see below, the first species of *Homo* were neither particularly large nor well armed in terms of sharp teeth or claws. Moreover, they lacked the tools and skills used by even the most primitive of modern human cultures. How did they survive in hostile environments inhabited by large, hungry predators, poisonous snakes, and disease-carrying insects? It's clear that some *Homo* species did very well, given that they existed for hundreds of thousands of years. In fact, some earlier species have a longer evolutionary history than more recent species. Furthermore, did early *Homo* gain some fitness benefits from the gradual expansion of cranial capacity within our lineage (Figure 7.1)? As we'll see, there is tantalizing evidence that *Homo* rather than australopithecines created and used the first stone tools.

The question arises as to how exactly species in the genus *Homo* differ from preceding hominins? *Homo* is differentiated from *Australopithecus* by both absolute

Figure 7.1
Satirical view of lack of direction and goal in the expansion of cranial capacities in the hominin lineage.

Table 7.1		
DIFFERENCES BETWEEN EARLY *HOMO* AND *AUSTRALOPITHECUS*		
Feature	**Early *Homo***	***Australopithecus***
Sagittal and nuchal crests	Absent	Present (males)
Brain size	Relatively larger	Relatively smaller
Face	Relatively smaller	Relatively larger
Mandible	Less robust	More robust
Incisors and canines	Smaller	Larger
Premolars and molars	Smaller	Larger

differences (better) and relative differences (worse) in morphology (Table 7.1). *Absolute differences* refer to unique features that distinguish one species from another. For example, the highly distinctive flat face of *Kenyanthropus platyops* distinguishes this hominin from other early hominins. In evolutionary anthropology, *relative differences* typically refer to slight variations in a trait between taxa. For example, the position of the foramen magnum is relatively closer to the back of the skull in quadrupedal apes than in bipedal hominins. The relative differences make taxonomic and phylogenetic assessments difficult. Why? Because use of a relative measure requires that the paleoanthropologist has knowledge of one fossil to help differentiate it from another. Theoretically, a budding researcher would have to be holding an early *Homo* skull in one hand and an *Australopithecus* skull in the other hand in order to differentiate between the two. Thus, despite the clear importance of knowing when and why our genus first evolved, there is little consensus among paleoanthropologists on just how to define the genus *Homo* and the species therein! Put simply, the systematics and phylogenetics of early *Homo* are highly debatable, which can be great fun! Thus, we focus our review on a very conservative taxonomic and phylogenetic perspective.

Before we begin, we need to understand a few common terms used extensively in paleoanthropology. First, researchers refer to the designated representative of a species and genus as a *type specimen*. Each time researchers think they have a replicate specimen of a species, they consult the type specimen as the guide for what constitutes the features of that taxon. Every specimen recovered by a researcher is given a unique catalogue number, which assists in organizing and studying specimens. Each catalogue number is made up of a combination of letters, which typically refer to the location of the find or where the specimen is housed, and numbers, which refer to specific specimens located at a digging site. For example, OH 7 stands for Olduvai Hominin #7; and KNM ER 1470 stands for Kenyan National Museum (where the specimen is housed), East Rudolph (where the specimen was found), and 1470 (the unique numerical ID of the specimen).

Homo habilis and Homo rudolfensis

Homo habilis (2.3–1.6 MYA), which translates loosely to "handyman," was discovered by Mark and Louis Leakey at Olduvai, Tanzania (Leakey et al., 1964). Eventually, other specimens were found in Kenya and Ethiopia. The **type specimen**, OH 7, comprises a mandible, some postcranial bones, and parts of the skull. The Leakeys and their colleagues placed this specimen within *Homo* based on a few morphological features, such as estimated brain size (Figure 7.2), and on the behavioural feature of being able to make stone tools. Primitive stone tools, which we'll talk about soon, were found in

Type specimen ▪ The original specimen from which the description of a new species is made.

Figure 7.2

Reconstruction of a *H. habilis* skull.

Note the flat-topped skull and prognathic face of this primitive hominin.
© S. M. Lehman

association with OH 7 and *A. boisei* in the same level. Thus, the question arises as to whether *H. habilis* or *A. boisei* made and used the stone tools. The controversial use of a behavioural feature to determine hominin taxonomy was challenged for years because the *H. habilis* skeleton is remarkably similar to contemporaneous australopithecines. For example, *H. habilis* shares with *A. afarensis* the ape-like traits of having very long forelimbs and robust hand bones, which are ideal for climbing in trees. However, *H. habilis* brain size averages 635 cc, which is larger than that measured in *A. afarensis*.

The discovery of a contemporaneous fossil, known as KNM ER 1470, temporarily substantiated *H. habilis* as a legitimate taxon. In time, some researchers decided that the morphological differences between OH 7 and KNM ER 1470 are too great to represent conspecifics. Thus, KNM ER 1470 and other associated specimens are placed into a new species of early hominin, *Homo rudolfensis* (Wood, 1991). How do you tell the difference between specimens of *H. habilis* and *H. rudolfensis*? Compared to *H. habilis*, *H. rudolfensis* has a flatter, broader face and molars with thicker enamel. Although there are few postcranial remains for *H. rudolfensis*, what we do have indicates that the hind limbs were longer than in *H. habilis*. In this scenario, *H. habilis* is represented only by the Olduvai specimens. Some extreme assessments call for all specimens of *H. habilis* to be reassigned to *Australopithecus,* leaving *H. rudolfensis* as the first representative of our genus. These taxonomic issues are important to determining whether modern humans are descendants of *H. habilis* or *H. rudolfensis*. In other words, is *H. habilis* or *H. rudolfensis* the earliest, direct ancestor to modern humans? The debate on these issues rages on!

Homo erectus and *Homo ergaster*

Homo erectus (1.8 MYA–27 **KYA**) has been found in Africa, Asia, and Southeast Asia, making it the first definitive hominin to be found outside of Africa. Compared to australopithecines and *H. habilis*, *H. erectus* has a long, low cranial vault, thicker cranial bones, larger cranial capacity (732–1266 cc), larger brow ridges, smaller premolars and molars, and a more gracile mandible (Figure 7.3). A complete 1.6 MYA skeleton of a young *H. erectus* was discovered at West Turkana, Kenya. Analysis of this remarkable specimen, known as Turkana Boy, indicates an estimated adult height of 1.8 m and limb proportions similar to those in modern humans. However, the skeleton is more robust than those of modern humans, implying greater strength. The recent discovery of an almost complete pelvis from an adult female *H. erectus* in Africa reveals that the shape of this structure was changing, presumably to accommodate increased brain and skull size within the *Homo* lineage (Simpson et al., 2008). Evidence exists that *H. erectus* used fire and preyed or scavenged on a variety of large land mammals (e.g., elephants, horses, and deer). They produced more sophisticated stone tools than those made by earlier hominins. Based on certain skull features, some paleoanthropologists place the earlier African specimens, such as Turkana Boy, in a separate species, *Homo ergaster*. Moreover, proponents of

Figure 7.3

H. ergaster skull.

Note the more rounded cranium, larger brow ridges, and flatter face of this skull compared to the *H. habilis* specimen.
© *S. M. Lehman*

H. ergaster classify this hominin as the ancestor of modern humans, thereby relegating *H. erectus* to an evolutionary dead end. Others classify *H. ergaster* as an evolutionary dead end, and draw a direct relationship between *H. erectus* and the modern human lineage.

Homo heidelbergensis and Homo antecessor

Homo heidelbergensis (700–130 KYA) encompasses an assemblage of fossils from Europe and Africa. *H. heidelbergensis* is the new taxonomic designation for specimens that used to be called archaic *H. sapiens*. Compared to *H. erectus*, *H. heidelbergensis* has smaller teeth, a larger average cranial capacity (1250 cc), and a divided supraorbital torus (brow ridge; Figure 7.4). Moreover, body size estimates for *H. heidelbergensis* reach upwards of 100 kg, marking a major increase in overall body size within the *Homo* lineage. Like *H. erectus*, *H. heidelbergensis* produced more sophisticated stone tools and either hunted or scavenged large mammals for food. Some researchers designate ancient (1.2 MYA–800 KYA) specimens from a Spanish cave site as a controversial new species, called *Homo antecessor* (Bermudez de Castro et al., 1997). However, not all paleoanthropologists accept this species designation because the type specimen is a 10-year-old male. Hominin youths have incomplete skeletal development, making it difficult to know what they looked like as adults.

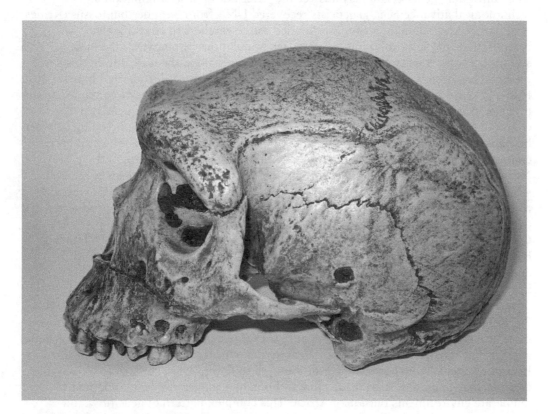

Figure 7.4

H. heidelbergensis skull.

Note how the low braincase slopes back from the large brow ridges, like in *H. ergaster*. However, *H. heidelbergensis* has a larger cranial capacity.
© S. M. Lehman

Homo neanderthalensis

Homo neanderthalensis (300–35 KYA) has been discovered at numerous Pleistocene sites in Europe and the Middle East. Moreover, paleoanthropologists have recovered complete Neanderthal skeletons because they were purposely buried in shallow graves. Neanderthals are characterized by a large cranial capacity (1065–1745 cc), strong supraorbital torus, large nose, **retromolar gap** (a space between the third molar and the rear end of the mandible), weak chin, and **taurodont** molars (that is, molars with large pulp cavities and reduced root size). Neanderthal body proportions are similar to those of modern humans living in polar regions—that is, adapted for life in cold climates. Specifically, both species have short, stout limbs, which are thought to be an adaptation to prevent heat loss in outer extremities. Adult male Neanderthals stood approximately 1.68 m in height. Their postcranial bones are thick and heavy, with evidence of powerful muscle attachments. Consequently, paleoanthropologists speculate that Neanderthals were extraordinarily strong, even by modern standards. Many Neanderthals have broken bones and other evidence of physical traumas. Neanderthals exploited a variety of game animals as food resources, made shelters, exploited caves for shelter, used fire, and produced advanced stone tools. Despite their advanced lifestyle and great physical strength, Neanderthals went extinct about 35 KYA.

Two of the most hotly debated issues in evolutionary anthropology are understanding why Neanderthals disappeared and determining whether or not they contributed some of their genes to modern humans. Only speculative answers exist for the first question, but some intriguing genetic data may answer the latter question. In a remarkable technological advancement, geneticists recovered DNA from Neanderthal fossils (Krings et al., 1997)! Initial analysis of these data led the researchers to conclude that Neanderthals did not evolve into any modern populations of humans. Like most scientific advancements, there have been a few hiccups along the way, and in this case, the issue has been with human and bacterial contamination of Neanderthal bones. Most fossils have been handled by hundreds of humans, which can hopelessly contaminate the little Neanderthal DNA left on a fossil (Wall and Kim, 2007). Consequently, contamination issues may have led to the erroneous conclusion of interbreeding between humans and Neanderthals. Conversely, analysis of fossils free from human and bacterial contamination reveal that the most recent common ancestor of humans and Neanderthals existed about 500 to 700 KYA (Green et al., 2006; Noonan et al., 2006), which, as we see below, is long before the emergence of modern humans. However, more recent research by scientists involved in the Neanderthal Genome Project produced a compelling dataset of four billion base pairs of Neanderthal DNA (i.e. the pairs A-T or C-G found in DNA and RNA). To put this number into perspective, modern humans have about three billion base pairs in our haploid genome (eggs and sperm) and approximately six billion base pairs in our somatic cells (all the other cells). This international team of scientists concluded that about 1-4% mixture of genes had occurred between Neanderthals and non-African modern humans (Green et al., 2010). Put differently, if you or your recent ancestors are come from Asia or SE Asia, then you may have some Neanderthal DNA in you! Further research revealed that human genetic regions that have a high frequency of Neanderthal alleles are enriched for genes affecting keratin filaments, which provide tensile strength to tissue. Thus, some of these Neanderthal genes may have made modern humans stronger and better adapted to temperate environments outside of Africa. This complex pattern of gene flow and genetics was further detailed when researchers recovered a rather innocuous finger bone from a 30,000-48,000 years old fossil in the Denisova Cave in Russia. Geneticists were able to recover mitochondrial DNA (mtDNA) from this bone. A few of the important aspect of mtDNA are that it makes up only a small proportion of the DNA in our cells, evolves (changes) very slowly over time, and is inherited exclusively from the mother.

Retromolar gap ■ Space between the third molar and the rear portion of the mandible.

Taurodont ■ Very large pulp cavities combined with reduced root size.

Consequently, mtDNA is an invaluable tool for understanding evolutionary relationships in extinct and extant organisms, like modern humans and our extinct congenera. So, what did the researchers find in this mtDNA from the finger bone? Well, to everyone's surprise, the mtNDA revealed a genetic pattern different from known human patterns. This difference was so great that the people from which the finger bone was recovered have been called Denisova hominins, which may represent an extinct hominin species (Reich et al., 2010). Moreover, the mtDNA analyses revealed that these Denisovans hominins were related to the Neanderthals and interbred with the ancestors of modern Melanesians, which are the modern humans found on islands in the tropical Pacific Ocean (e.g., New Guinea, Solomon Islands, Fiji). Amazing science! Evolutionary anthropologists are not alone in being fascinated by Neanderthals. Writers have produced engaging fictional stories about Neanderthals, including Jean Auel's *The Clan of the Cave Bear* and John Darton's aptly titled *Neanderthal*. Up until just recently, many scientists thought Neanderthals were the last hominin species to evolve before the advent of modern humans; they were wrong!

Homo floresiensis

The scientific community was flabbergasted by the recent discovery of *Homo floresiensis* (95–13 KYA), the so-called hobbit-like hominin, on Flores Island in Indonesia (Brown et al., 2004). No word as yet on whether or not they had hairy feet! Although not a hobbit, an adult female *H. floresiensis* was only 1.06 m in height, and it is clearly an obligate biped, which means that like modern humans, these small hominins employed only bipedal locomotion. This unique hominin has a small brain size of 417 cc, equal to that of a modern chimpanzee. *H. floresiensis* has other interesting primitive and derived features: human-like teeth, an ape-like receding forehead, and no chin. Furthermore, this hominin controlled fire, produced unique stone tools, and hunted large animals, including the deadly **Komodo dragon**. The discoverers hypothesize that *H. floresiensis* represents a dwarf hominin derived from *H. erectus* (Brown et al., 2004). On some islands, biological evolution produces dwarf forms of large mammals. However, other scientists assert that *H. floresiensis* represents an aberrant individual suffering from either **microcephaly** (a condition in which the head is smaller than normal and the brain does not develop properly) or a hormonal disease that inhibits brain and body growth (Martin et al., 2006; Hershkovitz et al., 2007), either of which would mean that the bones represent only a pathological specimen of *H. sapiens*. In hopes of resolving the issue of microcephaly, Falk and colleagues (2007) compared a brain scan from *H. floresiensis* to those of 9 microcephalic humans and 10 normal humans. Based on this research, it was determined that *H. floresiensis* did not suffer from microcephaly. Furthermore, its brain morphology is similar in some ways to modern humans yet differs enough in other ways to warrant a unique species designation. Subsequent discoveries of smaller *H. floresiensis* remains substantiate the view that this hominin warrants species recognition (Roberts et al., 2005). The researchers hope that DNA can be extracted from the bones, which can then be compared to DNA from modern humans. No doubt the debate will continue for years. Sounds like fun!

Komodo dragon The largest extant lizard, with adults reaching up to 3 m in length and a body mass of approximately 70 kg!

Microcephaly A condition in which adults typically achieve small brain capacity and have moderate to severe intellectual disabilities.

Homo sapiens

At last we come to the final hominin species you need to learn! The first *Homo sapiens* evolved 160 KYA in Africa (White et al., 2003). *H. sapiens* then appear for the first time about 100 KYA in the Middle East and 40 KYA in Europe. In time, humans colonized all the major continents, except for Antarctica.

Paleoanthropologists use a variety of cranial and postcranial features to distinguish *H. sapiens* from earlier species of *Homo* (Table 7.2). For example, the average cranial capacity of *H. sapiens* ranges from 1090 to 1614 cc, with the low end representing the older specimens. There are exceptions to this morphological model. For example, many size-related features of *H. sapiens* are larger than those in *H. floresiensis,* whereas others (e.g., brain size) are smaller than those in *H. neanderthalensis.* The first humans were likely hunters and gatherers. Early humans exploited new food resources in new habitats, such as fish in marine environments, and used fire to cook foods. Cooking softens and detoxifies some foods, which likely contributed to reduced robusticity of our cranial and dental morphologies (Fleagle, 1999). Early humans eventually produced a variety of materials with only cultural or artistic purposes. For example, 35 KYA humans created incredibly beautiful cave paintings near Lascaux, France. There were also concomitant changes in human stone tool technology, which we cover in the following section.

Table 7.2

MORPHOLOGICAL DIFFERENCES BETWEEN EARLY *HOMO* AND *HOMO SAPIENS*

Feature	Early *Homo*	*Homo sapiens*
Brain size	Smaller*	Larger
Mandible	More robust	Less robust
Face	Relatively longer	Relatively shorter
Brow ridges	More robust	Less robust
Tooth size	Relatively larger	Relatively smaller
Postcranial skeleton	More robust	Less robust

*Except in H. neanderthalensis.

Early Hominin Tools: From Pebbles to Works of Art

The earliest example of hominin culture is represented by stone tools dated to 2.5 MYA in East Africa. There is considerable debate among paleoanthropologists as to whether non-stone tools, such as those made from plant parts, were made earlier but did not fossilize. Paleoanthropologists often team with archaeologists and geological chemists to determine the purpose of the earliest stone tools. Were the tools only for chopping plants and carcass processing, or were they also used for predator defence? Hominins eventually produced differing **tool traditions**—that is, the tools were created in consistent ways. Some traditions remain unchanged for millennia across broad geographic areas. Other traditions reflect subtle, regional variations in manufacturing techniques. Early hominins gained expertise in finding and identifying the ideal stones with which to make tools because some type of stones are best suited for use as a **hammerstone**, a stone used as a tool for making other tools, whereas others are ideal for producing sharp **flakes**, pieces of stone that are removed from a core stone.

Archaeologists recognize approximately 20 to 30 tool traditions in the time span from 2.5 MYA to the advent of modern humans. Furthermore, there are considerable regional variations for each tradition. Because the focus of this book is on biological and evolutionary anthropology, we employ a chronological view of only the main stone tool traditions within the following Palaeolithic periods: lower Palaeolithic, middle Palaeolithic, and upper Palaeolithic. As we'll see, many of these tool traditions have French names, resulting from extensive research on stone tool technology recovered from sites in modern-day France. However, it is important to recognize that many of the earlier traditions originated elsewhere, and were brought by hominins to France.

Tool tradition ■ A tool or tools with a generally consistent pattern of production.

Hammerstone ■ A large, often spherical stone used for making other tools, to detach flakes from a core by percussion or striking.

Flake ■ The thin piece of stone that has been removed from a core.

Low Palaeolithic Period

The lower Palaeolithic period (2.5 MYA–100 KYA) encompasses tool traditions that remained largely unchanged over the course of millennia. Two main tool traditions are associated with this period, the Oldowan and the Acheulian.

OLDOWAN   This tool tradition gets its name from the stone tools found in association with *H. habilis* and *A. boisei* at Olduvai, Tanzania. These tools are also sometimes referred to as "pebble tools" because they look remarkably similar to slightly damaged pebbles. However, detailed studies indicate that they are, in fact, tools rather than just rocks damaged by natural occurrences. The earliest examples date to 2.5 MYA at Gona, Ethiopia, and continue through to sites dated to about 1.5 MYA. Oldowan tools are made by striking the edge of a **core** stone with another hard object, such as a hammerstone. The resulting tool has a sharp edge, typically 5 cm in length, which can then be used to cut, scrape, or smash stuff. The Oldowan tradition was dominated by **unifacial tools,** which were worked on only one side, although some **bifacial tools** (tools worked on both sides) were produced (Figure 7.5). Oldowan tools encompass large scrapers, hammerstones, a variety of stone flakes, and **choppers,** which are simply hand-sized tools with one sharpened edge. Archaeologists are debating whether early hominins sought to produce stone flakes or stone cores.

It should not be assumed that Oldowan tools are easily made; they're not. Just finding suitable stone material with which to make the tools can be a difficult and laborious process. The first attempts at tool manufacture always result in more bruised knuckles and cut fingers than useful implements. In fact, it can take years of training and practice to make Oldowan tools. Thus, Oldowan tools mark an important technological change in the lifestyles of early hominins.

ACHEULIAN   This tool tradition gets its name from the Saint-Acheul site in modern-day France, where 19th-century researchers first identified this specialized tool. It's

Core ▪ The raw stone from which flakes will be removed and which can be modified and used as a tool itself.

Unifacial tool ▪ A tool worked on only one side.

Bifacial tool ▪ A tool worked on two sides.

Chopper ▪ A tool made by flaking the edge of a round or spherical stone on one side. The resulting tool is best suited for powerful "chopping" activities, such as breaking animal bones or cutting up vegetation.

Figure 7.5

Oldowan chopper (left) and flake (right).

Scale bar is 1 cm.
© S. M. Lehman

Figure 7.6

An Acheulian hand axe.

Note the characteristic pear-shaped pattern to this stone tool.
Courtesy of Werner Forman/Getty Images

important to note, however, that this tradition was first developed in Africa long before it was brought to Europe. The Acheulian tool tradition is associated with three early hominins: *H. erectus, H. ergaster,* and *H. heidelbergensis* (1.5–0.5 MYA). This tradition is best known by the distinctive oval- and pear-shaped "hand axes," which get their name from their axe-like shape and the premise that the tool was held in the user's hand (Figure 7.6). These hand axes have been recovered from sites across Africa, Europe, and Asia.

This tradition also includes fairly distinctive cleavers and picks. The Acheulian tradition marks two major shifts in tool production. First, Acheulian toolmakers perfected the controlled use of flaking techniques. Specifically, most Acheulian tools are made by striking flakes off both sides of a stone core (i.e., bifacial tools). Second, although the first Acheulian tools were created using a hammerstone, later tools were formed using bone or antler as the "hammer." This shift in percussive techniques results in tools that are thinner, sharper, and more complex in shape. Compared to the Oldowan, the Acheulian tradition is characterized by fairly standardized tools with more workable, sharper edges: The average Acheulian tool has about 20 cm of edge, almost four times as much as that seen in Oldowan tools. At the end of the Acheulian period, toolmakers developed a way of producing standardized flakes from a single core, which is now known as the Levalloisian method because it was first described by 19th-century archaeologists working near Levallois-Perret, France. Researchers have also documented regional variations in tool kits. For example, eastern European toolmakers focused on the production of simple flaked choppers. In Asia, toolmakers produced a variety of Acheulian tools, including scrapers and burins (chisel-like tools). Thus, the Acheulian tradition is characterized by greater control over raw stone materials to produce a desired tool.

Middle Palaeolithic Period

The middle Palaeolithic period lasted from approximately 300 to 40 KYA in Europe, Africa, and Asia. This period is associated mainly with tools produced by *H. neanderthalensis* and *H. sapiens*. Collectively, these tools are classified as the Mousterian tool tradition.

MOUSTERIAN   This tool tradition gets its name from the stone tools found near Le Moustier, France. Compared to the Acheulian tradition, the Mousterian tradition produces more small-flake tools, such as side scrapers, and fewer large tools, such as hand axes (Figure 7.7). Moreover, many Mousterian flakes bear evidence of retouching, in which the toolmaker further refines the edge of the flake. In other words, most Acheulian flakes were utilized as they came off the core, but a Mousterian toolmaker would work to sharpen or extend the edge of a flake. It has been suggested that some retouched flakes were attached to a wooden shaft, presumably to ease scraping of animal hides or wood. Retouched flakes are extremely sharp, although they can lose their edge quite quickly when used on a tough substance. In time, Neanderthals perfected the Mousterian tradition by creating the Levalloisian method, which involves pre-shaping stone cores to produce ready-to-use flake tools. The Levallois method provided the toolmaker with a means for standardizing the size and shape of the flake tool as well as specialized flake points. Also, use of this method allowed for the production of a relatively greater quantity of edged tools than would be produced using Acheulian methods. Therefore, compared to the Acheulian tradition, the Mousterian tradition reflects improved control of the tools produced from raw stone materials.

Upper Palaeolithic Period

The upper Palaeolithic period is dated to approximately 40 to 20 KYA in Europe, Africa, and Asia. This period is associated mainly with tools produced by *H. sapiens*. Lithic experts recognize at least five tool traditions in this period, each of which can be further subdivided into regionally varying tool cultures. We focus on the following three main traditions: Aurignacian, Solutrean, and Magdalenian.

Figure 7.7

A Mousterian flake.

Note how the tool maker reworked the edge (i.e., removed small pieces of obsidian).
© S. M. Lehman

Burin ■ A chisel-like stone tool for engraving.

AURIGNACIAN   The Aurignacian tradition, named for the Aurignac site in southwestern France, was developed and used predominantly by *H. sapiens* over the course of approximately 6000 years (32–26 KYA) in Europe. Compared to middle Palaeolithic traditions, the Aurignacian is characterized by innovations in blade production and standardization of tool types. Aurignacian toolmakers perfected the art of making long blades rather than flakes. Thus, they maximized the amount of usable edge that could be obtained from the raw materials. The tool types are more standardized than in past traditions, with a focus on producing scrapers and **burins**, chisel-like tools used for engraving wood or bone. There is also evidence for the production of projectile points made from non-lithic materials, such as antler, bone, and ivory.

SOLUTREAN   This tool tradition gets its name from the stone tools found near Solutré, in eastern France. The Solutrean tradition lasted for only a few thousand years (21–17 KYA) in what is present-day France. Despite the short existence of this period, Solutrean tools are considered by anthropologists to be among the most beautiful ever produced during the Palaeolithic period. Compared to those of the Aurignacian tradition, Solutrean toolmakers produced incredibly symmetrical, bifacial tools and spear points. Rather than striking the core stone, the Solutrean tradition involves use of a new process called **pressure flaking**, which involves steadily applying pressure to the core until a flake breaks off. This innovation produced incredibly light, sharp tools and flakes. Solutrean toolmakers also excelled at producing knives, saws, scrapers, points, and perforators.

Pressure flaking ■ Removing flakes from a core by applying pressure steadily until the flake breaks off.

MAGDALENIAN   The Magdalenian tool tradition (18–10 KYA), named for the archaeological site of La Madeleine in central France, marks one of the final stone tool traditions before tool production transitioned to almost exclusive use of non-lithics, such as organic materials and metal. The Magdalenian underwent considerable changes over the course of a few thousand years. In the early phase of the period, toolmakers produced long, thin blades and a variety of scrapers. The middle phase is characterized by the emergence of **microliths** (small, flaked stone tools) and **denticulated microliths** (small, flaked stone tools with notches). In the last phase, people produced various harpoons made from bone, antler, and ivory; nets woven from plant materials; spear throwers; and bows and arrows. The Magdalenian also presaged the first domesticated plants and animals. Because these developments fall within the archaeological subfield, we will not discuss them further. Instead, we conclude this chapter by looking at the hypothesized phylogenetic relationships in Plio-Pleistocene hominins.

Microliths ■ Small (1–4 cm in length), flaked stone tools.

Denticulated microliths ■ Small (1–4 cm in length), flaked stone tools set with little notches.

Hominin Phylogenetic Relationships

It can be argued that the ultimate goal of evolutionary anthropology is determining phylogenetic relationships in hominins. After all, paleoanthropologists seek answers to the following, mind-blowing questions: Where did we come from, and what is it to be human? By seeking answers to these questions, we also gain perspectives on human biogeography, ecology, and behaviour. Not surprisingly, efforts to attain this goal and answer the above questions energize people, whether or not they believe in evolutionary anthropology. For example, type the species name of any of the above fossils into an Internet search engine. You're likely to find blogs and postings discussing how a fossil supports evolutionary anthropology or the pseudo-science of "intelligent design." Contrary to claims made by proponents of intelligent design, there is broad consensus among paleoanthropologists that hominins evolved in Africa. One question down, one to go!

In paleoanthropology, the second question—what is it to be human?—relates to hominin morphological characteristics, which are inherited from our common ancestors. So, what do fossils tell us about hypothesized phylogenetic relationships in hominins? Due to the nature of the fossilization process, most species are presented by crania and teeth. We focus on cranial features as the data source for our phylogenetic review (Figure 7.8). The addition of postcranial specimens can, and likely will, alter the tree. Before we review the tree, you should note that C-shaped nodes are better for interpreting phylogenetic relationships than E-shaped nodes. Even worse are nodes that look like multiple *E*'s all piled on top of each other. E-shaped nodes violate one of the key principles of cladistics, which states that lineage splitting produces two groups. As you can see, basal relationships, that is those closer to the root of the tree, remain largely unresolved (i.e., E-shaped nodes), in that we do not know with any degree of certainty which transitional or hominin species represents the last common ancestor to all other hominins (*O. tugenensis*, *S. tchadensis*, or *A. kadabba*). There is strong support for phylogenetic relationships between *A. ramidus* through *A. africanus*. In other words, this grouping is characterized by C-shaped node patterns. Things get a little muddled for *K. platyops* and the robust australopithecines (*A. robustus*, *A. boisei*, and *A. aethiopicus*). Why? Because these species are represented by only a few specimens that are fragmented or enigmatic, making it difficult to determine key morphological features. Resolving these nodes is critically important because

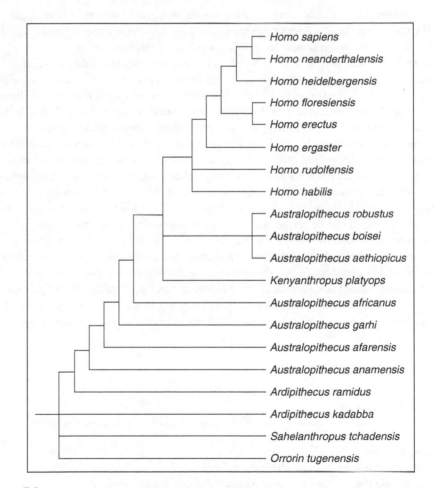

Figure 7.8

Hypothesized phylogenetic relationships based on cranial features in transitional hominins, australopithecines, and members of the genus *Homo*.

E-shaped nodes represent unresolved relationships. C-shaped nodes represent well-supported relationships.

Cladogram based on information in Strait et al., 2007.

they represent the last common ancestor linking australopithecines, and perhaps *K. platyops,* to the first representatives of our genus. The tree is further complicated by the unresolved E-shaped nodes linking early *Homo* (*H. habilis, H. rudolfensis*) to more derived species, such as *H. ergaster.* Although frustrating, these unresolved branching patterns do represent excellent opportunities for students, like you, to focus your research efforts! From these unresolved branches in early *Homo,* things get better, in that the cranial data indicates strong phylogenetic branching patterns from *H. ergaster* through *H. heidelbergensis* to the sister taxa of *H. neanderthalensis* and *H. sapiens.* Thus, the main phylogenetic issues involve basal taxa and the transition from australopithecines to *Homo* (Strait et al., 2007). There are also some taxonomic problems that need to be rectified, such as the validity of *Kenyanthropus* as a unique genus and species diversity in the genus *Homo.* These issues can and will be solved by work being conducted now by paleoanthropologists, and in the future by those of you eager to expand our understanding of why we, as a species, are here!

Summary

1. Despite considerable morphological variation among members of the genus *Homo,* there is a general pattern of reduced robusticity in the crania and postcrania, brain expansion, and the tendency for human beings to love lemurs (just kidding on this last one).

2. The lower Palaeolithic period (2.5 MYA–100 KYA) encompasses tool traditions that remained largely unchanged over the course of millennia. Two main tool traditions are associated with this period, the Oldowan and the Acheulian. Oldowan stone tools are predominantly unifacial tools, which look to the layperson remarkably like broken pebbles. Technological changes resulted in the production and use of Acheulian tools, which were standardized, bifacial tools best represented by the distinctive Acheulian hand axes, for almost one million years. The middle Palaeolithic period (300–40 KYA) is associated mainly with retouched stone tools produced by *H. neanderthalensis* and *H. sapiens.* Collectively, these tools are classified as the Mousterian tool tradition. The upper Palaeolithic period (40–20 KYA) is associated mainly with tools produced by *H. sapiens.* Lithic experts recognize at least five tool traditions in this period, each of which can be further subdivided into regionally varying tool cultures.

3. Hominin evolution is intimately linked with Africa. Despite lack of resolution at various points in the hypothesized phylogenetics of hominins, there is broad consensus for relationships in derived *Homo.* Specifically, the main phylogenetic issues involve evolutionary relationships among basal taxa, such as *Orrorin tugenensis* and both species of *Ardipithecus,* and the transition from australopithecines to *Homo.* There are also some taxonomic problems that need to be rectified, such as the validity of *Kenyanthropus* as a unique genus and species diversity in the genus *Homo.*

INTERNET RESOURCES

Human Origins Program at The Smithsonian Institution
http://humanorigins.si.edu/
See fossil hominins and learn about research being conducted by paleoanthropologists.

PBS: NOVA: Neanderthals on Trial
www.pbs.org/wgbh/nova/neanderthals/skul_vrs.html
See and manipulate the viewing angles of Neanderthal and human skulls.

PBS: Evolution
www.pbs.org/wgbh/evolution/humans
Great PBS website on human origins.

Old Stone Age
www.oldstoneage.com
Follow along with archaeologists as they dig for lithic treasures!

Time Line Index
http://lithiccastinglab.com/3timelineindex.htm
Everything you ever wanted to know about how to make lithic tools. See casts of the various tool traditions.

LITERATURE CITED

Bermudez de Castro, J., Arsuaga, J., Carbonell, E., Rosas, A., Martinez, I., and Mosquera, M. (1997). A hominid from the lower Pleistocene of Atapuerca, Spain: Possible ancestor to Neanderthals and modern humans. *Science,* 276(5317), 1392.

Brown, P., Sutikna, T., Morwood, M., Soejono, R., Saptomo, E., and Due, R. (2004). A new small-bodied hominin from the Late Pleistocene of Flores, Indonesia. *Nature,* 431(7012), 1055–1061.

Falk, D., Hildebolt, C., Smith, K., Morwood, M., and Sutikna, T. (2007). Brain shape in human microcephalics and *Homo floresiensis. Proceedings of the National Academy of Sciences, USA,* 104(7), 2513.

Fleagle, J. G. (1999). *Primate Adaptation and Evolution.* San Diego, Academic Press.

Green, R. E., Krause, J., Ptak, S. E., Briggs, A. W., Ronan, M. T., Simons, J. F., Du, L., Egholm, M., Rothberg, J. M., Paunovic, M., and Paabo, S. (2006). Analysis of one million base pairs of Neanderthal DNA. *Nature,* 444(7117), 330–336.

Green, R. E., Krause, J., Briggs, A. W., Maricic, T., Stenzel, U., Kircher, M., Patterson, N., Li, H., Zhai, W., Fritz, M. H.-Y., Hansen, N. F., Durand, E. Y., Malaspinas, A.-S., Jensen, J. D., Marques-Bonet, T., Alkan, C., Prufer, K., Meyer, M., Burbano, H. A., Good, J. M., Schultz, R., Aximu-Petri, A., Butthof, A., Hober, B., Hoffner, B., Siegemund, M., Weihmann, A., Nusbaum, C., Lander, E. S., Russ, C., Novod, N., Affourtit, J., Egholm, M., Verna, C., Rudan, P., Brajkovic, D., Kucan, Z., Gusic, I., Doronichev, V. B., Golovanova, L. V., Lalueza-Fox, C., de la Rasilla, M., Fortea, J., Rosas, A., Schmitz, R. W., Johnson, P. L. F., Eichler, E. E., Falush, D., Birney, E., Mullikin, J. C., Slatkin, M., Nielsen, R., Kelso, J., Lachmann, M., Reich, D. and Paabo, S. (2010). A draft sequence of the Neandertal genome. *Science* 328(5979): 710-722.

Hershkovitz, I., Kornreich, L., and Laron, Z. (2007). Comparative skeletal features between *Homo floresiensis* and patients with primary growth hormone insensitivity (Laron syndrome). *American Journal of Physical Anthropology,* 134(2), 198–208.

Krings, M., Stone, A., Schmitz, R., Krainitzki, H., Stoneking, M., and Pääbo, S. (1997). Neandertal DNA sequences and the origin of modern humans. *Cell,* 90, 19–30.

Leakey, L. S. B., Tobias, P. V., and Napier, J. R. (1964). A new species of the genus *Homo* from Olduvai Gorge. *Nature,* 202, 7–9.

Martin, R., MacLarnon, A., Phillips, J., and Dobyns, W. (2006). Flores hominid: New species or microcephalic dwarf? *The Anatomical Record Part A: Discoveries in Molecular, Cellular, and Evolutionary Biology,* 288A(11), 1123–1145.

Noonan, J. P., Coop, G., Kudaravalli, S., Smith, D., Krause, J., Alessi, J., Chen, F., Platt, D., Paabo, S., Pritchard, J. K., and Rubin, E. M. (2006). Sequencing and analysis of Neanderthal genomic DNA. *Science,* 314(5802), 1113–1118.

Reich, D., Green, R. E., Kircher, M., Krause, J., Patterson, N., Durand, E. Y., Viola, B., Briggs, A. W., Stenzel, U., Johnson, P. L. F., Maricic, T., Good, J. M., Marques-Bonet, T., Alkan, C., Fu, Q., Mallick, S., Li, H., Meyer, M., Eichler, E. E., Stoneking, M., Richards, M., Talamo, S., Shunkov, M. V., Derevianko, A. P., Hublin, J.J., Kelso, J., Slatkin, M. and Paabo, S. (2010). Genetic history of an archaic hominin group from Denisova Cave in Siberia. *Nature* 468(7327): 1053–1060.

Roberts, R., Maeda, T., Wasisto, S., and Djubiantono, T. (2005). Further evidence for small-bodied hominins from the Late Pleistocene of Flores, Indonesia. *Nature,* 437, 13.

Simpson, S.W., Quade, J., Levin, N.E., Butler, R., Dupont-Nivet, G., Everett, M., and Semaw, S. (2008) A female *Homo erectus* pelvis from Gona, Ethiopia. *Science* 322(5904):1089-1092.

Strait, D., Grine, F., and Fleagle, J. (2007). Analyzing hominid phylogeny. *Handbook of Paleoanthropology* (ed. by W. Henke and I. Tattersall), pp. 1781–1806. New York: Springer.

Wall, J. D. and Kim, S. K. (2007) Inconsistencies in Neanderthal genomic DNA sequences. *PLoS Genetics,* 3(10), e175.

White, T. D., Asfaw, B., DeGusta, D., Gilbert, H., Richards, G. D., Suwa, G., and Clark Howell, F. (2003). Pleistocene *Homo sapiens* from Middle Awash, Ethiopia. *Nature,* 423(6941), 742–747.

Wood, B. (1991). *Koobi Fora Research Project. Volume 4: Hominid Cranial Remains.* Oxford: Clarendon Press.

CHAPTER 8

Human Variation

GOALS

By the end of this chapter you should understand:

1. The main hypotheses on human origins.
2. How natural selection has produced adaptations in humans.
3. How evolutionary anthropologists refute human race concepts.

CHAPTER OUTLINE

Human Origins: Replacement or Multiregional Hypotheses?

Natural Selection and Human Adaptation

Are There Human Races?

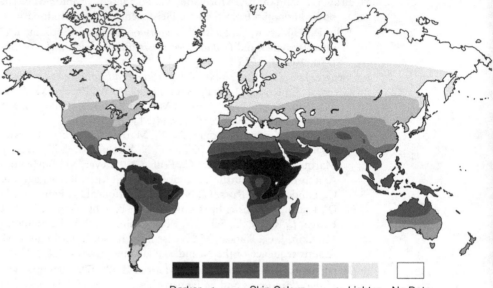

Darker ← Skin Colour → Lighter   No Data

Introduction

Although variation is a good thing in evolution, having unique features can have negative consequences for individuals in some human societies. Even subtle forms of racism can be insidiously hurtful, particularly for innocent children. During a survey of a remote jungle site in Madagascar, local people kindly offered to let me and my research team of Malagasy scientists set up a temporary camp near their village. None of the villagers had ever seen, let alone talked with, a North American *vaza,* their term for a stranger or foreigner. The children soon overcame their fear of me, watching everything I did with considerable interest. All the children, but for one little girl, eventually grew bored and moved on to other activities. Each day, this little girl silently followed me through the village to the edge of the forest, her blue-green eyes taking in my every move. She was still there when I emerged after 12 to 14 hours of searching for lemurs. All my attempts at conversation were met with a shy silence. Just before we decamped, one of my Malagasy colleagues gently informed me of the reasons for the little girl's curiosity and persistence. She was teased by other children because of her blue-green *vaza* eyes. I suddenly realized that all the other villagers had hazel eyes. My visit represented the first time the little girl had ever seen someone sharing her eye colour, which provided some comfort in a place where even slight phenotypic differences result in ostracism. I'll never forget the little girl with *vaza* eyes standing silent and alone as we departed her village.

Evolutionary anthropologists are at the forefront of science in documenting phenotypic and genetic diversity of modern humans. This research seeks to provide us with an improved understanding of where we came from and why we look the way we do. In the sections below, we discuss the evolutionary anthropology of human variation. We start with looking at the main hypotheses on human origins. We then review human adaptations, ranging from body size to disease. Finally, we look at how evolutionary anthropologists view the concept of human races.

Human Origins: Replacement or Multiregional Hypotheses?

Despite decades of research, evolutionary anthropologists still lack a definitive answer to the following question: Where did humans come from? Although there is consensus on the successful dispersal of early humans out of Africa, researchers vigorously debate whether *H. erectus, H. heidelbergensis,* or *H. neanderthalensis* represents our most recent common ancestor. Moreover, researchers question whether *H. sapiens* displaced other hominins across the globe or evolved due to gene flow between Africa, Asia, and Europe. These fascinating issues were originally investigated predominantly from the perspective of skeletal and dental specimens. The advent of powerful genetic tools for investigating human origins has contributed much to the debate. Consequently, support has careened back and forth between differing hypotheses. In the sections below, we first review the two main hypotheses on human origins: the replacement hypothesis and the multiregional hypothesis. We then look at the morphological and genetic evidence used to test each hypothesis.

Replacement Hypothesis

The replacement hypothesis is also known as the single-origin and out-of-Africa hypotheses (Figure 8.1). This hypothesis states that about 2 million years ago (MYA), *H. erectus* evolved in Africa and then dispersed into Europe and Asia. Approximately 160 thousand years ago (KYA), early *H. sapiens* evolved in Africa. Starting around

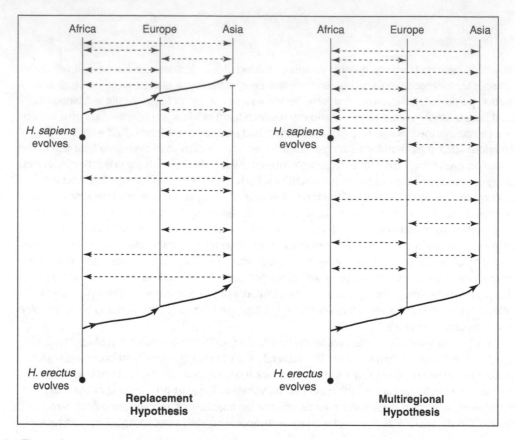

Figure 8.1

Two hypotheses on human origins.

Thick lines represent hominin dispersals. Dashed lines represent gene flow between regions. Note that each starts in the same way: *H. erectus* and *H. sapiens* evolve in and then disperse out of Africa. From there, the hypotheses differ considerably on how the dispersal happened (i.e., displacement or interbreeding).

100 KYA, *H. sapiens* migrated to and displaced contemporaneous hominins (*H. erectus*, *H. heidelbergensis*, and *H. neanderthalensis*) in Africa, Europe, and Asia. The model makes the following three predictions: (1) there was only one wave of human dispersal and replacement of other congenera out of Africa, (2) modern humans are descendants of African *H. sapiens*, and (3) *H. neanderthalensis* is an evolutionary dead end. The replacement hypothesis also holds that the anatomical traits associated with modern humans evolved approximately 200 KYA.

Multiregional Hypothesis

The multiregional hypothesis holds that *H. erectus* evolved in Africa and then migrated to Europe and eventually Asia (Figure 8.1). *H. sapiens* evolved about 160 KYA in Africa and then dispersed into Europe and Asia 100 KYA. In each region, gene flow spread *H. sapiens* traits among local populations (i.e., interbreeding). Thus, *H. sapiens* did not replace or displace other hominins. Furthermore, *H. neanderthalensis* is not an evolutionary dead end because this species contributed to the gene pool of European *H. sapiens*. Put differently, the model makes three predictions: (1) there was no wave of *H. sapiens* replacements, (2) *H. erectus* represents the most recent common ancestor of all modern humans, and (3) *H. neanderthalensis* contributed to the gene pool of some modern human populations. We should, therefore, be able to trace our genetic history back all the way to *H. erectus*.

The Evidence!

Each of the above hypotheses starts out quite similarly: *H. erectus* evolved in Africa and dispersed to Europe and Asia. Also similarly, both hypotheses hold that *H. sapiens* first evolved in Africa. The main difference between the hypotheses is whether African *H. sapiens* replaced other contemporaneous hominins in Europe and Asia. We leave the question of the fate of Neanderthals to more advanced classes. As we see below, the evidence for replacement is controversial, irrespective of the data source. So, what does the morphological and genetic evidence say about each theory?

MORPHOLOGICAL EVIDENCE   Morphological evidence for the replacement and multi-regional hypotheses centres on whether *H. sapiens* interbred with contemporaneous congenera, particularly *H. neanderthalensis*. The replacement hypothesis states that no such interbreeding occurred, whereas the multiregional hypothesis states that it did. Thus, the multiregional hypothesis will be supported if we find transitional forms exhibiting characteristics of both *H. sapiens* and *H. neanderthalensis*. As we discussed in Chapter 7, there are many morphological distinctions between *H. sapiens* and *H. neanderthalensis*. For example, early *H. sapiens* is characterized by a skull with a vertical forehead, rounded occipital bone, and reduced supraorbital tori. Conversely, *H. neanderthalensis* has a larger, longer skull with a well-developed double-arched brow ridge. These divergent features existed despite 20 000 to 60 000 years of coexistence of *H. sapiens* and *H. neanderthalensis* in the Middle East and Eastern Europe (Fleagle, 1999). The lack of transitional forms provides strong support for the replacement hypothesis. This lack of evidence was challenged by the 1999 discovery of a fossil skeleton of a four-year-old child dated 24 to 25 KYA in Portugal (Duarte et al., 1999). The discoverers suggested that the suite of transitional morphological features in this fossil indicates gene flow between *H. neanderthalensis* and early *H. sapiens,* which supports the multiregional hypothesis. However, the young age of the child complicates taxonomic analyses, as we noted in Chapter 7 regarding the *H. antecessor* specimens. Moreover, there has been, to date, no independent verification of the Neanderthal features of this specimen. Thus, the morphological evidence is equivocal, supporting certain aspects of both the replacement and multiregional hypotheses.

GENETIC EVIDENCE   You may be thinking, "Oh no, aren't we finished with genetics?!" As before, take a deep breath, let it out slowly, and relax. Ahhh, feel better? Good! We focus on only a general review of the genetic evidence for each hypothesis. The major genetic breakthrough on human origins resulted from a 1987 study by Cann and colleagues on the **mitochondrial** DNA (mtDNA) of humans (Figure 8.2). Why focus on mtDNA? Because mtDNA has a higher mutation rate relative to nuclear DNA, meaning that researchers access a stronger signal, and because mtDNA is transmitted without changes through the matrilineal line (i.e., from the mother to her offspring). Thus, mtDNA does not undergo recombination processes, like nuclear DNA. What this means is that you received your nuclear DNA from each of your parents, but you received all your mtDNA from your mother. A similar pattern holds for Y-chromosome DNA, except that this DNA is transmitted along the male lineage. Initially, it was thought that the mtDNA revealed that modern humans are ultimately descended from African populations and that there is a rather recent female progenitor for modern humans. The press cleverly labelled this common ancestor as the mitochondrial Eve (i.e., as in the biblical Eve from the Garden of Eden). These results seemed to support the replacement hypothesis, and led to a flurry of research on the genetics of human

Mitochondria ■ Structures in eukaryotic cells that turn nutrients into energy for the cells (i.e., the "power plants" of cells).

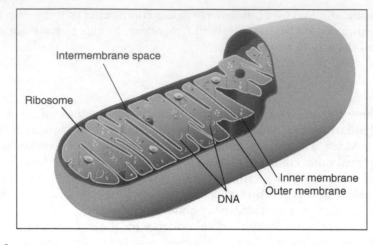

Figure 8.2

Graphical representation of some of the internal structures within a mitochondrian.

origins. In time, many studies lent further support to the primacy of the replacement hypothesis over the multiregional hypothesis. Researchers eventually discovered the so-called Y-chromosome Adam, representing the African male who is the most recent common patrilineal ancestor of modern humans.

The good times did not last for proponents of the replacement hypothesis, due largely to the work of Alan Templeton. Dr. Templeton is one of the world authorities on human genetics and biological evolution. In a series of seminal articles (Templeton, 2005, 2007), he noted problems with many genetic studies of human origins. For example, he pointed out that many earlier studies failed to correctly identify the basic tenets of each hypothesis on human origins. For example, Templeton suggested that some researchers simply sought support for only a few aspects of one hypothesis, largely ignoring contradictory data that refuted other aspects of the hypothesis. Thus, Templeton noted that some researchers focused on hypothesis compatibility rather than on hypothesis testing. Not sure what this means? Go back to Chapter 1 (pages 6–7) and review how scientists ensure a hypothesis is falsifiable. Most important, Templeton warned against relying on inferences drawn from only two DNA regions, mtDNA and Y-DNA. Put differently, how strong do you think a hominin phylogeny would be if the researcher focused only on two traits? The answer is, not very strong. Phylogenetics and biogeography require total evidence for DNA data just as they do for skeletal or dental data. After Dr. Templeton corrected for errors in the genetic data and expanded his analysis to include 24 DNA regions, he found little support for either the replacement or multiregional hypotheses. In fact, the genetic data supports a unique model of human origins, in which there were two population expansions of *H. sapiens* out of Africa and then one dispersal from Asia back to Africa (Templeton, 2005)! As more DNA regions become available for study, geneticists will further refine our understanding of speciation and dispersal in *Homo*.

Natural Selection and Human Adaptation

Since *H. sapiens* evolved approximately 160 KYA in Africa, our species has spread across the planet, occupying and exploiting resources in an incredible variety of environments. Humans exist or have existed in environments ranging from equatorial jungles through scorching deserts to the awesome expanses of the Arctic ice shelf. Only in the most extreme environments, such as atop the highest mountains or in Antarctica, is there no evidence of permanent human habitation. Consequently, modern humans have been subject to environmentally specific selection pressures. In turn, humans have evolved biological adaptations due to varying environmental conditions. So, should we expect to see Arctic dwellers covered in a thick layer of insulating hair or people living in high rainfall areas having prominent brow ridges to shield their eyes? No! But don't laugh: these were valid anthropological questions only 100 to 200 years ago. Today, evolutionary anthropologists study evolutionary correlates to body size, body shape, and skin colour in humans.

Body Size and Shape

Modern humans are a remarkably diverse species in terms of body size and shape. For example, we range in height from an average of 1.5 m in the pygmies of Central Africa to 1.85 m in the mountainous regions of Croatia. Here, we look at two **ecogeographic patterns** associated with **latitude**: Bergmann's Rule and Allen's Rule. Before we begin, it's important for you to understand that these so-called rules are best interpreted as biogeographic patterns. Why? Because body size variations result from geographic patterns of heredity, nutrition, and changes in response to environmental factors, called **phenotypic plasticity**. We explore the effects of nutrition on human health and biology in the next chapter.

BERGMANN'S RULE   This ecogeographic rule holds that humans possessing smaller body size tend to range into lower latitudes (warmer regions) whereas those having larger body size tend to exist in higher latitudes (cooler regions). The underlying cause of these body size patterns relates directly to area and volume changes we discussed in Chapter 4. Specifically, basic physics and thermodynamics state that larger body sizes have less surface area relative to their total volume. Consequently, larger-bodied humans lose heat more slowly, relative to their size, than smaller humans, which is a good thing in colder climates. In hotter climates, body heat needs to be dissipated rather than stored. Smaller-sized humans in hot climates have a higher surface area to volume relationship, thereby cooling their bodies. There are plenty of exceptions to Bergmann's Rule, particularly in modern humans because we wear heavy clothing in cold climates. By wearing insulative clothing, modern humans may reduce natural selection for larger body size in cold regions. This may explain, in part, why people are not extremely tall in polar regions. For example, the average height of an adult Inuit, who resides in Arctic regions of northern Canada, is approximately 1.57 m, which is only slightly smaller than the average for an adult Canadian (1.67 m). You should not assume, however, that Inuit exhibit no adaptations to the cold, as we see below.

ALLEN'S RULE This ecogeographic rule also relates to the effects of latitude on body size. Specifically, Allen's Rule states that human populations living in colder climates should have shorter limbs or appendages compared to populations living in warmer regions. Why does this happen? Well, we need to return yet again to basic physics and thermodynamics. If you've been exposed to very cold ambient temperatures, then you also likely experienced the cold first in your extremities (e.g., nose, face, hands, or feet). The human body's response to cold is to undergo narrowing of the blood vessels, or **vasoconstriction**, which maintains a steady supply of warm blood to the organs in your head and torso. In other words, we would expect the arms, legs, ears, or nose of humans to be smaller for a population living in polar regions. Allen's Rule does hold for the Inuit, in that they have relatively shorter arms and legs, but not torsos, compared to people living in more temperate climates.

Ecogeographic patterns ▪ Similar patterns of variation within and across species and their correlation to biogeography.

Latitude ▪ Geographic distance north or south of the equator.

Phenotypic plasticity ▪ Variation in organisms in response to environmental factors rather than genetic factors.

Vasocontriction ▪ Narrowing of blood vessels. This reduces the amount of blood flowing to that part of the body.

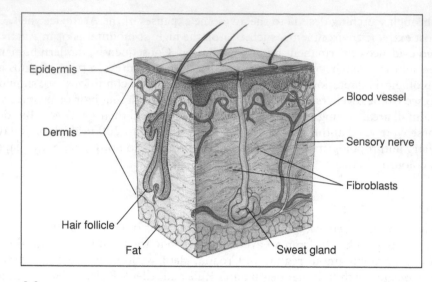

Figure 8.3

Basic structure of human skin.

The cells primarily responsible for skin colour are located in the thin outer layer known as the epidermis.
Courtesy of National Institute of General Medical Sciences

Skin Colour Adaptations

Melanin ■ A mixture of biopolymers that give colour to the skin, hair, and parts of the eye.

Perhaps no other feature of modern humans varies as much as and is of more interest to evolutionary anthropologists than skin colour or pigmentation. So, what are the biological causes of skin pigmentation? Skin pigmentation results primarily from variations in the colour, size, and density of **melanin** granules produced by melanocytes in the cells of the upper layers of the skin (epidermis; Figure 8.3). Thus, lighter skinned individuals typically have melanin granules that are light coloured, small, and lower in density. In individuals with darker skin, the melanin granules are typically darker in colour, larger, and higher in density.

The question arises as to why humans evolved geographic variations in skin pigmentation. As we now know, humans evolved in African environments that are characterized by high-intensity **ultraviolet radiation** (UVR). As our early human ancestors dispersed across the globe, they became exposed to differing climates and UVR intensities. The distinction between UVR intensities is particularly pronounced between equatorial regions and regions near the poles. In fact, some very high latitudes are characterized by complete darkness for weeks or months at a time. Moreover, people living near the poles typically have lighter skin compared to those living near the equator. Evolutionary anthropologists have formulated three theories on this pattern: UVR protection, nutrient protection, and vitamin D synthesis.

Ultraviolet radiation ■ Electromagnetic radiation, similar to visible light but of shorter wavelength, which is emitted from the sun.

MELANIN AND UVR PROTECTION   Proximity to the equator results in people having darker skin, representing an adaptation to filter harmful sunlight away from the skin (Figure 8.4). Exposure to sunlight actually involves exposure to UVR. Through a complex series of biochemical steps, exposure to UVR initially causes immediate darkening of existing melanin in skin. A slower, secondary process causes an increased production of new melanin granules, which produces a tan. Thus, melanin acts as a natural sun screen. Individuals with naturally dark skin have immediate and long-lasting protection from UVR. Conversely, individuals with few melanocytes do not tan. Thus, natural selection has favoured naturally dark-skinned individuals in equatorial regions. Why did this occur?

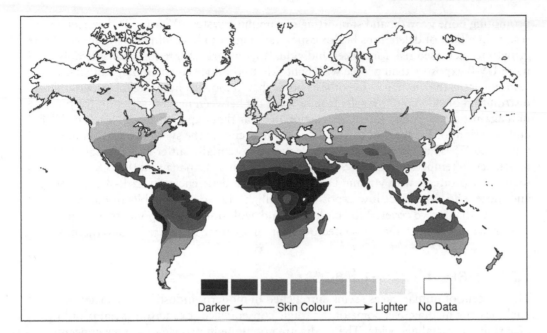

Figure 8.4

World map showing human skin coloration.

The map is based on the work of the Italian geographer R. Biasutti.
Updated information from Chaplin (2004) and Jablonski and Chapman (2000).

The scientific community is divided on whether natural selection favoured protection from sunburn or skin cancer in equatorial regions. Initially, scientists noted that dark-skinned individuals have reduced rates of some forms of skin cancer, which supports skin pigmentation as an adaptation for skin cancer. However, some forms of skin cancer are rarely lethal. Those forms that are lethal typically affect individuals who are past their reproductive years, resulting in a reduced effect on their fitness. In this view, dark skin pigmentation as an adaptation for skin cancer is only "piggybacking" on some other feature, just like the child's selection toy we discussed in Chapter 2. One theory is that melanin may be a nutrient essential to a variety of human biological systems.

MELANIN AND NUTRIENT PROTECTION   Melanin also plays a role in protecting **folate** or folic acid. Where do you find folate? It's abundant in the vegetables you may have avoided eating as child: spinach, turnip greens, lettuces, and peas. Because folate plays such an important role in human reproduction, it represents a nutrient whose maintenance would be strongly favoured by natural selection. Put differently, adequate folate levels support infant health, which improves the evolutionary fitness of the parents and their offspring. Despite the critical role played by folate in human health and reproduction, this vitamin is highly sensitive to UVR. Even brief exposure to UVR can reduce folate levels in human blood. Thus, selection would be rather strong for dark-skinned individuals in low latitudes.

MELANIN AND VITAMIN D SYNTHESIS   The above hypotheses support strong selection pressures in favour of individuals with dark skin. Yet humans in temperate regions have relatively lighter skin pigmentation than others living in tropical parts of the world (Figure 8.4). Why then would selection favour light-skinned individuals in high latitudes? The answer to this question relates to a benefit of UVR exposure. Humans require exposure to a specific kind of UVR, known as UV-B, to synthesize vitamin D in our skin. Unlike folate, vitamin D is found in only a few food resources, such as some fish species. Vitamin D is necessary for absorbing other essential nutrients in our food,

Folate ▪ A B-complex vitamin associated with reduced risk of birth defects and cardiac events, and improved cognitive function.

promoting bone growth, and supporting our immune system. Vitamin D deficiency results in a host of deleterious health issues, ranging from liver ailments to reduced bone growth to increased risk for cancer. Individuals with dark skin require considerably more UV-B exposure than people with light skin to produce equal amounts of vitamin D. Consequently, the vitamin D hypothesis holds that in modern humans, the geographic distribution of skin colour results from a trade-off between natural selection for protection against sunburn and folate destruction in areas that experience high levels of UVR, and selection for lighter skin in high latitudes to facilitate the synthesis of vitamin D (Parra, 2007). Thus, dark-skinned people would potentially suffer from a vitamin D deficiency in temperate regions. Some countries, such as Canada and the U.S., fortify their dairy products with vitamin D to guard against deficiencies in dark-skinned people and those who experience low exposure to sunlight due to work habits or culture.

Now that we've covered the biological and evolutionary components of skin colour, we can turn to the associated question of whether there are human races.

Are There Human Races?

The concept of human races seems entrenched in modern, industrialized societies. Each day the media cover some of the tragic consequences of racism: racial profiling, race riots, or racial genocide. The media are not alone in propagating race concepts. Health officials gauge their advisories in terms of increased risk factors based on racial classifications rather than populations. For example, American medical researchers have noted differences in diabetic complications between minority races compared to "white" Americans, despite no differences in the quality of health care between the so-called races (Karter et al., 2002). Members of some fundamental religions are vocal supporters of human races, particularly in their theological interpretations of the divine origin of our species. Government elections involve politicians and pundits arguing and dissecting the various strategies used to secure votes within specific races. In Canada and the U.S., government agencies identify and provide specialized support for individuals based on race. Thus, each of us has completed or someone has completed on our behalf a government form indicating our self-identified race or ethnicity.

Despite the seemingly pervasive support of race concepts, there exists a glaring weakness in how to define a human race and just how many races exist. The U.S. Census Bureau employs 10 racial categories, which are usually grouped into five generalized races: Whites, Blacks, Asian/Pacific islanders, Indians/Alaskan Natives, and Hispanics (U.S. Census Bureau, 2008). These races seem to be based on a confusing mixture of skin colour (White, Black), regions of origin (Asian/Pacific islanders, Indians/Alaskan Natives), and ethnicity (Hispanics). The U.S. government states that its racial classifications "reflect a social definition of race recognized in this country. They do not conform to any biological, anthropological or genetic criteria" (U.S. Census Bureau, 2001). In other words, respondents are free to self-identify with any race(s). For example, the so-called White race comprises everything from "White alone" through "White and Black or African American," to "White and Asian and American Indian and Alaska Native." Yet few people know their complete ancestry beyond two or three generations. In order to make some sense of this mess, we need to consider what evolutionary anthropology has to say about the divisive issue of human races.

Evolutionary Anthropologists and Human Races

Few evolutionary anthropologists employ the term *race* when studying modern humans. Why? Because the term is considered ambiguous, crude, and misleading (Cartmill, 1998). When the term is used by biologists, it typically refers to a uniform, genetically distinct population of a species, called a **subspecies**. However, many evolutionary anthropologists

Subspecies ■ A uniform, genetically distinct population of a species, often in a specific geographic region.

are unconvinced that subspecies designations have any biological or evolutionary value. Why? Because physical traits and their associated genes are often independent of each other in geographical space (Templeton, 1998). What does this mean? Put simply, local populations can be distinguished by an unlimited numbers of phenotypic and genetic traits. Consequently, there are, in theory, millions of races of extant humans, rendering race concepts useless. Evolutionary anthropologists also reject race concepts because they rely almost exclusively on only a few arbitrary physical traits, such as skin colour. Under this concept, it's just as meaningless to designate a human race based on skin colour as it is to base it on fingernail shape.

This crude classification system becomes particularly ineffectual when complex things like intelligence and athleticism are arbitrarily assigned to so-called racial groups. In other words, why are only a few phenotypic features used exclusively to define a human race, and, for that matter, who picked these features? Why do proponents of human races ignore all the other features that conflict with specific racial classification? After all, people in sub-Saharan Africa and southern India have similar skin pigmentation, yet they supposedly represent separate human races. The blame for choosing skin colour as a dominant racial feature lies, in part, at the feet of some early 20th-century scientists. At that time, researchers from various scientific disciplines measured human physical features with the goal of identifying specific races. In time, most anthropologists came to realize that these efforts were scientifically futile because the original researchers imposed races on their data rather than seeing if statistical analyses extracted races from the data. Thus, there is no scientific evidence for physical traits defining human races.

Despite the above reasoning and scientific data, some researchers persist in supporting human race concepts (Murray and Herrnstein, 1994; Sarich and Miele, 2004). In a nutshell, they argue that ancestry can be defined by specific genetic variants between populations. Furthermore, there are rare genetic variants, such as those associated with genetic diseases, that are typically found in only some individuals within a population. For example, Tay-Sachs disease is a potentially fatal genetic disorder that at one time was particularly common in Ashkenazi Jews. Some researchers note that African Americans consistently receive lower IQ scores on standardized tests than people of European and Asian descent, which is trumpeted as further evidence of genetically determined race concepts. In other words, European and Asian races are supposedly genetically predisposed to being smarter than the African race. So, what's the deal here? Scientific proponents of human race concepts consistently share three fatal flaws in their logic and science. First, these researchers assume that biological and genetic differences result in social differences between races, when in fact it can be the other way around. Put differently, human abilities are the result of a complex pattern of nature and nurture, and not just genetics. Aptitude at IQ tests results from a complex mixture of educational opportunities, economics, peer networks, and upbringing. Second, scientific proponents of human races consistently err when they extrapolate findings from a few local populations into broad generalizations about racial groupings. For example, do you think that the students in your class represent a hypothetical "race" of university or college students? No! Thus, Ashkenazi Jews are not a specific human race; rather, they represent a group of humans defined by their cultural affinities. Finally, scientific defenders of race as a biological reality consistently fail to define what constitutes a human race, beyond vague descriptions using a few arbitrary phenotypic features, and just how many human races exist. Skin colour is not a determinant of intelligence; it's an adaptation for exposure to UVR.

Perhaps there exists a certain level of genetic differentiation between populations that can be used as a threshold for determining geographically separated species. In other words, we can overcome the issue of a "race" being synonymous with a local population by defining a minimal threshold of genetic differentiation between subspecies. In this sense, a subspecies can be defined as a unique evolutionary lineage within a species. We can use subspecific, genetic variations in other relatively large-bodied, widely distributed mammals as a benchmark value with which to determine races or subspecies in humans. Put differently, we can determine empirically how much genetic variation exists in mammal subspecies. This empirical threshold can then be compared to genetic variation in humans to see if there is evidence of subspecies and races. When this evolutionary perspective is applied to humans and certain mammals, modern humans fail to meet the minimum levels of genetic variation needed to support races or subspecies (Templeton, 1998). If human races did exist, then the majority of genetic variation should exist between populations. The fact is that there is more genetic variation among individuals *within* human populations than there is between human populations. Finally, the genetic data indicate that there are no distinct lineages within modern *Homo sapiens*. There has never been nor will there ever be "pure" human races. Human evolution is characterized by the existence of locally differentiated populations. Gene flow has existed and is accelerating due to modern transportation methods between all human populations to such a degree that we represent a single lineage. Therefore, there are no genetically distinct human races.

What's the Deal with "Racial" Abilities?

Although quality science refutes the existence of human races, people persist in supporting certain racial stereotypes or abilities, particularly those evident in some professional athletes. After all, it doesn't take a rocket scientist to note that members of the so-called Black race dominate a few North American sports, such as basketball, football, and certain running events. Consequently, some writers perpetuate outdated race concepts by suggesting that black athletes are biologically predisposed to be superior athletes (Kotkin, 1993; George, 1999). A simple internet search turns up websites supporting athletic stereotypes. The authors of these sites base their arguments predominantly on alleged racial differences in body proportions, muscle fibres, and lung capacities. For example, African Americans of West African descent are supposedly graced with an abundance of special muscle fibres that enable them to excel at sprinting events but reduce their abilities in long-distance running. Conversely, East Africans are supposedly endowed with another type of muscle fibre, thereby enabling them to dominant long-distance events but do poorly at sprint running. As before, the most significant flaw in any arguments supporting racial abilities is that each so-called race is almost always based on one superficial phenotypic trait, such as skin colour. How do the proponents of this racial viewpoint know that African American sprinters are descendants of West Africans? Did the writers do any genetic studies to assess just how much of Olympic champions' gene pool is West African in origin versus that which is European, Asian, or Native American? Has any adherent of racially based athletic abilities provided scientific support for differences in the types of muscle fibres between "whites" and "blacks" or between Americans of West Africans descent and East Africans? The answer to each of these questions is a resounding, irrefutable no.

But what about the citations used to support supposed racial abilities? Most sources cited by supporters of human race concepts come from newspaper articles and websites rather than scientific publications. Just about anyone with a computer and internet access can create a website, but that doesn't mean that the content is accurate or correct. In time, geneticists and evolutionary anthropologists will discover the complex patterns of genes (nature) and upbringing (nurture) that enable some individuals to achieve elite athletic prowess. However, this search for answers will not be enabled or accelerated by gauging the research in terms of simplistic phenotypic traits, such as skin colour (Figure 8.5). Put simply, there is no scientific evidence supporting the existence of human races!

Figure 8.5

Satirical view of the arbitrary criteria used to differentiate races and the common misconceptions regarding racial abilities and behaviour.

Summary

1. There are two prevailing hypotheses on human origins: the replacement hypothesis and the multiregional hypothesis. Although some aspects of each hypothesis are similar, they differ on whether African *H. sapiens* replaced other contemporaneous hominins in Europe and Asia. Recent analyses of multiple DNA regions fail to support either hypothesis, suggesting instead that there were multiple expansions of *H. sapiens* out of and into Africa.
2. The global dispersal of humans has resulted in phenotypic plasticity within our species. Various ecogeographic rules associated largely with latitude have been used to explain regional differences in human body size and shape. For example, human skin colour represents adaptations for UVR protection, nutrient protection, or vitamin D synthesis.
3. Despite the pervasive use of human race concepts in media and by governments, evolutionary anthropologists find no support for either human races or subspecific variation in modern humans. Similarly, there is no valid scientific evidence supporting so-called racial abilities.

INTERNET RESOURCES

PBS: NOVA: Neanderthals on Trial
www.pbs.org/wgbh/nova/neanderthals/mtdna.html
Learn about the differences between nuclear DNA and mtDNA, and investigations of mtDNA variations between modern humans and Neanderthals.

Science Daily
www.sciencedaily.com/releases/2006/02/060209184558.htm
Read about Dr. Alan Templeton's work on genetic correlates to human origins.

Reacting to Climate Extremes
http://anthro.palomar.edu/adapt/adapt_2.htm
Learn about human adaptations to life in the Arctic climate.

Website of Dr. Esteban Parra
www.utm.utoronto.ca/~parraest/profile/eparra.htm
Read about the work being conducted by geneticist Dr. Esteban Parra on human variation, including his investigation of genetic correlates to human skin colour.

LITERATURE CITED

Cann, R. L., Stoneking, M., and Wilson, A. C. (1987). Mitochondrial DNA and human evolution. *Nature, 325,* 31–36.

Cartmill, M, (1998). The status of the race concept in physical anthropology. *American Anthropologist, 100,* 651–660.

Chaplin, G. (2004). Geographic distribution of environmental factors influencing human skin coloration. *American Journal of Physical Anthropology, 125,* 292–302.

Duarte, C., Mauricio, J., Pettitt, P., Souto, P., Trinkaus, E., van der Plicht, H., and Zilhao, J. (1999). The early upper Paleolithic human skeleton from the Abrigo do Lagar Velho (Portugal) and modern human emergence in Iberia. *Proceedings of the National Academy of Sciences, USA, 96,* 7604.

Fleagle, J. G. (1999). *Primate Adaptation and Evolution.* San Diego: Academic Press.

George, N. (1999). *Elevating the Game: Black Men and Basketball.* Omaha: University of Nebraska Press.

Jablonski, N., and Chaplin, G. (2000). The evolution of human skin coloration. *Journal of Human Evolution, 39,* 57–106.

Karter, A., Ferrara, A., Liu, J., Moffet, H., Ackerson, L., and Selby, J. (2002). Ethnic disparities in diabetic complications in an insured population. *Journal of the American Medical Association, 287,* 2519–2527.

Kotkin, J. (1993). *Tribes: How Race, Religion, and Identity Determine Success in the New Global Economy*. New York: Random House.

Murray, C., and Herrnstein, R. (1994). *The Bell Curve: Intelligence and Class Structure in American Life*. New York: Free Press.

Parra, E. (2007). Human pigmentation variation: Evolution, genetic basis, and implications for public health. *Yearbook of Physical Anthropology, 50*, 85–105.

Sarich, V., and Miele, F. (2004). *Race: The Reality of Human Differences*. Boulder, CO: Westview Press.

Templeton, A. (1998). Human races: A genetic and evolutionary perspective. *American Anthropologist, 100*, 632–650.

Templeton, A. R. (2005). Haplotype trees and modern human origins. *American Journal of Physical Anthropology, 128*, 33–59.

Templeton, A. R. (2007). Genetics and recent human evolution. *Evolution, 61*, 1507–1519.

U.S. Census Bureau. (2001). Questions and answers for Census 2000 data on race. www.census.gov/Press-Release/www/2001/raceqandas.html (accessed October 15, 2008).

U.S. Census Bureau. (2008). *Projections of the Total Resident Population by 5-Year Age Groups, and Sex with Special Age Categories: Middle Series, 1999 to 2100*. Washington, DC: U.S. Census Bureau.

CHAPTER 9

Applied Anthropology

GOALS

By the end of this chapter you should understand:

1. How primatologists are involved in applied anthropology.
2. Links between medical anthropology and applied anthropology.
3. What forensic anthropology is and how it relates to applied anthropology.

CHAPTER OUTLINE

Primatologists and Applied Anthropology

Medical Anthropologists and Applied Anthropology

Forensic Anthropology: Cool TV Shows, Cooler Science

Introduction

While visiting the lush, beautiful jungles in southeastern Madagascar, I learned about a unique, applied solution to local conservation issues. In the mid-1980s, Dr. Patricia Wright, a noted primatologist, discovered a new lemur species, the golden bamboo lemur, and rediscovered another lemur species, the greater bamboo lemur (Figure 9.1), thought to have gone extinct within a large forest block subject to logging and lemur hunting. These discoveries led, in part, to the creation of Ranomafana National Park, home to hundreds of unique plants and animals. While she was assisting government authorities with determining compensation packages for logging companies that had lost their concessions within the confines of the new park, Dr. Wright asked the director of one of the largest companies what he wanted as compensation. His response was, "I want to be a building contractor." Seeing a rare synergy between logging and conservation, Dr. Wright acquired funding from international donors and support from local people to enable the former logger to build the first natural history museum in the region (Wright, 1992). To this day, the museum staff educates thousands of local, national, and international visitors about the importance of sustainable development and biodiversity conservation in Madagascar.

Figure 9.1

A Greater Bamboo Lemur (*Prolemur simus*) eating giant bamboo in Ranomafana National Park, Madagascar.
© S. M. Lehman

Applied anthropology refers to the application of anthropological knowledge to solve practical problems. In the course of conducting their research, many evolutionary anthropologists have an opportunity to assist with resolving environmental issues for their study animals or social and health problems for local human populations. Moreover, forensic anthropologists employ their expertise in skeletal biology to issues in a legal setting. In the sections below, we discuss specifics of the practical application of anthropological knowledge in primatology, medical anthropology, and forensic anthropology.

Primatologists and Applied Anthropology

Primate-source country ■ A country with naturally occurring primate populations.

Protected area ■ An area that has a protected designation according to legal statute.

In Chapter 4, we discussed how primates are endangered by human activities, particularly habitat disturbance and hunting pressures. In many **primate-source countries**, where primates occur naturally, people living near **protected areas** suffer from extreme poverty (Figure 9.2), necessitating exploitation of nearby forests for food, medicine, and building materials. You've likely seen infomercials requesting money to enable a conservation organization to protect endangered animals. Often implicit in these

Figure 9.2

Impoverished village near a forest edge.
Villagers lack electricity, potable water, medical facilities, and a school. Note the bare brown agricultural field on the steep mountain slope.
© S. M. Lehman

infomercials is the assumption that local people represent the main problem affecting conservation. In other words, there is a common misconception that primates can be protected simply by "kicking" people out of protected areas. However, local people have typically resided in the areas for considerable time periods. Relocating residents represents an intrusive threat to their lifestyles and culture, resulting in resentment among the local people for **conservation biologists** and their study populations (Chatty and Colchester, 2002). Not surprisingly, many anthropological studies reveal that conservation efforts work best when local people are actively involved in decision making and management of nearby protected areas. After all, most primatologists are only visitors to primate-source countries, so they must return home at some point, thereby leaving the local people to determine the fate of resident primate populations. In the following sections, we look at practical solutions to primate conservation issues.

Conservation biology
■ Multidisciplinary, scientific study of biodiversity, with the goal of protecting species.

Applied Anthropology and Habitat Disturbance

Primatologists have successfully applied their knowledge of the forest to issues associated with habitat disturbance, particularly localized logging and agriculture. To promote sustainable use of forest resources, some loggers have shifted from trees critical to primate survival to those not exploited by the animals. If there are no possibilities for sustainable use of local forests, then primatologists have started programs in which local communities set up and maintain small plantations for economically desirable plant species. Recent primatological studies in Indonesia have shown that creating forest corridors between tree plantations and undisturbed forests can actually sustain local primate populations in industrial landscapes (Nasi et al., 2008). Finally, many field primatologists have made the serendipitous discovery that their presence deters forest disturbance within a study area. For a variety of cultural or legal reasons, local people are often reticent to interfere with research activities, although this reluctance can pass over the course of a long-term study.

In Chapter 4, we also discussed that in many primate-source countries, people living in proximity to primate habitats are forced by circumstance, culture, and lack of training to maintain the destructive practice of slash and burn agriculture. Primatologists often team with agricultural scientists to train local people to shift to more sustainable farming methods. For example, some local people growing rice, their main food resource, near Ranomafana National Park in the highland regions of eastern Madagascar have successfully transitioned from using unsustainable slash and burn methods to more sustainable tiered rice fields (Wright, 1997). Although creating these tiered fields is initially very labour intensive, in the long run, doing so results in increased food production and a marked reduction in the conversion of local forests to cropland (Figure 9.3).

Applied Anthropology and Primate Hunting

As we noted in Chapter 4, many primates are subject to hunting pressures from local people. Hunting pressures range along a continuum of intensities (low to high) and utilization (local to international). Primatologists seek to mitigate primate hunting, in part, by striking accords with local hunters, targeting alternative employment for hunters, and by participating in international conservation efforts. Although in the past primatologists sought to prevent all hunting of primates, there is a growing consensus that in some cases local people should be assisted in determining what levels of legal hunting can be sustained in circumscribed areas. By doing so, researchers hope to gain some level of protection for primates and their forests from the disastrous effects of large-scale logging, mining, and oil projects. For example,

Figure 9.3

Two forms of rice agriculture.

On the left, tiered rice fields; on the right, slash and burn plots.

© S. M. Lehman

Yasuni National Park is located in the Amazon rainforest of eastern Ecuador, which also overlies some of the richest oil-bearing strata in South America. The park was instituted with the critical support of the local Huaorani people, who until just 50 years ago were unknown to the outside world. In order to achieve preservation of both local biodiversity and Huaorani culture, a private reserve was established beside the new national park. Within this reserve, the Huaorani people practise their traditional lifestyle, including primate hunting (Franzen, 2006). In turn, hunters agree not to target habituated primates in the adjacent national park. The accord between the researchers and local people has been, for the most part, successful in protecting local primates and indigenous culture. Another simple but highly effective method for reducing hunting pressures is for researchers to hire local hunters. With their knowledge of the forest and local animals, hunters typically make excellent research assistants (Figure 9.4). An interesting aspect of this method is that very few of these research assistants return to hunting.

As well, primatologists participate in national and international efforts to curtail unsustainable hunting of primates, particularly those taken as part of the bushmeat trade. Bushmeat is typically sold to employees of large, international logging and mining companies. Some of the meat even finds its way into ethnic restaurants in large European and North American cities. The international scope of this biodiversity crisis necessitates the involvement of primatologists in everything from education programs for local hunters to lobbying governments and working with large, multinational companies for improved protection of animals in protected areas and near logging camps. Thus, some famous primatologists, such as Dr. Jane Goodall, travel the world giving talks about primate conservation and development projects.

Applied Anthropology and Primate Ecotourism

Starting in the 1980s, primatologists took advantage of the upsurge of interest in **ecotourism** by providing tourists with paid access to habituated groups of charismatic primate species (Fennell, 1999). For example, it's possible for tourists to get within metres of the famous and awe-inspiring mountain gorillas in central Africa. In turn, local people derive financial benefits by leading tour groups, working with tour operators, and selling items to the tourists. Moreover, less charismatic species gain

Ecotourism ■ A form of low-impact, culturally sensitive tourism that can generate income for local people.

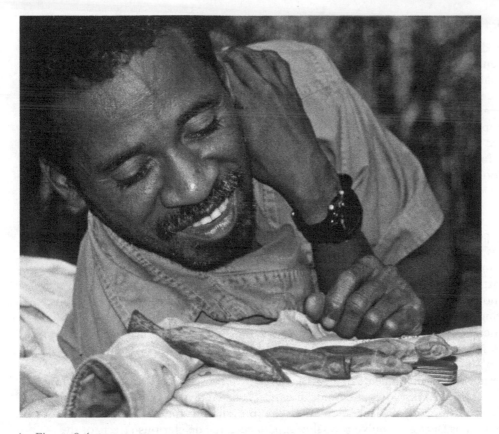

Figure 9.4

Emile Rajeriarson of Madagascar.

He is a former logger and sometime lemur hunter who now works as a specialized naturalist.
He's seen here with some of his animal carvings, which he sells to ecotourists and researchers.

© S. M. Lehman

conservation benefits due to their coexistence with tourist-friendly primates. Put differently, primates become more valuable to local people as a long-term revenue source than they do as a one-time food source. Seems like a win-win situation for biodiversity and people. Well, not quite. Even well-habituated primates sometimes exhibit signs of stress, such as fleeing and screaming, when large and often loud groups of tourists tramp through their home range (Cowlishaw and Dunbar, 2000). Stress levels can be particularly pronounced when tourists feed primates, thereby causing conflict between individuals within a group for access to the food. Ecotourism is also an unreliable conservation measure because many charismatic primates are endemic to areas experiencing armed conflicts and political instability. In some cases, these armed conflicts have led to the complete cessation of tourism and research at research sites. Finally, there is a growing concern among primatologists that disease transmission may occur between well-intentioned ecotourists and the primates they come to see (Wallis and Rick Lee, 1999). Despite these concerns, many researchers feel that the benefits to local economies and conservation outweigh the presumably short-term stress experienced by the primates. The question arises as to whether the short-term benefits of ecotourism extend to primates in the long run. We need people, like you, to study this question!

Medical Anthropologists and Applied Anthropology

As we discussed in Chapter 1, medical anthropologists investigate, in part, how environmental and biological factors influence human health at the community, regional, national, and global levels. Researchers in this field come from a variety of scientific disciplines, ranging from medical doctors and evolutionary anthropologists investigating diseases to researchers looking at links between nutrition and health. Medical anthropology serves to unite these seemingly different scientific enterprises by seeking applied solutions to disease and health in humans. Next, we review the biological and evolutionary reasons for health issues in humans, and look at the effects of too little and too much food on human health.

Applied Anthropology, Biological Evolution, and Disease

Many people take for granted the serious health consequences of even minor ailments, such as an infected blister. Before the advent of antibiotics, a simple foot blister could result in fatal septicemia (blood poisoning). The potentially fatal consequences of illness are particularly relevant to humans exposed to new, **infectious diseases** for which they have no immunity. These diseases have decimated some modern human populations, resulting in the deaths of millions of people. As we evolve and adapt, so, too, do the microscopic creatures that make us ill, necessitating a review of **co-evolution**. Human diseases encompass more than just those we are exposed to in various environments. Medical anthropologists are at the forefront of research investigating how human biology results in certain ailments that can have negative consequences for our evolutionary fitness. Thus, we must look at **chronic disease**. Then, we review an interesting evolutionary viewpoint on why we lack adaptations that prevent infectious and chronic diseases.

INFECTIOUS DISEASE   You've probably experienced the deleterious effects of the flu: fever, aching muscles, lethargy, headache, and nausea. People afflicted with this seemingly annual ailment sometimes mutter, "We can put people on the moon, so how come we can't cure the common flu?" Indeed, why not? Because putting someone on the moon is a matter of engineering and lots of money. The common flu represents symptoms associated with an infection by a highly contagious RNA **virus** that is itself the result of millions of years of natural selection, mutation, and biological evolution. Some RNA viruses are incredibly lethal. From 1918 to 1920, an estimated 40 to 100 million people throughout the world died from the Spanish flu and associated bacterial infections (Figure 9.5). Only people in isolated, quarantined areas avoided exposure and illness. In fact, there are many infectious diseases that cause illness and even death in tens of millions of people each year, including air-borne viruses such as tuberculosis and blood-borne parasites such as malaria and West Nile virus. Medical anthropologists from the World Health Organization estimate that each year approximately 14 to 15 million people across the planet die because of infectious diseases. Moreover, infectious diseases are the leading cause of death in developing countries. For example, in 2002 infectious diseases caused a death rate of 1152 per 100 000 people in Liberia. During the same year, infectious diseases were responsible for relatively fewer deaths in Canada (10 per 100 000) and the U.S. (22 per 100 000).

However, some people do not become ill after exposure to infectious parasites and viruses. Even in its most virulent form, the Spanish flu infected about 50 percent of the people exposed to the virus. Put differently, many people knowingly or unknowingly exposed to the virus did not become infected or ill. Why? Medical anthropologists hold that some people were exposed to a low **pathogenic** strain of the virus. But what about people exposed to high pathogenic strains, such as medical staff in hospitals? Although the biological answer to this question is complex, the evolutionary perspective is rather

Infectious disease ▪ Illness that can be transmitted from person to person or from organism to organism, and that is caused by a microbial agent.

Co-evolution ▪ Evolution of two or more ecologically interacting species, each of which evolves in response to selection pressures imposed by the other.

Chronic disease ▪ A disease that is more or less permanent, leaves residual disability, and is caused by a non-reversible pathology.

Virus ▪ A microscopic, infectious organism composed of RNA or DNA that relies on the genetic machinery of living cells to grow and reproduce.

Pathogenic ▪ Causing disease or capable of doing so.

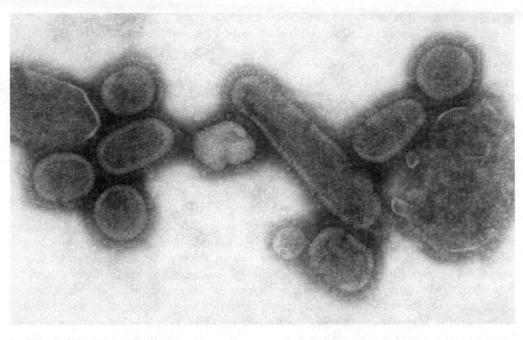

Figure 9.5

Micrograph showing re-created 1918 influenza collected from an infected dog's kidney.
Image courtesy of Cynthia Goldsmith, CDC USA.

straightforward: increased genetic variability provides a greater chance for natural resistance. The same process of bacterial resistance to antibiotics we discussed in Chapter 2 holds here for human immune system resistance to infectious diseases. Medical anthropologists have determined that small, inbred populations are typically characterized by genetic homogeneity, which can result in catastrophic loss of life when exposed to a new infectious disease. Consequently, history is replete with tragic examples of the death of entire human populations and cultures after their exposure to diseases introduced by explorers.

Although vaccination programs and antiviral drug treatments have mitigated the effects of some infectious diseases, two types of mutations to viruses over time result in the biological evolution of infectious diseases that are resistant to medical intervention: **antigenic drift,** in which small changes to a virus gradually accumulate, and **antigenic shift,** in which major changes occur rapidly. For example, many parts of the world are experiencing the resurgence of particularly virulent forms of tuberculosis, smallpox, and yellow fever. These relatively rapid antigenic shifts outpace the development of medical interventions, which explains, in part, why doctors can't cure the common cold or virus. In other words, the micro-organisms that cause infectious diseases can, in some cases, evolve faster than human defences, resulting in a perpetual pathogen–prey war. Many parasitic infectious diseases, such as malaria, have so far defied scientists' attempts to develop perfectly effective preventative treatments. In the modern world, we are experiencing increased gene flow between regions and high population densities in urban environments, both of which increase the chances of a potentially catastrophic **pandemic.** Thus, the question arises as to why humans have not evolved adaptations that overcome infectious diseases.

Antigenic drift ■ Minor changes in a virus due to gradual accumulation of mutations over time.

Antigenic shift ■ Rapid, major changes in a virus due to mutations.

Pandemic ■ Spread of an infectious disease throughout a country, continent, or the world.

CO-EVOLUTION OF HUMANS AND OUR PATHOGENS   The natural world is a marvellous, complex web of species interacting with each other. Interactions can range from each species negatively influencing each other to neither being affected by the interaction to each species benefiting from the interaction. In turn, a species can experience and exert selective pressures on other species. Things can change with the addition of multiple pathogens infecting a host, and not necessarily in a bad way. Depending on the circumstances, it can actually be beneficial to be infected by multiple pathogens rather than just one pathogen! Why? Because relatively benign pathogens out-compete more virulent forms for resources.

Of the many co-evolutionary processes known to exist, medical anthropologists tend to focus on two that relate directly to humans and our pathogens: specific co-evolution and co-speciation. First, specific or "arms race" co-evolution occurs when each change in one species results in a counter-change in another. For example, as the human immune system adapts to an infectious pathogen, the micro-organism sometimes evolves new ways of maintaining its relationship with us. This co-evolutionary "arms race" can occur in two ways: progressive or escalatory. If pathogens experience progressive co-evolution, then later pathogens will achieve higher infection rates than those measured in earlier forms. Conversely, escalatory co-evolution occurs when later pathogens are no better than their ancestors at infecting hosts because the hosts evolved adaptations to deal with the new pathogenic strategy. The catch here is that if pathogens that underwent changes in escalatory co-evolution are let loose on a distant, isolated population, then these "super" pathogens can decimate the new hosts. This scenario has occurred in the past when human populations from 16th-century Europe, which experienced waves of pathogenic "arms races," visited native populations in other regions of the world. In some pandemics, native populations declined by 90 percent after exposure to European pathogens.

The second co-evolutionary process, co-speciation, occurs when the biological evolution of new species in one lineage causes or correlates with the formation of new species in another lineage. Evidence for co-speciation can be found in congruent phylogenies for the pathogen and host species. For example, certain parasites specialize in one primate species, such that any changes in the host species result in rapid changes to the parasite species. Scientists studying the genetics of primate lice recently made the rather uncomfortable discovery that gorillas gave pubic lice (*Pthirus pubis*) to early hominins about 3 or 4 million years ago (MYA) (Figure 9.6)! Transfer of pubic lice occurs primarily by sexual contact between conspecific hosts. Although it's not possible to rule out some kinky hominin–gorilla sex, a more plausible scenario involves lice transferring from a gorilla carcass to hunters or scavengers. It's just amazing how genetics can be applied to a variety of evolutionary questions.

We now turn to evolutionary approaches to diseases that are related more to biology than to infectious pathogens.

CHRONIC DISEASE   Chronic diseases include cardiovascular diseases, cancer, and respiratory illnesses. Cardiovascular illness and cancer are the primary causes of death in developed nations. In 2002, the death rate due to cardiovascular diseases was 245 deaths per 100 000 in Canada and 317 deaths per 100 000 in the U.S. During the same year, cardiovascular diseases were responsible for almost half as many deaths in Liberia (138 per 100 000). The proximal reasons for this disparity in death rates between people in developed and developing countries relates, in part, to a complex pattern of longevity, lifestyle, health care, and economic power. For example, people live longer in developed countries than in developing countries, which results in more "wear and tear" on the body. The human body contains numerous biological systems, each of which eventually wears down, particularly the cardiovascular system. After

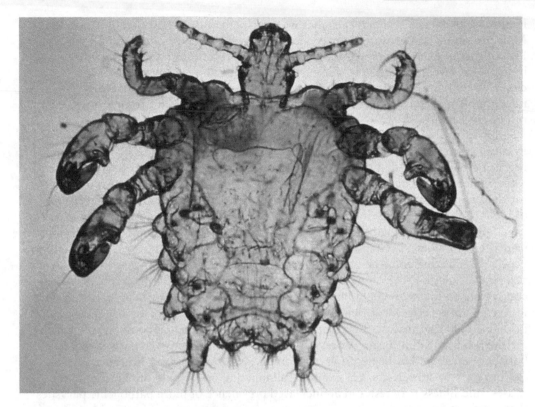

Figure 9.6
Phthirus pubis.
The pubic louse infests the pubic hair and eyelashes of its host.
Image courtesy of Cynthia Goldsmith, CDC USA.

all, the human heart beats an estimated 3 billion times over the course of a 72-year lifespan! But why hasn't biological evolution produced better organs that don't wear out over time and become prone to chronic diseases? The ultimate cause of chronic diseases seems to represent an evolutionary conundrum because they often affect individuals in their post-reproductive years. Human evolutionary fitness is closely linked to our reproductive output rather than just our longevity. However, post-reproductive individuals can provide enormous fitness benefits to their descendants through financial aid, housing, wisdom, and child care. The evolutionary consequences of what appears to be an inability of humans to deal with chronic disease are issues rarely considered by doctors practising modern medicine.

DARWINIAN MEDICINE   In a fascinating evolutionary perspective, researchers argue that disease treatment should include Darwinian or evolutionary medicine (Nesse and Williams, 1999). Darwinian medicine follows standard evolution principles, in that all organisms have experienced biological evolution by natural selection. Put simply, Darwinian medicine is a two-step process seeking evolutionary answers to the following question: Why are we vulnerable to diseases and how has natural selection produced **maladaptations**? Put differently, Darwinian medicine holds that the evolutionary processes that produce an adaptation inevitably result in a maladaptation. For example, humans have adaptations of our upper and lower limbs for specialized,

Maladaptation ■ An adaptation that is no longer beneficial to an organism.

habitual bipedalism, which means that we are maladapted for arboreal locomotion. Maladaptations also exist as defence mechanisms within our bodies and organs. Proponents of Darwinian medicine use biological evolution to understand why humans get fevers so high they cause seizures. In this sense, a fever is seen as a defensive adaptation of the body because heightened temperatures can ward off infection. Conversely, a fever is also a maladaptation because in extreme cases it can cause seizures.

But what about cardiovascular disease? Given the power of biological evolution by natural selection to produce something as powerful and complex as the mammalian heart, it seems logical that it would also produce an organ free from deadly chronic disease. Nope! Biological evolution is not about producing perfect organisms, or organs for that matter. Darwinian medicine holds that we are vulnerable to disease because of biological design compromises associated with biological evolution by natural selection. For example, biological evolution by natural selection results in limitations and tradeoffs in biological systems, such as the mammalian cardiovascular system. Suppose genetic engineering could be used to reduce chronic heart disease by altering the structure of the human heart. Sounds good, right? The problem is that basic physiological constraints on the heart could be violated by the change, resulting in a heart that no longer operates properly or that is prone to other diseases. Proponents of Darwinian medicine hold that diseases have both genetic and environmental components, which are the result of evolutionary processes. In other words, effective treatment requires both proximate and ultimate viewpoints on illness. Otherwise, medical intervention can have severe side effects. For example, eliminating one species of parasite that causes mild illness may result in an increased prevalence of more pathogenic parasites that were out-competed by the less virulent parasite at the microecological level. Despite the importance of an evolutionary perspective on human health and adaptation, most medical schools and students have been reluctant to apply Darwinian medicine (MacCallum, 2007). Perhaps you'll establish a new medical school dedicated to training physicians in Darwinian medicine!

Applied Anthropology, Nutrition, and Health

An individual's health is more than the result of evolutionary processes or environmental factors. Nutrition also relates directly to a person's well-being. Thus, medical anthropologists operating within a biological framework are active in determining the effects of nutrition on health. Unfortunately, it is estimated that approximately 16 percent of the people in the world are undernourished, with the greatest numbers residing in sub-Saharan Africa and southeast Asia (Figure 9.7). Moreover, there is a growing movement within the field of medical anthropology to reduce the disparities between nutritional recommendations for young children and actual child-rearing systems in industrialized and developing nations. Given that proper nutrition is essential to the health and development of young children, the question arises then as to why there are so many malnourished children. Conversely, why is childhood **obesity** on the rise in the industrialized world? Although medical anthropologists conduct their research and seek applied solutions to health issues at various geographic levels, we explore these questions next in terms of the "big picture," or at a global level.

MALNUTRITION Malnutrition results from inadequate ingestion of food or poor eating habits. Medical anthropologists have identified two major forms of malnutrition: **protein malnutrition** (not enough proteins in the diet) and **micronutrient malnutrition** (not enough essential vitamins and amino acids in the diet). Protein malnutrition is one of the leading causes of death in children in developing nations. If protein requirements

Obesity ■ Condition characterized by excessive weight or adipose tissue.

Protein malnutrition ■ Insufficient intake of nitrogen-containing food (protein).

Micronutrient malnutrition ■ Insufficient intake of essential vitamins and amino acids.

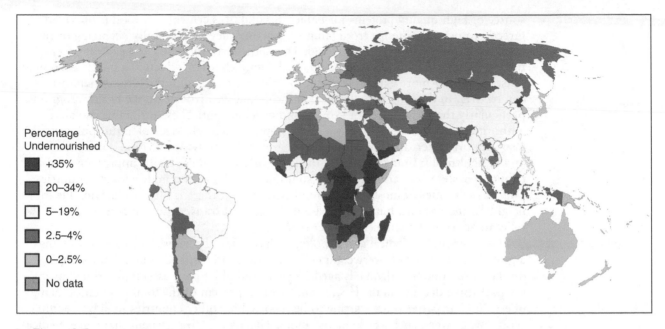

Figure 9.7
World map showing the proportion of undernourished people by country.
Note the variability in Africa.
Data from the United Nations World Food Programme.

are not met, then muscle tissue begins to waste away, resulting in serious health issues and eventually death. The predominant sources of dietary protein come from animal flesh (e.g., beef, pigs, chicken), eggs, cereal grains, legumes, and dairy products (milk, cheese). Furthermore, some food resources provide higher-quality protein than others, in the sense that a greater proportion of the available protein can be taken up during digestion. For example, egg protein is more readily absorbed than plant protein. Protein availability is often negatively influenced by wars, famine, and overpopulation. Even when protein sources are available, poor people, who often make up the bulk of the population in developing countries, lack the financial means to purchase meat and dairy products. This issue is exasperated by the presence of local cattle cultures, which emphasize animals as signs of power and wealth rather than food resources. Lack of refrigeration precludes the safe storage of milk and other dairy products.

Micronutrient malnutrition is more difficult to assess given that such minute quantities are needed to maintain health. Nonetheless, each person requires nine essential amino acids, various vitamins, iron, iodine, and many other dietary minerals, all of which come from food resources. The consequence of micronutrient malnutrition on human populations is potentially more devastating than even protein malnutrition. People living with inadequate access to essential macronutrients rarely die quickly. Instead, they suffer from reduced cognitive abilities, poor disease resistance, and a host of other debilitating health issues.

So, what can be done to eliminate malnutrition? Medical anthropologists have identified three applied solutions to the issue of malnutrition in developing countries. First, one of the best and easiest applied solutions to infant protein malnutrition is to ensure that breastfeeding is maintained to the exclusion of dietary supplements for as long as possible (Sellen, 1998). Why? Because human breast milk represents the best source of high-quality proteins for babies. Second, it is critical that food is provided directly to people suffering from famines, whether they are naturally occurring or the result of human activities, such as war. This short-term solution can head off potentially long-term health issues in infants and young children, which in a purely economic sense can be far more expensive than providing nutrients until the local agriculture can recover. In the long term, medical anthropologists advocate public health programs, particularly those that monitor growth and development. These programs can alert authorities to pending health crises at the population level. Medical anthropologists also support the creation of education programs that provide nutritional information and agricultural training specific to the local environments. Finally, improving food distribution systems is a critical applied solution to malnutrition in developing countries. One of the ironies of most regional food crises is that there is often food available in neighbouring nations, but there are limited means of transporting emergency food relief to areas hit by famines or other disasters.

OBESITY CRISIS   Medical anthropologists have played a significant role in studying a global health crisis of overweight children, young adults, and adults. For example, obesity rates among individuals aged 15 years and older have essentially tripled over the past three decades in the U.S., resulting in 32 percent of the total population being obese. Similar patterns are starting to be reported for other countries with burgeoning economic powers, such as China and India. This issue is so prevalent that some medical anthropologists estimate that at present the number of overweight people actually exceeds the number of underweight people in the world. Obese children often experience health issues, such as joint degeneration, and are more likely to become overweight adults. Obese adults often have serious health issues, including **diabetes**, heart disease, and liver disease. Consequently, obese adults often have significantly shorter lifespans than people closer to their ideal body weight.

So, what's causing this health crisis? As with many global issues, the obesity crisis reflects, in part, complex and regionally varying patterns of socioeconomics, changes in physical activity levels, and food marketing. In a nutshell, this crisis is not a result of too little food, but rather too much of the wrong kinds of food. Research shows that people in lower socioeconomic households tend to consume more calories and fat than people in higher socioeconomic households. Moreover, there has been a global shift in food selection and dietary choices. For example, take a look at the food that you and your fellow students consume while at school. On many campuses, students are enticed by billboards and other media to eat lots of hot dogs, hamburgers, pizza, and french fries. Many students eschew fruits and vegetables for days at a time. Thus, there is a pattern of people being stimulated by mass media to fill up on what are essentially empty calories, lacking in required amino acids and protein. There is also a growing consensus among medical anthropologists that a progressive increase in sedentary lifestyles combined with a decline in overall physical activity play a significant role in the obesity pandemic. Put differently, people in many populations are not as active now as they were even 10 years ago.

So, what are medical anthropologists doing to alleviate this global health crisis? Because of the immense scale of the problem, applied solutions are most likely to achieve success when managed within a framework of international institutions and agreements. For example, medical anthropologists are working within the World Health Organization to develop national and international policies to provide people with healthy foods and to promote the benefits of physical activity. Furthermore, medical anthropologists work with governments and global food marketers to ensure that food companies do not target vulnerable societies for consumption of high-profit but low-quality foods. For example, many medical anthropologists advocate cessation of

Diabetes ▪ Serious health disorder associated with elevated blood glucose (sugar) levels.

all commercial advertising that promotes children consuming high-fat and high-sugar treats instead of healthy foods, such as local fruits and vegetables. These broad solutions to a global health crisis represent only a small fraction of the fascinating work conducted by medical anthropologists. In fact, medical anthropology is one of the fastest-growing fields of research in anthropology.

We turn now to forensic anthropology, which is perhaps the most popular aspect of anthropology thanks to a host of popular television shows, books, and movies.

Forensic Anthropology: Cool TV Shows, Cooler Science

Forensic anthropology represents the most applied field within biological and evolutionary anthropology. Although forensic science involves everything from genetics to toxicology, forensic anthropology focuses on the skeletal remains of deceased humans (Figure 9.8). Forensic anthropologists employ their osteological expertise to assist law enforcement and the court system in understanding various aspects of the skeletal remains at crime scenes. Forensic anthropologists involved in academia also conduct research on refining skeletal analysis and assessments. Although in the past most forensic anthropologists worked only on a single skeleton at a crime scene, some forensic anthropologists are now participating in large-scale excavations of multiple human remains as part of international investigations of alleged genocides. In the sections below, we review some of the basic methods used by forensic anthropologists to determine age, sex, and trauma in skeletal remains.

Forensic anthropology ■ The application of the study of the human skeleton (osteology) in a legal setting.

Determining Age from Skeletal Remains

Forensic anthropologists study the relative aspects of bone size and **ossification** (the process of bone formation) to estimate the approximate age of a deceased individual (Byers, 2007). The resulting age estimate typically falls into one of the following seven age groups, ranging from youngest to oldest: **perinatal**, **neonatal**, infants and young children, older children, adolescents, young adults, and older adults. In perinatals, age can be determined by observing the overall bone size and composition, which tends to be small and composed of varying proportions of **cartilage** and bone. Although it is difficult to distinguish perinatals from neonatals, neonatals do exhibit a slightly greater degree of bone ossification, particularly in older babies. Infants and young children as well as those in late childhood are characterized by a relatively greater degree of bone ossification in the long bones of the legs and arms. Adolescents exhibit an increased lengthening of the long bones, such as the femur. Starting with this age group, forensic anthropologists can apply more precise methods to estimate age. How do they do this? By noting the degree of fusion of the end of a bone (epiphysis) to a shaft (diaphysis). Through exhaustive study of thousands of individuals, forensic anthropologists have determined the rate and timing of bone fusion. They then compare the relative amount of bone fusion in the deceased individual to a table of values, thereby determining the approximate age of the deceased. This method works well with adolescents and young adults, but not so well with older adults. In fact, older adults are difficult to assess for age because all their bones have ossified. It is only when bones begin to deteriorate due to advanced age that it becomes possible to arrive at a more specific age estimate for adults. Finally, it's important for you to note that these age estimates can be affected by a variety of external factors,

Ossification ■ Process of bone formation, in which connective tissue (e.g., cartilage) is converted to bone or bone-like tissue.

Perinatal ■ Period of time before, during, and immediately after birth.

Neonatal ■ Period of time from birth to 4–6 weeks of age.

Cartilage ■ Dense connective tissue, which is mostly converted to bone in adults.

Figure 9.8
Contrary to what is portrayed in popular television shows, forensic anthropologists work only on human remains, and these specialized anthropologists do not determine cause of death.

such as nutrition and lifestyle, which alter the pattern and timing of bone growth and deterioration.

Determining Sex from Skeletal Remains

Forensic anthropologists use sexual dimorphism in the human skeleton to determine sex (male or female) in deceased adolescents or adults. Sex is more difficult to determine in younger skeletons due to a lack of sexual dimorphism in these individuals. Compared to females, males tend to have larger bones with larger muscle attachments. The pelvic bones provide some of the best evidence for determining sex in the deceased (Figure 9.9). Why? Because only females give birth, requiring morphological changes to allow the passage of a large-headed baby through the birth canal (pelvic inlet). For example, females have a wider subpubic angle and larger pelvic inlet than males (Klepinger, 2006). Although there are other useful skeletal features, and other things to look for, the above represent some of the most common methods used by forensic anthropologists to determine the sex of a skeleton.

Determining Trauma from Skeletal Remains

Forensic anthropologists also assess the type, origin, and timing of any **skeletal trauma**. Trauma types include, but are not limited to, lesions or bone defects. Lesions typically result from a pathogen that has altered the natural shape or condition of the bone. Some diseases, such as advanced tuberculosis, result in the deformation of the outer surface of bone, resulting in a "Swiss cheese" look. Bone defects represent changes in bone shape or structure due to physical trauma of some kind. When referring to the timing of skeletal trauma, forensic anthropologists use three mutually exclusive categories: premortem (before death), perimortem (at time of death), and postmortem (after death). Premortem lesions and defects can provide vital clues regarding the health of the deceased, which can then be compared to health records to assist in individual identification. For example, many people have had bone breaks,

Skeletal trauma An injury, such as a wound, to skeletal tissue resulting from an agent, force, or mechanism.

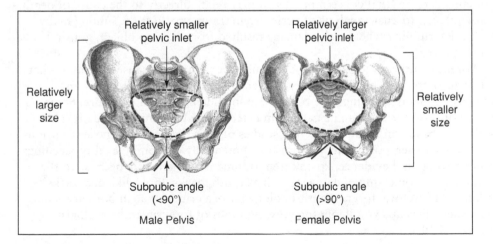

Figure 9.9

Three morphological differences of the pelvis between adult males and females.

Figure 9.10

Two students participating in a forensic anthropology field school conducted by Dr. Tracy Rogers from the University of Toronto-Mississauga.
© T. Rogers

which can still be seen faintly in X-rays of their skeletal remains. Perimortem trauma is of considerable legal concern because it may relate directly to the cause of death. Consequently, forensic analysis of perimortem trauma focuses on, among many things, determining whether the damage resulted from a sharp object, gunshot, or blunt force.

Forensic anthropologists don't determine the manner or cause of death—that task is accomplished by a medical examiner or coroner. Postmortem trauma typically results from things like reburial, animal damage, and exposure. Some aspects of postmortem trauma can aid in determining the timing of death. This estimate is based on detailed, forensic studies of how bodies decompose in various settings. However, postmortem trauma can potentially confound legal proceedings by destroying vital evidence. Postmortem trauma is also an issue because to the untrained eye some animal damage, such as tooth marks, looks like cut marks on bones. Therefore, forensic anthropology plays a critical role in both academics and society. Perhaps you'll join the growing ranks of forensic anthropologists (Figure 9.10)!

Summary

1. Primatologists employ a variety of applied solutions to the deleterious effects of habitat disturbance and primate hunting. Ecotourism represents one of the best-known applied solutions to conserving charismatic primates and other species within a protected area.

2. Medical anthropologists are at the forefront of local, regional, and international applied solutions to infectious diseases, chronic diseases, and health issues. In addition to the standard biological aspects of disease intervention, medical anthropologists also investigate evolutionary causes of disease via Darwinian medicine. Medical anthropologists are working closely with international relief agencies to alleviate health issues associated with both malnutrition and obesity.

3. Forensic anthropology is cool! This field is the most applied aspect of biological and evolutionary anthropology, with a focus on the application of osteology in a legal setting. Forensic anthropologists examine skeletal remains to determine, in part, the age, sex, and any skeletal trauma of a deceased individual.

INTERNET RESOURCES

International Ecotourism Society
www.ecotourism.org
Learn about various aspects of ecotourism.

YouTube
http://youtube.com/watch?v=Bz8NQdgj-iY
See a YouTube video "Me and a gorilla" on just how close some ecotourists get to the rare, majestic mountain gorillas in Rwanda.

Evolution and Medicine Network
http://evolutionandmedicine.org
Learn about the role of Darwinian medicine in modern Western medical sciences.

Society for Medical Anthropology
www.medanthro.net
Learn about the academic and applied work being conducted by medical anthropologists.

World Health Organization: Nutrition Programme
www.who.int/nutrition/en
Read about efforts being made to combat global issues of malnutrition and obesity.

World Obesity Federation
http://www.worldobesity.org/
The WOF is working to lead and drive global efforts to reduce, prevent and treat obesity.

American Board of Forensic Anthropology
http://www.theabfa.org/
Learn about special programs and career opportunities in forensic anthropology.

LITERATURE CITED

Byers, S. (2007). *Introduction to Forensic Anthropology: A Textbook*. Boston: Allyn and Bacon.

Chatty, D., and Colchester, M., eds. (2002). *Conservation and Mobile Indigenous Peoples: Displacement, Forced Settlement, and Sustainable Development*. Oxford/New York: Berghahn Books.

Cowlishaw, G., and Dunbar, R. (2000). *Primate Conservation Biology*. Chicago: University of Chicago Press.

Fennell, D. (1999). *Ecotourism: An Introduction*. New York: Routledge.

Franzen, M. (2006). Evaluating the sustainability of hunting: A comparison of harvest profiles across three Huaorani communities. *Environmental Conservation, 33,* 36–45.

Klepinger, L. (2006). *Fundamentals of Forensic Anthropology*. New York: John Wiley & Sons.

MacCallum, C. J. (2007). Does medicine without evolution make sense? *PLoS Biology, 5,* e112.

Nasi, R., Koponen, P., Poulsen, J., Buitenzorgy, M., and Rusmantoro, W. (2008). Impact of landscape and corridor design on primates in a large-scale industrial tropical plantation landscape. *Biodiversity and Conservation, 17,* 1105–1126.

Nesse, R., and Williams, G. (1999). What is Darwinian medicine? *Life Science Research, 3,* 1–17.

Sellen, D. (1998). Infant and young child feeding practices among African pastoralists: The Datoga of Tanzania. *Journal of Biosocial Science, 30,* 481–499.

Wallis, J., and Rick Lee, D. (1999). Primate conservation: The prevention of disease transmission. *International Journal of Primatology, 20,* 803–826.

Wright, P. C. (1992). Primate ecology, rainforest conservation, and economic development: Building a national park in Madagascar. *Evolutionary Anthropology, 1,* 25–33.

Wright, P. C. (1997). The future of biodiversity in Madagascar: A view from Ranomafana National Park. *Natural Change and Human Impact in Madagascar* (ed. by S. M. Goodman and B. D. Patterson), pp. 381–405. Washington, D.C.: Smithsonian Institution Press.

Absolute   A complete measure without restriction or qualification.   *120*

Acclimatization   The short-term process of an organism adjusting to chronic change in its environment (i.e., within one organism's lifetime).   *37*

Adaptation   An organismal character that performs a function that is of utility to the organisms possessing it and that evolved by natural selection for that particular function.   *58*

Adducted   Toward the midline of the body.   *122*

Agnostic   A person holding the belief that God is unknown and unknowable.   *15*

Allele   One of several forms of the same gene.   *17*

Allergen   A substance that causes an allergic reaction.   *66*

Allopatric speciation   Species formation that occurs following the geographic isolation of populations.   *48*

Amino acid   One of a class of 20 molecules that are combined to form proteins in living things.   *26*

Anthropology   The global and holistic study of human culture and biology.   *2*

Anticodon   A complementary three-nucleotide site on the tRNA that recognizes and binds to a specific codon on the mRNA during protein synthesis.   *27*

Antigenic drift   Minor changes in a virus due to gradual accumulation of mutations over time.   *177*

Antigenic shift   Rapid, major changes in a virus due to mutations.   *177*

Autosome   Chromosome(s) not involved in determining an organism's sex.   *24*

Average   The middle or most common value in a set of data.   *35*

Bifacial tool   A tool worked on two sides.   *149*

Binomial nomenclature   The scientific method for assigning names to species and genera.   *7*

Biogeography   The scientific study of the geographic distribution of organisms.   *7*

Biological evolution   Change in allele frequencies within a population, or a change in the genetic makeup of a population of organisms over time, or the process by which all forms of plant and animal life change slowly over time because of slight variations in genes that one generation passes down to the next.   *58*

Biostratigraphy   The study of fossilized animals in vertical sequences of rock layers.   *125*

Bipedal locomotion   Moving upright using two legs.   *35*

Bipedalism   Habitual upright locomotion on two feet.   *120*

Botanist   A scientist who studies plants.   *7*

Botany   The scientific study of plants.   *11*

Bottom-up processes   Interactions between organisms involving physical or chemical factors such as temperature or nutrient availability.   *79*

Brachiation   Travel involving two-armed swinging from branch to branch.   *73*

Breccia   A coarse-grained rock composed of angular fragments of pre-existing rocks.   *125*

Bunodont molars   Teeth possessing four major cusps arranged in a rectangle.   *71*

Burin   A chisel-like stone tool for engraving.   *152*

Callitrichidae   Primate family comprising marmosets, tamarins, and Goeldi's monkeys.   *70*

Canines   Teeth between the incisors and premolars.   *93*

Canopy   System of horizontal branches and foliage formed by tree crowns (i.e., the leafy parts).   *79*

Cartilage   Dense connective tissue, which is mostly converted to bone in adults.   *183*

Catarrhini   Infraorder comprising Old World monkeys, apes, and humans.   *67*

Catastrophism   The idea that catastrophic events altered geological features and caused the extinction of plants and animals.   *9*

Cathemeral   Varying active cycles from nocturnal to diurnal depending on food availability.   *65*

Cercopithecidae   Primate family comprising Old World monkeys.   *71*

Cercopithecinae Primate subfamily comprising various Old World monkeys. *71*

Character state Alternative expressions of a character. For example, each character is described in terms of its states, such as "hair present" or "hair absent," where "hair" is the character, and "present" and "absent" are its states. *46*

Chopper A tool made by flaking the edge of a round or spherical stone on one side. The resulting tool is best suited for powerful "chopping" activities, such as breaking animal bones or cutting up vegetation. *149*

Chromosome Double-stranded DNA molecule in nucleus of eukaryotic cells that carries genes and functions in the transmission of hereditary information. *23*

Chronic disease A disease that is more or less permanent, leaves residual disability, and is caused by a non-reversible pathology. *176*

Clade A group of organisms that contains an ancestral taxon and all of its descendants. *51*

Cladistics A system of biological taxonomy based on the quantitative analysis of comparative data that is used to reconstruct the (assumed) phylogenetic relationships and evolutionary history of groups of organisms. *46*

Cladogram A branching diagram used to illustrate phylogenetic relationships. *49*

Classify The scientific method of placing an organism in a system based on order by classes or categories. *7*

Co-evolution Evolution of two or more ecologically interacting species, each of which evolves in response to selection pressures imposed by the other. *176*

Codon Genetic information encoded in a sequence of three nucleotides. *27*

Colobinae Primate subfamily comprising various Old World leaf-eating monkeys. *71*

Common theory An idea based only on conjecture or personal opinion. *6*

Comparative anatomy The study of anatomical features of animals of different species. *8*

Complex stomach Amazing adaptation to allow bacterial fermentation of leaves. *72*

Conservation biology Multidisciplinary, scientific study of biodiversity, with the goal of protecting species. *173*

Conspecifics Members of the same species. *45*

Continuous variation Phenotypic variation that falls along a continuum rather than in discrete units or categories (e.g., body mass in modern humans). *31*

Core The raw stone from which flakes will be removed and which can be modified and used as a tool itself. *149*

Core area Most frequently used part of the home range. *80*

Correlation A statistical relationship between two variables such that high values on one factor tend to go with high values on the other factor. *96*

Cranial skeleton Bones of the head. *94*

Creationism The largely Christian belief that all life was created by a supernatural deity (typically God), the existence of which is presupposed. *13*

Critically endangered Extremely high risk of extinction in the wild. *88*

Crown The part of the tooth that is visible above the gum. *93*

Cusp Pointed or rounded part of the biting surface of a tooth. *93*

Cytoplasm Internal fluid (called cytosol), dissolved materials, and cellular organelles in a cell, except for the nucleus. The cytoplasm is the primary site for chemical activity in the cell. *27*

Daily path length Refers to the one-dimensional distance travelled by a primate during its daily active period. *80*

Day range Two-dimensional area used by a primate throughout a 24-hour period. *80*

Denticulated microliths Small (1–4 cm in length), flaked stone tools set with little notches. *152*

Depth perception Visual ability to judge distance. *62*

Derived feature A character state that differs from that of a common ancestor. *67*

Diabetes Serious health disorder associated with elevated blood glucose (sugar) levels. *182*

Diphyodonty Having two successive sets of teeth. *92*

Discontinuous variation Phenotypic variation that falls into discrete categories (e.g., yellow or green seeds in Mendel's pea plants). *31*

Diurnal Active during the day and sleeping at night. *65*

Dominance hierarchy A social order sustained by aggression, affiliation, or other behaviour patterns. *81*

Dominant Allele that is fully expressed in the phenotype. *18*

Ecogeographic patterns Similar patterns of variation within and across species and their correlation to biogeography. *161*

Ecological niche Sum of all the interactions between an organism and its ecosystem. *79*

Ecology The study of interrelationships of organisms and their environment. *2*

Ecotourism A form of low-impact, culturally sensitive tourism that can generate income for local people. *174*

Ectothermy The ability to regulate body temperature by environmental exposure. *62*

Emergent layer Topmost level of the tree, which is usually exposed to sunlight. *79*

Enamel Outer surface of a tooth, the hardest biological substance in the body. *93*

Endangered Very high risk of extinction in the wild. *88*

Endemic Restricted to a specified locality. *63*

Epoch A unit of geological time that is a subdivision of an era. *100*

Era One of approximately 11 units of geological time that cover the ca. 4.6-billion-year age of Earth (e.g., Cenozoic Era from 65.5 million years ago to present). *100*

Euprimates Primates of modern aspect. *103*

Evolutionary radiation A geologically rapid diversification of members of a single lineage into a variety of forms. *53*

Evolutionary synthesis A modern theory of evolutionary processes that emphasizes the combined action of the four mechanisms of change: random mutation, natural selection, genetic drift, and gene flow. *57*

Extant Living representatives of aspecies exist. *4*

Extinct No living representative of a species exists. *4*

Falsifiable A study design that enables the researcher to makeobservations thatdisprove a hypothesis. *6*

Female philopatry A female spends her entire life in her natal (birth) group, and males typically emigrate upon reaching sexual maturity. *84*

Fitness The average contribution of an allele or genotype tosucceeding generations. *13*

Fixity of species A theory that derives from Biblical creation, in which each living thing has always existed and will always exist by God's acts of creation. *9*

Flake The thin piece of stone that has been removed from a core. *148*

Folate A B-complex vitamin associated with reduced risk of birth defects and cardiac events, and improved cognitive function. *163*

Foraging coherence Which individuals forage together in time and space. *84*

Forensic anthropology The application of the study of the human skeleton (osteology) in a legal setting. *183*

Fossils Organic remains that have been transformed by geological processes into a mineralized form. *4*

Gamete A sex cell; asperm or egg. *23*

Gene flow The movement of individuals, and therefore genes, between populations. *33*

Genes Basic, functional units of heredity. *17*

Genetic engineering Removing, modifying, or adding genes to a DNA molecule to change the information it contains. *31*

Genotype Genetic makeup of an organism. *17*

Genus (pl. genera) A taxonomic group of species exhibiting similar characteristics. *7*

Geology The scientific study of the Earth, what it is made of, and how it changes over time. *9*

Germ cells Sex cells (sperm or egg). *28*

Germinate To grow from a seed. *38*

Glaciology The study of glaciers and other natural phenomena involving ice. *9*

Gracile Slight, slender. *120*

Great chain of being The belief that all things and creatures in nature are organized in a hierarchy from inanimate objects at thebottom to God at the top. *40*

Habitat A place that provides adequate nutrients, water, and living space. *78*

Habituate To allow a primate group to become used to the presence of human observers by quietly and carefully following the group. *81*

Hammerstone A large, often spherical stone used for making other tools, to detach flakes from a core by percussion or striking. *148*

Haplorhini Primate suborder comprising tarsiers, monkeys, apes, and humans. *62*

Hemoglobin The iron-protein component in the red blood cells that carries oxygen to the tissues. *30*

Heterodonty Different kinds of teeth. *93*

Heterozygous Different rather than identical alleles in the corresponding loci of a pair of chromosomes. *17*

Hibernate Spend time, typically months, in a state of reduced metabolic activity. *65*

Holistic Considering all aspects of the research subject. *2*

Homeothermic The ability to use energy from food to produce heat and self-regulate internal body temperature. *61*

Home range Two-dimensional area used by a primate throughout months or years. *80*

Hominidae Primate family comprising apes and humans. *71*

Hominini Tribe within the Homininae comprising humans (Homo), chimpanzees (Pan), and our most recent common ancestors. *119*

Homoplastic character A feature in two or more taxa whose similarity is not due to common descent (e.g., body forms in whales and fish, or eyeball morphology in an octopus and primate). *50*

Homozygous Identical rather than different alleles in the corresponding loci of a pair of chromosomes. *17*

Hybrid zone A region in which genetically distinct populations come into contact and produce at least some offspring of mixed ancestry. *45*

Hybrid Offspring produced from mating plants or animals from different species, varieties, or genotypes. *45*

Hylobatidae Primate family comprising gibbons and siamangs. *71*

Incisors Front teeth between the canines *93*

Infectious disease Illness that can be transmitted from person to person or from organism to organism, and that is caused by a microbial agent. *176*

Inference A process of reasoning in which a conclusion is derived from one or more facts. *6*

Intelligent design The largely Christian belief that living things occur because of intelligent cause, not as a result of undirected processes, such as evolution and natural selection. *13*

Ischial callosities Well-developed sitting pads. *71*

Knuckle-walking Walking on four limbs by partially supporting body weight on the middle phlanges (bones in finger). *74*

Komodo dragon The largest extant lizard, with adults reaching up to 3 m in length and a body mass of approximately 70 kg! *147*

KYA Abbreviation for thousands of years before present (BP). Thus, 27 KYA = 27000 years BP. *144*

Latitude Geographic distance north or south of the equator. *161*

Lemuroidea Primate superfamily comprising five lemur families (Cheirogalidae, Lemuridae, Indriidae, Lepilemuridae, and Daubentoniidae). *63*

Lorisidae Primate family in the Lorisiformes. *65*

Lorisoidea Primate superfamily comprising Lorisidae, known as lorises and galagos. *63*

Maladaptation An adaptation that is no longer beneficial to an organism. *179*

Male philopatry A male spends his entire life in his natal (birth) group, and females typically emigrate upon reaching sexual maturity. *84*

Mandible Lower jaw. *93*

Mass extinction The disappearance of numerous species over a relatively short time. *54*

Mastication Chewing of food. *96*

Mating system Mating patterns exhibited by individuals. *84*

Maxilla Part of the upper jaw from which the teeth grow. *92*

Meiosis Cellular division resulting in each daughter cell receiving half the amount of DNA as the parent cell. Meiosis occurs during formation of egg andsperm cells in mammals. *23*

Melanin   A mixture of biopolymers that give colour to the skin, hair, and parts of the eye.   *162*

Microcephaly   A condition in which adults typically achieve small brain capacity and have moderate to severe intellectual disabilities.   *147*

Microevolution   Evolutionary changes within populations.   *22*

Microliths   Small (1–4 cm in length), flaked stone tools.   *152*

Micronutrient malnutrition   Insufficient intake of essential vitamins and amino acids.   *180*

Mitochondria   Structures in eukaryotic cells that turn nutrients into energy for the cells (i.e., the "power plants" of cells).   *159*

Mitosis   Cellular division resulting in two identical daughter cells with the same number of chromosomes as theparent cell.   *23*

Molars   Teeth behind the premolars.   *93*

Morphology   The study of the form and structure of organisms.   *2*

Mosaic evolution   The evolution at different rates of various related or unrelated features within a lineage or clade.   *120*

Mutation   An error or alteration of a nucleotide sequence, which represents the ultimate source of new genetic material in populations.   *28*

Natural history   The study of animals, plants, and minerals.   *7*

Neck   Part of the tooth that is at the gum line.   *93*

Neonatal   Period of time from birth to 4–6 weeks of age.   *183*

Neuron   A specialized cell that delivers information within the body.   *120*

Nocturnal   Active at night and sleeping during the day.   *64*

Node   The start point (internal) or end point (terminal) of a line segment in a cladogram.   *51*

Non-human primate   Any primate that is not a human.   *2*

Nuchal crest   A horizontal ridge of bone where large neck muscles attach to the back of the skull.   *131*

Nucleotide   A building block of DNA, consisting of a base, sugar, and phosphate group.   *24*

Nucleus   Part of a eukaryotic cell containing genetic material.   *22*

Obesity   Condition characterized by excessive weight or adipose tissue.   *180*

Ossification   Process of bone formation, in which connective tissue (e.g., cartilage) is converted to bone or bone-like tissue.   *183*

Paleontology   The study of fossilized life forms.   *8*

Palynology   The study of fossilized pollen.   *125*

Pandemic   Spread of an infectious disease throughout a country, continent, or the world.   *177*

Parasite   An organism living upon or in, and at the expense of, another organism.   *37*

Pathogenic   Causing disease or capable of doing so.   *176*

Perinatal   Period of time before, during, and immediately after birth.   *183*

Phenetics   The classification of organisms based on their overall phenotypic similarities, regardless of their evolutionary relationships.   *46*

Phenotype   Observable traits or characteristics of an organism.   *17*

Phenotypic plasticity   Variation in organisms in response to environmental factors rather than genetic factors.   *161*

Phylogenetic tree   A graphical representation of the evolutionary interrelationships among various taxa that have a common ancestor, based on paleontological, morphological, molecular, or other evidence.   *53*

Plate tectonics   Geological theory that the plates of the Earth's crust move, resulting in changes in the position, size, and shape of continents and oceans.   *102*

Platyrrhini   Infraorder comprising New World monkeys.   *67*

Pleiotropic   The phenotypic effect of a single gene on more than one trait.   *31*

Point mutation   Mutation resulting from a change in a single base pair in the DNA molecule.   *30*

Pollinator Agent that transports small amounts of nectar and pollen, e.g., on fur or by mouth, between flowers. *80*

Polygenic A trait that results from the interaction of multiple genes. *31*

Population genetics The study of distribution of allele frequencies and changes under the influence of the four main mechanisms of evolution: mutation, genetic drift, gene flow, and natural selection. *31*

Postcranial skeleton Bones below the head. *94*

Postorbital bar A ring of bone around the eye socket. *63*

Precision The closeness of repeated measurements to the same value. *125*

Prehensile tail A tail that can support the entire body weight of the animal. *69*

Premolars Teeth between the canines and molars. *93*

Pressure flaking Removing flakes from a core by applying pressure steadily until the flake breaks off. *152*

Primate-source country A country with naturally occurring primate populations. *172*

Primate Any extant or extinct member of the order of mammals that includes lemurs, tarsiers, monkeys, apes, and humans. *4*

Primitive feature A trait that is old on a phylogenetic scale of development. *62*

Procumbent Teeth that project forward. *96*

Prognathic A forward or projecting aspect of anatomy, typically referring to the face. *111*

Protected area An area that has a protected designation according to legal statute. *172*

Protein malnutrition Insufficient intake of nitrogen-containing food (protein). *180*

Protein A large molecule composed of a specific sequence of amino acids. *26*

Quadrumanous climbing The use of varying combinations of all four limbs to move through an arboreal habitat. *74*

Quadruped The use of all four limbs to travel. *64*

Qualitative data Information based on observations that cannot be reduced to numerical expression. *7*

Quantitative data Information measurable or quantifiable on a numeric scale, such as body mass or the number of primate species in a protected area. *7*

Radioactive decay The process of a material giving off particles to reach a stable state. *126*

Recessive Allele that is fully expressed in the phenotype only when its paired allele is identical. *18*

Recombination The process by which two homologous chromosomes exchange genetic material during gamete formation. *24*

Red list A comprehensive listing of the conservation status of plant and animal taxa on a global scale. *87*

Red Queen hypothesis As species evolve, continuing development is required to maintain fitness in the systems with which they are co-evolving. *56*

Residence group composition Primate social groupings based on the number of individuals in differing age-sex classes. *84*

Resource defence Active defence of a food resource by an individual or group. *84*

Retinal fovea A characteristic of the eye that reduces night vision but improves visual acuity. *67*

Retromolar gap Space between the third molar and the rear portion of the mandible. *146*

Ribosome A structure within cells that manufactures proteins by linking together amino acids according to the coded sequence on a strand of mRNA. *27*

RNA Single-stranded nucleic acid. The primary function of RNA in a cell is the step between DNA and protein synthesis. *27*

Robust Physically strong, durable. *120*

Root Part of the tooth that is below the gum line. *93*

Sagital crest A lengthwise (front to back) ridge of bone along the top of the skull where strong chewing muscles attach to the top of the skull. *131*

Sampling error An error that results from a mistake in sampling procedure. *32*

School of thought A group of people united in their shared belief in some ideas or concepts. *9*

Sectorial premolar First lower premolar with a shearing edge for the upper canine. *130*

Seed dispersal Specific fruit characteristics to entice animals to eat the juicy parts and then disperse the seeds in feces dropped away from the parent plant. *79*

Sexually dimorphic Males and females of the same species having different physical features. *71*

Skeletal trauma An injury, such as a wound, to skeletal tissue resulting from an agent, force, or mechanism. *185*

Slash and burn Involves the burning and clearing of forests for planting of agriculture. *85*

Social Darwinism The misguided application of the concepts of natural selection and biological evolution to the historical development of human societies, placing special emphasis on the idea of "survival of the fittest." *13*

Sociobiology The study of animal (and human) behaviour based on the assumption that behaviour is controlled by the genes. *38*

Somatic cells Any cells in the body that are not sperm or egg cells. *28*

Speciation Evolutionary process involving the formation of a new species. *44*

Standard deviation Measure of dispersion, typically 67% of data from the average. *125*

Stasis Reduced or non-existent morphological changes over long time periods within a lineage. *53*

Stereoscopic vision Organism has overlapping fields of vision. *62*

Stratigraphy The study of rock layers (strata) and the relationships among them. *9*

Strepsirhini Primate suborder comprising lemurs, lorises, and galagos. *62*

Subspecies A uniform, genetically distinct population of a species, often in a specific geographic region. *164*

Substrate Surface on which an organism moves. *97*

Sweat glands Sweat-producing and ear wax–producing glands. *62*

Tapetum lucidum An extra layer of tissue in the eye that reflects light, thereby enhancing night vision. *63*

Tarsiiformes Infraorder comprising tarsiers. *67*

Taurodont Very large pulp cavities combined with reduced root size. *146*

Taxa Groupings of organisms given a formal scientific name such as species, genus, family, etc. (singular is taxon). *44*

Taxonomy The theory and practice of describing, naming, and classifying extant and extinct organisms. *7*

Temporal fossa A large space between the eye orbit and the cheek bone (zygomatic). *136*

Territory An area actively defended by an individual or group. *80*

Theology The study of religion from a religious perspective. *15*

Tool tradition A tool or tools with a generally consistent pattern of production. *148*

Top-down processes Influence of consumers, such as predators, on prey. *79*

Transcription Process by which genetic information from DNA is transferred into RNA. *26*

Translation Process by which information coded in sequence of mRNA is translated into sequence of amino acids in a protein. *27*

Tree topology Patterns of evolutionary relatedness among the taxa within a cladogram. *51*

Tropical rainforests Forest habitats typically near the equator that are characterized by high annual temperatures and rainfall. *78*

Type specimen The original specimen from which the description of a new species is made. *142*

Typological The study or systematic classification of types that have characteristics or traits in common. *44*

Ultraviolet radiation Electromagnetic radiation, similar to visible light but of shorter wavelength, which is emitted from the sun. *162*

Understorey Area between the ground and the lowest horizontal branches. *79*

Ungulates Mammals with hooves (e.g., horses, deer, sheep). *102*

Unifacial tool A tool worked on only one side. *149*

Uniformitarianism A theory that natural processes, such as erosion, operating in the past are the same as those that operate in the present. *9*

Vasocontriction   Narrowing of blood vessels. This reduces the amount of blood flowing to that part of the body.   *161*

Vertical clinging and leaping   Clinging to vertical or inclined substrate in upright position and then leaping toward and grasping another vertical or inclined substrate.   *64*

Virus   A microscopic, infectious organism composed of RNA or DNA that relies on the genetic machinery of living cells to grow and reproduce.   *176*

Zoology   The scientific study of animals.   *9*

Note: Entries for figures are followed by "f"

CPSIA information can be obtained
at www.ICGtesting.com
Printed in the USA
LVHW02s0031270918
591461LV00005B/12/P